A Review of the
CORNISH FLORA
1980

by
L.J. MARGETTS
and
R.W. DAVID

INSTITUTE OF CORNISH STUDIES
1981

Published by
The Institute of Cornish Studies
Trevenson House, Pool, Redruth, Cornwall
and printed in G.B. by Cornwall Lithographic Printers Ltd.

ISBN 0 903686 34 1

PREFACE

We have called this book A Review of the Cornish Flora inasmuch as it attempts to sum up the botanical records of the last 50 years in Cornwall and to assess how the vegetation of the county has changed in this last half-century. Our account is necessarily comparative, and the basis of the comparison, the standard, is F.H. Davey's excellent *Flora of Cornwall* (1909) and E. Thurston and C.C. Vigurs' *Supplement* to it (1922), reissued together in a single volume in 1978. By that standard we have measured the subsequent additions to and subtractions from the flora of the county; but we have also noted some earlier records that escaped both Davey and his successors.

Under each genus we first list those species that are so generally distributed in Cornwall that individual records are of little significance. We then particularise the less common taxa, listing records subsequent to Thurston and Vigurs' *Supplement*, and also commenting where the plants seem to have disappeared from previously recorded localities. A very few of the earlier records can now be shown to be erroneous, and we have pointed these out.

As J.E. Lousley's *Flora of the Isles of Scilly* appeared as recently as 1971, we have not included Scillonian records except when these add information to Lousley's; and we are grateful to Mrs Dorothy Lousley for allowing us to see and to use the notes which her husband entered into his copy of his book. We have also omitted any detailed discussion of the Lizard specialities, for these will be fully covered in the study of that area now being compiled by Dr D.E. Coombe, Dr L.C. Frost, and others.

The introduction to Davey's *Flora* gives an account of the Topography, Climate, and Geology of the county, and of the principal botanical workers who had been active in it up to that time. We have supplemented this with a summary of recent changes in the environment, with descriptions of some of the most characteristic ecological habitats, and with notes on later Cornish botanists.

We acknowledge here the considerable help and advice freely given by a large number of both amateur and professional botanists, many of whose initials appear in the text. In particular, we would like to thank the following for help in identification:

C.E.A. Andrews
P.M. Benoit
Professor J.P.M. Brenan
E.J. Clement
Dr M.G. Daker
E.S. Edees
Dr D.J. Hambler
Dr R.M. Harley
R.C.L. Howitt
Dr C.E. Hubbard
P.F. Hunt
A.C. Jermy

Dr R. Melville
A. Newton
Dr C.N. Page
Dr A.J. Richards
R.H. Roberts
P.D. Sell
Dr A. Sleep
V.S. Summerhayes
P. Taylor
P.J.O. Trist
Dr C. West
Dr P.F. Yeo

We owe a double debt to Mr D.H. Kent, who not only checked for us a number of Cornish specimens in national herbaria, but also read the typescript and made a number of valuable suggestions.

We also wish to thank Mr R. Penhallurick, Assistant Curator of Truro Museum, for the map of the county, the late Mr H.B. Sargent, who started the card-index from which most of the records have been taken, and Dr G. Allsop, for continuing this time-consuming but important work.

L.J.M. has undertaken the compilation of the body of records (with the exception of *Carex*), and collected the information on Cornish botanists. R.W.D. wrote the note on changes in the last fifty years. For the rest of the contents of this book, and for its general planning, we are jointly responsible.

L.J. Margetts
R.W. David

A REVIEW OF THE CORNISH FLORA, 1980

ILLUSTRATIONS

MAP OF CORNWALL

INTRODUCTION

The Cornish flora: changes in the last fifty years

Thurston and Vigurs published their supplement to Davey's
Flora of Cornwall in 1922, and the date may almost be taken as
symbolising a critical turning point in the history of the Cornish
flora. Most of the major changes in the vegetation that have
occurred since then have resulted directly or indirectly from
changes in transport that began to be manifest about that date.
When R.W.D.'s family first came to Cornwall in 1920 they
travelled by the old London and South Western Railway to
Port Isaac Road and made the rest of the journey to Polzeath
very slowly in Mr Prout's wagonette. By 1925 Mr Old had set
up his garage with two cars and made a regular business of
ferrying travellers to and from the trains. In 1931 the family
acquired a car of its own.

The intensification of traffic with the arrival of the motor
car and, a little later, the caravan, had two obvious botanical
effects. In the first place the county became very much more
accessible, the influx of tourists much greater, and the human
pressure upon even the remoter localities much more intense.
Lonely paths became well-trodden, dune-areas were flattened
or excavated for car-parks (one of the two colonies of *Centaurium
scilloides* was extinguished in this way), and more than one
coastal marsh was converted to a caravan site and could no
longer sustain *Cyperus longus.*

A subsidiary phenomenon has been the widening and tidying
of roads to accommodate greater and faster traffic. In Cornwall
this must often entail the destruction of the characteristic stone
"hedges" which provide a congenial habitat for many plants,
and the equally characteristic tree-belt that often crowns and
sometimes replaces the "hedge". Even when the tree-belt has
not been grubbed it is frequently trimmed to ground-level to
improve visibility. In this way the shrubby *Rosaceae*, such as
Wild Service, Medlar, and Dwarf Cherry, have become much
rarer than they seem to have been in Davey's time, while the
Plymouth Pear and *Sorbus devoniensis* have not recently been
seen at all in the county.

With the arrival of the car began the decline of the railways,
but the latter has not much affected the flora. In the past the
railway clearly fostered the spread of some species, especially
aliens: *Erica lusitanica* is found scattered beside the track of
the Great Western, as is *Campanula alliariifolia* along the London

and South Western. This means of access is now limited, but the plants that benefited are still there, and the lines that have been closed provide an attractive habitat for colonists.

A quite different change in the transport system has been the virtual ending of the coasting trade. As late as the 1920s the small ports such as Fowey, Par, Penzance, Hayle, Portreath, Padstow, and Bude were regularly visited by small tramp steamers and even ketches and schooners carrying stone, coal, grain, and other commodities for local use. The casuals introduced in this way, more probably from other British docks than from overseas, made such places a Mecca for the hunter of aliens. Nowadays the two Bur-parsleys are no longer to be found on Eastern Green, Penzance, and Par Harbour has lost *Reseda alba* and *Eryngium campestre.*

Other plants have disappeared for less easily explicable reasons. It is, presumably, because it is no longer used as a herb that Motherwort has died out from several cottage sides; the true Catmint, *Nepeta cataria*, on the other hand, just survives in one farmyard where it has been known for at least a hundred years, while the true Balm, *Melissa*, has enormously increased its hold throughout the county. The decline of Pennyroyal, *Mentha pulegium*, a decline that seems to have been general throughout southern Britain, is more of a mystery. *Vicia orobus* has so far eluded twenty years of persistent search in its recorded Cornish localities.

The increase in accessibility, while it has endangered some plants, has assisted the discovery of others. It is now appreciated how plentifully some of the "Lizard plants" re-appear on the north coast: *Genista pilosa* is more widespread and abundant there than on the Lizard, and the northern colony of *Hypochoeris maculata* is more splendid than the one at Kynance. The apparent loss of *Carex montana* from what was so long its only Cornish station has been more than compensated by the finding of two extensive colonies elsewhere.

Also against the decline of certain plants must be set the spectacular increase of others. In 1894 the discovery of a few plants of *Juncus tenuis* on an East Cornish roadside was hailed as a first county record of high importance; now it lines paths and woodland rides in many parts of the county. *Allium triquetrum*, once a rarity confined to the Lizard area, is locally abundant near the coast as far east as the Devon border and beyond it. *Veronica filiformis* has a similar expansionist record, while another introduction, the hybrid "Montbretia", *Tritonia crocosmiflora*, has become one of the commonest plants near the coast, together with *Carpobrotus* and *Disphyma.*

All in all the gains in the Cornish flora over the last fifty years much outweigh the losses. Very little, in fact, has been wholly lost. Farm organisation and methods have not changed so radically as, for example, in East Anglia or the South Downs, where the mechanisation of agriculture in the first, and in the second the switch from sheep to cattle, have produced drastic alterations in the vegetation patterns. Where, however, the expansion of tourism and of leisure activities are being so deliberately increased, there must be danger to the plants from sheer human pressure.

In the early fifties botany in Cornwall, as in other counties, received a boost when the Botanical Society of the British Isles launched its scheme for an Atlas of the British flora, and its members were encouraged to search the country, ten kilometre square by square, and record all the flowering plants found. In Cornwall the operation was handicapped by the fact that very few botanists were resident in the county; even the Society's official "recorders" for the two vice-counties did not live there permanently. Most of the records were therefore made by visitors, and the plants recorded were preponderantly those that were conspicuous in holiday seasons or on the coast, while, for example, the spring annuals and the bog-plants of the hinterland were overlooked. Nevertheless the exercise added much to knowledge of the general vegetation-patterns in the county, opened up a few under-explored areas, and added *Centaurium scilloides*, *Eleocharis uniglumis*, *Epilobium brunnescens* and *E.ciliatum* to the Cornish list. Still later additions have been the newly described species *Atriplex longipes*, *Gentianella anglica* subsp. *cornubiensis*, and *Trifolium occidentale*, together with *Equisetum variegatum*, *Juncus acutus*, and *Poa bulbosa.*

In 1962 the Cornish Naturalists' Trust was founded. Botany was not, at first, a major interest of the Trust; but the new organisation gradually brought together all those in the county who were interested in natural history, provided them with an efficient and continuing means of communication, and enabled them to offer a concerted and informed programme in matters such as conservation policy. The publication, in 1968, of Mrs Paton's popular book *Wild Flowers in Cornwall* was some compensation for the absence of an up-to-date County Flora, offering, as it did, an incentive and helpful guide to botanising in Cornwall. Botanical interests in the county are now soundly based. The recorders for both vice-counties are now permanent residents, and in constant touch with other botanists who also live in Cornwall as well as with experts in the "difficult" genera such as *Rubus* and *Taraxacum*, who are being called in to help disentangle the county's endemics. It seems an appropriate moment to take stock of the work of the generation that succeeded that of Davey, Vigurs, and Thurston, and so provide a base-line for the further investigations that are now likely to proceed vigorously.

Plant habitats in Cornwall

In Cornwall no place is further than twenty miles from the coast, and the greater part of the county is within ten miles of it. Almost all ecological habitats, then, as they are generally understood, are in Cornwall to some extent modified by the proximity of the sea. For example, rivers and streams tend to be short, and in their upper reaches steep; while on the south coast the sinking of the land, and elsewhere erosion, have created rias or drowned valleys at the rivers' mouths. Again, as a result of exposure to ocean weather, trees are in general restricted to narrow valleys and sheltered combes below the skyline inland, while those near the coast are stunted and bent at a sharp angle by the wind. Overall the pressing need for plant communities is to make the most of the available shelter, and in consequence those communities, with the possible exception of the inland moors, tend to be small and sharply localised.

In what follows we very briefly characterise the main types of Cornish habitat and note some plants typical of each.

1. MARITIME

(a) **Rocky cliffs.** The highest cliffs are on the north coast, in the culm measures of Morwenstow and Cambeak and the Old Red Sandstone (with igneous intrusions) of Port Isaac and Watergate Bays. Almost equally imposing are the cliffs of diabase projecting from the overlying granite between St Ives and Cape Cornwall, (Plate 1, above). On the south coast the serpentine and hornblende of the Lizard, the Cambrian Rock of Dodman Point, and the cliffs between Fowey and Looe (Old Red Sandstone again) produce substantial elevations. Many of these cliffs are more or less sheer and offer only scattered ledges for colonisation by plants. Characteristic species are *Armeria, Asplenium marinum, Crithmum, Silene vulgaris* subsp. *maritima*, and *Spergularia rupicola; Adiantum capillus-veneris, Brassica oleracea, Inula crithmoides, Lavatera* *arborea*, and *Limonium binervosum* are found locally.

(b) **Cliff-top sward.** The level ground above the cliffs is often grassland, cropped close by wind and spray, the dominant grass being *Festuca rubra*, with *F.ovina* in the stonier patches, and some *Dactylis*. Associated plants are *Anthyllis*, *Daucus carota* subsp. *gummifer*, *Euphrasia tetraquetra*, *Plantago coronopus*, *Scilla verna* (with *S. autumnalis* abundant in a few stations), and *Viola riviniana*. Where the cliffs are not sheer but, as in much of the north coast, include long slopes and hanging valleys, these may carry extensive colonies of *Pteridium* and, where this is not dominant, a variety of plants normally associated with woodland, such as *Arum maculatum*, *Brachypodium sylvaticum*, *Hyacinthoides*, *Primula vulgaris*, and *Teucrium scorodonia* (Plate 1, below).

(c) **Maritime heath.** An association characteristic of the Lizard and of the coast between St Ives and Perranporth. With *Calluna*, *Erica cinerea*, and *E.tetralix* (with *E.vagans* on the Lizard), grow *Dactylorhiza maculata* agg., *Festuca ovina*, *Genista pilosa*, *Ulex gallii*, and *Viola* spp., The *Scillas* are also frequently present.

(d) **Raised beaches.** The lower cliffs of the south coast often rise from a rock platform above high tide mark (Plate 2, above). These platforms are frequently irrigated by springs in the cliff above. Characteristic plants are *Carex distans* and *C. extensa* (with, very locally indeed, *C.punctata*), *Juncus gerardii*, *Lythrum*, and *Phragmites*.

(e) **Cliff flushes.** Raised beaches are less common on the north coast, but there spring-fed hollows in the cliffs support a somewhat similar vegetation including occasionally *Phragmites*. Other characteristic species are *Anagallis tenella*, *Festuca arundinacea*, *Juncus bufonius*, *Samolus valerandi*, *Scirpus cernuus*. Similar associations occur in the steep channels of streamlets arising in the western tableland and descending the cliffs precipitously. Here too *Sibthorpia* may not infrequently be found.

(f) **Sand and shingle beaches.** At the head of most beaches, immediately above high tide mark, a characteristic association is found, in which the main ingredients are *Atriplex* spp., *Cakile*, *Honkenya*, *Polygonum aviculare* and sometimes (on the south coast) *P.oxyspermum*. *Eryngium* and *Glaucium*, formerly frequent, are casualties of the increased pressure from visitors and have become rarities.

Rocky cliffs, eastward from Gunard Head (West 43)

Bluebell slope, above Compit (Pentire peninsula, East 98)

Raised beach, Rame (East 44)

Fixed dunes, Penhale Sands (West 75)

Saltmarsh, Polbathic (East 35)

Bodmin Moor and De Lank River (East 17)

Willow Carr, Trendrine (West 43)

Oak woodland, Merthen Wood (Helford River, West 72)

Mixed woodland, Luckett Nature Reserve (East 37)

Erica ciliaris heath, Silverwell (West 74)

Riverine marsh, Marazion (West 53)

Water meadow, North Tamerton (East 39)

A Lizard pool (Hayle Kimbro, West 61)

Tin-mine spoil-heap, South Crofty, Redruth (West 64)

China clay workings, Penwithick (East 05)

A Cornish lane, near Helland (East 96)

CORNWALL

The vice counties and ten kilometre squ

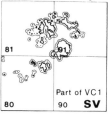

Isles of Scilly

81	91
	Part of VC 1
80	90 **SV**

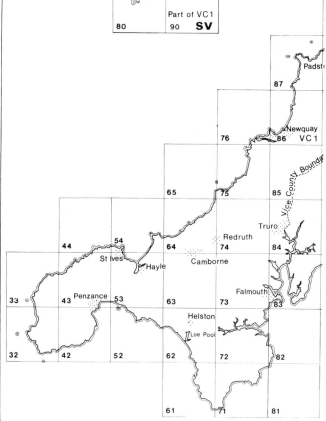

Padst○

87

Newquay
76   86   VC 1

65   75   85

Vice County Bound

Truro

Redruth
44   54   64   74   84
St Ives
     Hayle   Camborne

Falmouth
33   43   Penzance   53   63   73   83

Helston
32   42   52   Loe Pool   62   72   82

61   71   81

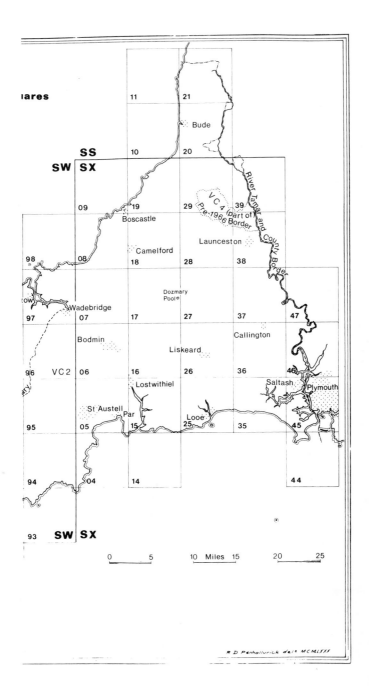

lares

11	21	
	Bude	

SS
SW SX

10	20	

09	19	29	VC 4 (part of) 39	
	Boscastle	Pre-1966 Border		

River Tamar and County Border

Launceston

98	08	Camelford 18	28	38	

Dozmary Pool

:ow					
97	Wadebridge 07	17	27	37	47

Bodmin

Callington

Liskeard

96	VC 2 06	16	26	36	46

Lostwithiel

Saltash Plymouth

St Austell Par

Looe

95	05	15	25	35	45

94	04	14		44

SW SX

93

0   5   10 Miles 15   20   25

R D Penhallurick del^o MCMLXXX

(g) **Sand-dunes and blown sand.** These areas are almost all on the north coast, where many are being reclaimed as camp sites. Within the dunes, which carry little except *Ammophila* and *Elymus (Agropyron)* species, with occasional *Calystegia soldanella, Euphorbia paralias,* and *E.portlandica,* the fixed sand nurtures a wide variety of plants, especially where there is a hollow to collect and hold moisture (Plate 2, below). Among many species characteristic of calcareous grassland (e.g. *Blackstonia* and *Viola hirta*) grow such local, and even national rarities as *Blysmus compressus, Gentianella anglica* subsp. *cornubiensis, Scrophularia scorodonia,* and *Verbascum virgatum.*

(h) **Salt-marsh.** Except in the estuaries of the Tamar and its associated rivers in the extreme south-east (Plate 3, above), this habitat is curiously rare in Cornwall and such salt-marshes as exist tend to be small. Many are being reclaimed for grazing or for caravan sites. The plants are for the most part the familiar ones for these conditions: *Aster tripolium, Carex extensa, Glaux, Oenanthe lachenalii, Puccinellia* spp., *Scirpus maritimus,* and *Suaeda.*

2. MOORLAND

(a) **Granite uplands.** The higher ground of the county consists of a series of granite intrusions which outcrop at intervals from Dartmoor (in Devonshire) to the rocky hills between St Ives and Land's End. Parts of these uplands support stands of *Erica cinerea* and *Pteridium,* with frequent *Carex binervis;* but large areas are acidic grassland with a very restricted flora dominated by *Nardus* with stunted *Calluna* and *Vaccinium myrtillus* (Plate 3, below). In the hollows between the tors are extensive mires (see 4 (a) below).

(b) **Dry heaths.** Small patches of dry heathland occur in many parts of the county, but there is a concentration of these sites in the north between Boscastle and Otterham in the west and Kilkhampton in the east. This is the area in which *Vicia orobus* was formerly found. Some characteristic plants are *Erica cinerea, Potentilla erecta, Senecio sylvaticus, Ulex gallii,* and *Viola riviniana.* In the more westerly heaths *Agrostis curtisii* is often dominant.

3. WOODLAND

(a) **Willow Carr.** This is probably the only ancient type of woodland occurring in the county in historic times, best seen to perfection along the small valleys of West Penwith (Plate

4, above). It forms a habitat of a very distinct kind, dominated by *Salix cinerea* subsp. *oleifolia* often to the exclusion of all other trees. The field layer is characteristically poor in species, but *Athyrium* and *Iris pseudacorus* are usually present, often with *Carex paniculata, Chrysosplenium oppositifolium* and *Viola palustris* subsp. *juressi. Osmunda regalis* is also a fairly frequent associate of this particular habitat, the larger units of which contain some *Alnus glutinosa.*

(b) **Oak Woodland.** The sheltered parts of the southern estuaries, such as those of the Helford River (Plate 4, below), and of the Fal, are fringed with woodland dominated by oak. Though both native species occur, the Durmast Oak, usually thought to be the western species, is surprisingly infrequent. The soil is usually rocky and thin, supporting only a scanty flora. Notable plants are the ferns *Dryopteris dilatata, D. filix-mas* and *D. pseudomas. Luzula sylvatica* and *Veronica montana* are fairly frequent, and *Melampyrum pratense* sometimes occurs in extensive colonies, but the familiar woodland plants of eastern England are noticeably absent from these acid oakwoods. Amongst other units of oak woodland in the county, a particularly interesting one is Peters Wood, in the Valency Valley near Boscastle, which is apparently quite old, with abundant *Quercus petraea.*

(c) **Mixed Woodland.** In the extreme east and north of Cornwall the woodlands are situated on richer soils by larger rivers, and are of a mixed type (Plate 5, above). Both *Quercus* species occur, together with the introduced *Q. cerris,* but there are also substantial stands of other trees such as *Acer pseudoplatanus, Betula* spp. *Fagus, Fraxinus, Prunus avium, Sorbus aucuparia,* and *Ulmus glabra. Aesculus hippocastanum* and *Castanea* have been commonly planted, and, in a few places, *Carpinus.* There is usually a shrub layer of *Corylus, Ilex,* and *Viburnum opulus,* sometimes with *Euonymus.* The field layer of these mixed woodlands is significantly richer than those of the west, though never anywhere approaching that of the coppice woodlands of south-east England. *Luzula pilosa* is frequent, as is *L. forsteri* locally, together with small populations of *Carex sylvatica, Festuca gigantea, Galium odoratum,* and *Lamiastrum galeobdolon.* Still further east, in the larger units of woodland along stretches of the Tamar and its estuaries, other species enter into the flora: *Bromus ramosus, Melica uniflora, Milium* *effusum*, and, occasionally, *Carex pallescens*. *Sorbus torminalis* is also found, usually in small numbers, in these eastern woods.

(d) **Commercial Woodland.** This is mostly the usual coniferous stand, some of it surviving from old plantings. Its flora is limited to the rides, but it is often rich in species such as *Anemone nemorosa, Epilobium angustifolium, Hieracium umbellatum* (with the subspecies *bichlorophyllum*), *Hypericum pulchrum*, but also with regional rarities like *Melittis* and *Physospermum*. On damp banks in these woods *Dryopteris aemula* is frequent, while *Sibthorpia* can often be found on the banks of streams.

More recently, mixed woodland has been planted, including some large stands of exotic trees such as *Eucalyptus* and *Nothofagus*, species of which thrive in the milder south-west. Clement Wood, near Truro, and Carthamartha Wood, on the Tamar, are both afforested with some of these newer introductions. It will be interesting to see what sort of flora will develop under such less sombre canopies, and whether the trees will regenerate naturally from seed.

(e) **Scrub.** A thick scrub cover soon develops wherever land is left untilled or unpastured. *Crataegus monogyna* and *Prunus spinosa* are the main species, the latter especially on cliffs, but *Ulex europaeus* is often the first to appear on dry hillsides. In coastal areas and particularly on dunes, a dense low scrub of *Ligustrum vulgare* is frequent, while in wetland areas *Frangula alnus* and *Salix aurita* are often the main species.

Isolated trees are widespread on Cornish hedges, in the corner of fields, and around farmhouses, where they have been originally planted as windbreaks. These tend to be species that are well-known to be wind-resistant, like *Acer pseudoplatanus, Fraxinus*, and the Cornish Elm, *Ulmus minor* var. *cornubiensis*. The origin and spread of the last-named remains to be investigated and described, but its presence probably owes much to its use as a windbreak by the earliest settlers.

4. WETLANDS

(a) **Upland mires.** In the hollows between the granite tors a certain amount of humus has collected and the flora is richer than that of the surrounding moorland. Characteristic plants are *Carex demissa* and *C.echinata, Potamogeton polygonifolius, Ranunculus omiophyllus*, and, locally,

Rhynchospora alba, sometimes with others *(Illecebrum, Wahlenbergia)* more regularly associated with the wet heaths of the west. In such upland mires *Hammarbya* has recently been refound and the first Cornish colony of *Vaccinium oxycoccus* discovered.

(b) **Wet heaths.** The triangle between Falmouth, Hayle, and Newquay contains a series of wet heaths which include most of the Cornish habitats of *Erica ciliaris* (Plate 5, below). This is often abundant, with *E. tetralix* and the hybrid between them. Associated plants are *Dactylorhiza* spp., *Drosera intermedia* and *D.rotundifolia*, *Molinia*, *Myrica*, *Narthecium*, *Scutellaria minor*, and *Succisa pratensis*. Where the vegetation is less dense, e.g. in ditches and around small ponds, *Cicendia filiformis*, *Illecebrum*, and *Pinguicula lusitanica* may be found.

Similar habitats outside the triangle tend to be more heavily overgrown with coarser and less varied vegetation, with a greater extent of *Molinia*, among which *Hypericum undulatum*, *Osmunda*, and *Schoenus* may be seen.

(c) **Riverine marshes.** Where the courses of the steeper streams flatten out, a marsh is often formed (Plate 6, above). Dominant plants are likely to be *Carex* spp., (especially *C. paniculata* and *C.riparia)*, *Deschampsia caespitosa*, *Filipendula ulmaria*, *Iris pseudacorus*, *Juncus* spp., and *Pulicaria dysenterica*. Nearer the coast *Phragmites* becomes a regular member of the community, and formerly there used to be here and there considerable stands of *Cyperus longus* though this is one of the plants that has been conspicuously reduced by human pressure on the sites.

(d) **Water meadows.** In the east of the county the deep-cut valleys often contain small enclosed fields which serve as cattle-pastures in summer but in winter become swamps. The grasses are mostly *Dactylis* and *Holcus*, with *Agrostis stolonifera* and some *Molinia* in the wetter parts, together with a number of plants characteristic of marshes and wet woods, such as *Carex laevigata, Hypericum undulatum, Juncus effusus, Mentha aquatica, Polygonum hydropiper*, and *Ranunculus flammula*. (Plate 6, below)

(e) **Lakes and tarns.** Natural lakes are very rare in Cornwall, most sheets of water being man-made or man-enlarged (see (f) below). The exceptions are Loe Pool near Helston, several pools on the Lizard (Plate 7, above), and Dozmary Pool on Bodmin Moor. Though the first of these was the only Cornish site for *Corrigiola* (now extinct), while Croft Pascoe Pool has *Pilularia* and Dozmary *Elatine hexandra* and *Isoetes echinospora*, none of these pools is species-rich, for the Lizard pools are largely overgrown with *Agrostis stolonifera* and the stony bottoms of Loe and Dozmary support little vegetation.

(f) **Pools and marshes on secondary sites.** A number of Cornish valleys have been dammed in order to create substantial reservoirs, but with the exception of a few such as Crowan (*Pilularia* again) the work has been so recent that the permanent vegetation has not yet declared itself although the margins, where the water-level fluctuates, already in many cases show a sward of *Littorella*. This plant is also characteristic of many smaller pools resulting from excavation in the China clay area, and in these *Myriophyllum* and *Utricularia* species may also appear.

(g) **Rivers and streams.** Except for Tamar in the east, Cornish rivers are short and, until they become tidal, small. They are also very acid. The species in them are limited and the only common ones are *Callitriche hamulata, Myriophyllum alterniflorum, Potamogeton polygonifolius,* and *Scirpus fluitans.* Near the coast the *Callitriche* and the *Potamogeton* may occasionally be replaced by *C.obtusangula* and *P.crispus.* The general scarcity in the county of Batrachian *Ranunculus* is remarkable.

5. MAN-MADE HABITATS

(a) **Arable.** As stated above (p. 3), agricultural methods have, largely on account of the topographical features, not changed so drastically as in some other counties. The walled fields tend to be of moderate size, and spraying has not become a fetish. Though *Agrostemma* is no longer seen, as it was before the second world war, many fields can still show a rich variety of cornfield weeds besides the ubiquitous *Anagallis arvensis, Mentha arvensis, Veronica* spp., and *Viola arvensis.* Four species of poppy may sometimes be found together, and with them *Anchusa arvensis, Kicksia elatine* (and more rarely *K.spuria*), and *Myosotis arvensis. Chrysanthemum segetum* and *Misopates* are frequent on more acid soils. *Briza minor* still occurs very locally in the south and west.

(b) **Pasture.** A high percentage of the land in Cornwall is permanent grazing, though some of this has been improved by the application of fertiliser, and also by ploughing and reseeding. The grasses are mostly *Agrostis* spp., *Cynosurus*, and *Holcus lanatus*, and common associates are *Carduus nutans*, *Centaurea nigra*, *Ononis*, and *Ranunculus acris*.

(c) **Waste-land from the extractive industries.** There are extensive tips in the neighbourhood of old tin-mines (Plate 7, below) and again by the china clay works north of St Austell (Plate 8, above). These spoil-heaps are very deficient in humus and their colonisation by plants is slow. Early arrivals are *Calluna*, *Logfia minima*, and the aliens *Cotoneaster microphylla*, *Epilobium brunnescens*, and *Reynoutria japonica*. Some attempt is being made to reclaim the china clay spoil-heaps by deliberate planting, especially of *Lupinus arboreus* and *Ornithopus sativus*.

(d) **Railway tracks, rubbish tips, and docks.** The spread of *Campanula alliariifolia* and *Erica lusitanica* along the Cornish railways has already been mentioned. *Verbascum virgatum* is another plant which can be seen on the embankments west of Saltash, and the occurrence of *Linaria supina* on the railway near Par is famous. The frequency with which *Chaenorhinum* turns up on the tracks is remarkable.

A feature of most tips is an abundance of *Fumaria*, a genus in which Cornwall is especially rich. The commonest species is *F.muralis (boraei)* but *F.bastardii* and *F.officinalis* are frequent with, in the west, *F.occidentalis* and, very occasionally, *F. purpurea*.

Though the rarer casuals have disappeared from the docks with the virtual ending of the coasting trade, Par can still show *Spergularia bocconii*, while *Cynodon* persists both at Penzance and at Portreath.

(e) **Walls, Cornish hedges, and road-banks.** The Cornish hedge or West Country wall, constructed of rough stone slabs cushioned and capped with earth, is the standard permanent fence, and it is satisfactory that the County Council is, of policy, continuing to use it to bound new or reconstructed roads. These walls offer an attractive habitat to many plants, and therefore usually reflect the surrounding vegetation; but regular constituents of the wall flora are *Sedum anglicum*, *Umbilicus*, and a variety of ferns, especially *Asplenium* spp. and *Polypodium* (all three species are found in the county). *Carex muricata* subsp. *lamprocarpa* is a frequent wall-plant in the west of the county; and walls near the sea often carry an abundance of *Cochlearia danica*, *Erodium cicutarium* subsp. *dunense*, and, locally, *Petroselinum crispum*, with *Smyrnium* at the wall-foot.   Other notable, but local, wall-plants are *Geranium purpureum* and *Linaria repens.*

Where roads are sunk (as is common in Cornwall), the banks are often crowned with a line of shrubs (Plate 8, below), especially of the family *Rosaceae.* Of these the most widespread are *Crataegus monogyna* and *Prunus spinosa,* but *Mespilus, Prunus cerasus,* and *Sorbus torminalis* are still to be found.

Field-walls are often characterised by *Arrhenatherum elatius* subsp. *bulbiferum* and a line of *Brassica nigra* and *Conium.*

Cornish Botanists

Davey's Flora of Cornwall gives a full account of the botanists active in the county until the turn of the 20th century, and, in the Supplement, Vigurs includes a biographical sketch of Davey himself. The following notes are intended only as brief glimpses of those botanists who were prominent in the twenties and thirties.

William Wise   (1843—1935) was the main contributor to Davey's Flora from the Launceston area, where he was a life-long resident, but he continued field-work well into the twenties. A local chemist, he was three times Mayor of Launceston. He had an unrivalled knowledge of the wild plants of NE Cornwall, and left a herbarium, bound in five volumes, which is preserved in Launceston Museum.

William Tresidder   (1851—1935) was headmaster of Goonhavern School, near Perranporth, for his entire professional career.   In his spare time he was undoubtedly the most active of the Cornish botanists of the period, and a close friend of Thurston and Rilstone, sharing the latter's interest in Brambles. The large number of critical taxa of all kinds that he recorded reveal him to have been a most discriminating observer.

Edgar Thurston   (1855—1935) retired to Cornwall after a distinguished career in the Indian Civil Service as Superintendent of the Madras Museum.   He soon became fascinated by the Cornish flora, as well as the trees and shrubs cultivated on the larger estates of the county. Thurston took more than a parochial view of the county flora and helped it to become better known nationally.

Chambré Corker Vigurs (1867—1940) was a well-known Newquay physician who spent his spare time recording the plants of that area, of which he was to become the accepted authority. Critical genera such as *Rubus* and *Euphrasia* were his special interests. He collaborated with Thurston in the publication of Cornish records in the Journals of the Royal Institution of Cornwall, and also in the writing of the Supplement of 1922.

Frank Hill Perrycoste (1864—1928), after a brief period lecturing in London, came to settle at Polperro, where he remained for the rest of his life. He became later known as a collaborator with Galton, the pioneer of fingerprints, but he was a trained botanist as well, and knew the area around Polperro especially well. His extensive herbarium is now in Truro Museum.

Mary Maud Perrycoste (1864—1938), wife of the above, was also widely known as a competent field-botanist, certainly a better one than her husband. With their son and daughter, they spent a great deal of time together botanising in various parts of the county. She kept a separate herbarium, which passed to Exeter Museum on her death.

Edgar Rees (1874—1959) was a well-known Penzance botanist, active in the twenties and thirties in West Penwith, an area not much covered by other botanists. Rees kept the flame of Cornish botany going when it was at a low ebb, from the late thirties to the end of the 1939—45 war, and spent a great deal of time revisiting sites of known rarities. The discovery of *Ajuga genevensis* on Upton Towans stands to his credit, but this has now gone, like *Euphorbia peplis*, which he refound near Marazion in 1934.

Laurence T. Medlin (1887—1959) lived most of his life at St Blazey Gate, near St Austell, and was a teacher at a local school. His botanical forays were largely limited to the area around Par, but this part he knew well, and eventually he became the authority on the aliens of Par and Charlestown Harbours, a veritable Mecca for botanists interested in foreign species.

Francis Rilstone (1881—1953), by profession a schoolmaster, first at St Agnes and later at Polperro, was Cornwall's greatest critical botanist, covering as he did virtually the whole field of plant life from Bryophytes and Fungi to Charophytes and Flowering Plants. He had a very special interest in microfungi, but it is in his life's work on Brambles that he will perhaps be known best to other botanists. Over a span of more than thirty years studying the Cornish taxa, he described 16 species as new to science. His Bramble collection is now in the British Museum.

THE PLAN OF THE FLORA, AND REFERENCES

Sequence. The arrangement of Families, Genera, and Species is that of *Flora Europaea*. Exceptions are in the ferns, where we have used the sequence in Jermy et al., *Atlas of Ferns*, in the genus *Rubus*, where we follow the arrangement in Dandy's *List of British Vascular Plants*, in *Taraxacum*, where we follow Dr Richards' *Taraxacum Flora* (though we have kept the sequence of sections as in *Flora Europaea*), and in *Hieracium*, where we follow the account in Perring's *Critical Supplement to the Atlas of the British Flora*.

Nomenclature. Here again we follow *Flora Europaea*, with the exception of a very few recent changes. Where the names used are radically different from those in British floras, we have supplied two forms of cross-reference: first, by prefixing each species name with the appropriate number in the Dandy *List*, and secondly by adding the names used in Davey's *Flora of Cornwall* wherever these differ from the current ones, Davey's names being placed in round brackets beneath the new names. The absence of a 'Dandy number' implies that the plant in question is not in that list.

English names. These are the common names used in Dony et al., *English Names of Wild Flowers*. In the case of species not listed in that book we have used common names from other sources.

Distribution. The records are grouped under vice-county headings: West = West Cornwall, vice-county 1; East = East Cornwall, vice-county 2; Scilly = Isles of Scilly, vice-county 1a. Under these headings the records, separated by semi-colons, are grouped under the appropriate 10 km squares. The Cornish squares are SW 32—97, SX 04—47, and SS 20 and 21. Squares 83, 84, 85, 95, 96, and 97 contain parts of both vice-counties. A few of the squares contain only very small areas of land, and these are put in round brackets following the number of the square to which they were annexed for recording purposes (e.g. records for these partial squares were in the *Atlas of the British Flora* allocated to the square adjoining). Scilly records are not grouped under 10 km squares but under individual islands, denoted by the initials used in Lousley's *The Flora of the Isles of Scilly*, viz.

M	St Mary's	A	St Agnes and	TN	Tean
T	Tresco		Gugh	AT	Annet
MN	St Martin's	B	Bryher	H	St Helen's
S	Samson	E	Eastern Isles		

Dates. The majority of the records are post-1950. They are entered undated, and it may be assumed that, unless otherwise stated, the plants are still there. Dates are, however, given for earlier records, or where an old record has been confirmed since 1950. In the case of very rare species, we have given the dates of the latest sightings. Where a new species has been added to the county flora, the record bearing a date may be taken to be the first record for the appropriate vice-county.

Authorities

(a) Individual recorders, 1922—1980

Canon F.W. Adams	F.W.A.	A.H.G. Alston	A.H.G.A.
Canon J.H. Adams	J.H.A.	W. Andrew	W.A.
W. Poynter Adams	W.P.A.	Dr T.H. Angel	T.H.A.
D.E. Allen	D.E.A.	Mrs J. Anslow	J.A.
Dr G. Allsop	G.A.	J.F. Archibald	J.F.A.
Mrs E. Almond	E.A.	Mrs Ashton	M.A.
S. Bannister	S.B.	Mr and Mrs J.B.	
P.T. Barbary	P.T.B.	Bottomley	J.B.B.
Miss L. Barnard	L.B.	Dr H.M. Bowen	H.M.B.
R.S. Barnes	R.S.B.	J.P. Bowman	J.P.B.
Miss M.E. Barnsdale	M.E.B.	R. Bradshaw	R.B.
W. Barratt	W.B.	R.R. Brenan	R.R.B.
H. Barrett	H.B.	Lady Anne Brewis	L.A.B.
D. Baster	D.B.	Miss C. Brewster	C.B.
Miss M. Bazeley	M.B.	T. Archer Briggs	T.A.B.
Rev. J. Beckerlegge	J.B.	A. Brisby	A. Br.
Mrs J. Bell	J. Bel.	Mrs E. Scott Brown	E.S.B.
R. Bere	R. Be.	Miss M. Brown	M. Bo.
J. Bevan	J.Be.	O. Buckle	O.B.
Mrs A. Bizley	A.Bi.	K.E. Bull	K.E.B.
Miss E. Blackett	E.B.	W.E. Bunney	W.E.B.
Mrs M. Blamey	M.Bl.	Miss A. Burns	A.B.
Squadron Leader C.J.		R. Burrows	R.Bu.
Booth	C.J.B.	R.M. Burton	R.M.B.

B. Boothby	B.B.	Mr and Mrs S. Burton	S.Bu.
W. Borlase	W.Bo.	J.T. Bury	J.T.B.
Mrs E. Campbell	E.Ca.	E. Cock	E.C.
Mr Carlton	M.Ca.	Dr D.E. Coombe	D.E.C.
S.J. Chamberlain	S.J.C.	F.H. Coon	F.H.C.
J.H. Chandler	J.H.C.	E.G. Cordiner	E.G.C.
W. Channon	W.Ch.	Dr R. Cotton	R.C.
E. Chicken	E.Ch.	C. Crooke	C.C.
A.D. Chisholm	A.D.C.	Mrs M. Cuddy	M.C.
C.K. Clutterbuck	C.K.C.	W. Curl	W.C.
T.O. Darke	T.O.D.	Dr and Mrs J.G. Dony	J.G.D. &
F. Hamilton Davey	F.H.D.		C.D.
R.W. David	R.W.D.	A.E. Dorey	A.E.D.
Dr J.H. Davie	J.H.D.	Dr E. Drabble	E.D.
J.C. Day	J.C.D.	Mrs H. Drabble	H.D.
H.F. Devis	H.F.D.	F. Druce	F.D.
Mrs J.R. Dick	J.R.D.	G.C. Druce	G.C.D.
Mrs L. Dickinson	L.D.	Miss D. Dudley	D.D.
Mrs R. Dingle	R.D.	Mrs D.S. Dudley-Smith	D.S.D.
T. Dingle	T.D.	W.S.D'Urban	W.S.D'U
E.S. Edees	E.S.E.	R.D. English	R.D.E.
W.N. Edwards	W.N.E.		
J.L. Faull	J.L.F.	Mrs C.H. Fox	C.H.F.
R. Flook	R.F.	Rev. H.E. Fox	H.E.F.
W.H. Foott	W.H.F.	Dr J.F. Frazer	J.F.F.
Miss N.J. Forbes	N.J.F.	Professor J. Fremlin	J.Fr.
G. Forster	G.F.	Dr L.C. Frost	L.C.F.
Miss C.P. Foster	C.P.F.	F.G. Fuller	F.G.F.
Mrs J. Foster	J.Fo.		
Mrs B.E.M. Garratt	B.E.M.G.	Rev. G.G. Graham	G.G.G.
Mrs I. Gatiss	I.G.	R.A. Graham	R.A.G.
P. Gay	P.Ga.	A.W. Graveson	A.W.G.
A.M. Geldert	A.M.G.	Mr and Mrs A. Gray	A. &
R. Gendall	R.Ge.		F.G.
Miss M.B. Gerrans	M.B.G.	Miss J. Greenham	J.G.
W. Goddard	W.G.	Miss M. Greenwood	M.G.
R. Gomm	R.Go.	A. Gregg	A.Gr.
Colonel and Mrs R.B.		Captain O. Greig	O.G.
Goodden	R.B.G.	E. Griffiths	E.G.
P.J. Goodman	P.J.G.	Mrs L. Grigg	L.G.
K.M. Goodway	K.M.G.	G. Grigson	G.G.
Miss V. Gordon	V.G.	R. Groom	R.G.
P. Goriup	P.G.	J.D. Grose	J.D.G.
Mrs B. Graham	B.G.	A. Guthrie	A.G.
E. Graham	E.Gr.	A.S. Gynn	A.S.G.

Miss Nichols	M.N.	C. Nicholson	C.N.
C.W. Nichols	C.W.N.	Miss I. Nicholson	I.N.
Mrs C. Orchard	C.O.	Major R. Orme	R.O.
Dr C.N. Page	C.N.P.	F.H. Perrycoste	F.H.P.
J.R. Palmer	J.R.P.	Mrs M.M. Perrycoste	M.M.P.
R.C. Palmer	R.C.P.	W.B. Perrycoste	W.B.P.
R. Pankhurst	R.P.	J.L. Peters	J.L.P.
Mrs J.A. Paton	J.A.P.	Miss R.M. Phillips	R.M.P.
H.W. Paynter	H.W.P.	Mrs L. Philpott	L.P.
Rev. G.T. Pearce	G.T.P.	K. Plummer	K.P.
R.D. Pearce	R.D.P.	T.J. Porter	T.J.P.
Rev. T.N. Smith Pearce	T.N.S.P.	C. Preston	C.P.
R. Pease	R.Pe.	Rev. A.L. Primavesi	A.L.P.
Miss H. Pendray	H.P.	Dr C.T. Prime	C.T.P.
Dr F.H. Perring	F.P.	H.W. Pugsley	H.W.P.
E.J. Perry	E.J.P.		
Dr O. Rackham	O.R.	T. Ricketts	T.R.
Dr D. Ranwell	D.R.	Rev. H.J. Riddelsdell	H.J.R.
J.E. Raven	J.E.R.	F. Rilstone	F.R.
E.A. Rees	E.A.R.	N. Robinson	N.R.
J.S. Rees	J.S.R.	R.B. Rogers	R.B.R.
C. Reid	C.R.	Rev. W. Moyle Rogers	W.M.R.
Mrs M. Reiss	M.Re.	Miss I.M. Roper	I.M.R.
Miss P.J. Renwick	P.J.R.	Miss E. Roseveare	E.R.
Dr A.J. Richards	A.J.R.	Miss J. Rowles	J.Ro.
Mrs J. Richards	J.R.	S. Russell	S.R.
M. Rickard	M.R.		
C.E. Salmon	C.E.S.	R.L. Smith	R.L.S.
N.Y. Sandwith	N.Y.S.	Mrs Watson Smyth	W.S.
H.B. Sargent	H.B.S.	Dr G. Soal	G.S.
J. Scott	J.S.	Dr C.A. Stace	C.A.S.
P.D. Sell	P.D.S.	Mrs B. Stanley	B.S.
Mrs D. Sharrock	D.Sh.	F.N. Stansfield	F.N.S.
B. Sheen	B.Sh.	Dr T.S. Stephenson	T.S.S.
Mrs Sheldon	M.S.	J.H.A. Steuart	J.H.A.S.
Mrs V. Shrieves	V.S.	C. Stevens	C.S.
A. Shrimpton	A.S.	Mrs S. Stewart	S.S.
Dr A.J. Silverside	A.Si.	A.L. Still	A.L.S.
F.W. Simpson	F.W.S.	D. Stoves	D.St.
N.D. Simpson	N.D.S.	D. Stoyel	D.S.
Mrs D.M. Sinclair	D.M.S.	Miss B.M. Sturdy	B.M.S.
Miss K.M. Skinner	K.M.S.	R.I. Sworder	R.I.S.
Dr A.J.E. Smith	A.J.S.	Mrs R.W. Sworder	R.W.S.
R. Smith	R.Sm.		
P.M. Taschereau	P.M.T.	W. Tresidder	W.D.
P. Taylor	P.Ta.	J. Trimen	J.T.

P.J. Terry	P.T.	P.J.O. Trist	P.J.T.
Miss E. Thomas	E.Th.	J. Trunson	J.Tr.
J.G. Thomas	J.G.T.	Mrs S.M. Turk	S.M.T.
Mrs H.S. Thompson	H.S.T.	Mr and Mrs D. Turner	D.T.
Rev. A. Thornley	A.Th.	Major General P.G.	
E. Thurston	E.T.	Turpin	P.Tu.
Miss E.S. Todd	E.S.T.	Professor T.G. Tutin	T.G.Tu.
C.C. Townsend	C.C.T.	Miss A. Tyley	A.T.
Miss D.E. de Vesian	D.E.V.	Miss C. Vivian	C.V.
C.C. Vigurs	C.C.V.	Miss A. Vowler	A.V.
Dr S.M. Walters	S.M.W.	Mrs G. White	G.W.
P. Ward	P.W.	Miss P. Wickham	P.Wi.
J.M. Watson	J.M.W.	E.B. Wilkinson	E.B.W.
W. Watson	W.W.	T. Willcocks	T.W.
W.D. Watson	W.D.W.	E.L. Williams	E.L.W.
C.H. Watts	C.H.W.	Mrs M. Williams	M.W.
Mrs M. Watts	M.Wa.	P.D. Williams	P.D.W.
E. Webster	E.W.	R.F. Williams	R.F.W.
Miss M. McCallum Webster	M.M.W.	Miss A. Wilson	A.W.
Dr C. West	C.We.	Mrs D.P. Wilson	D.P.W.
Mrs E. West	E.We.	W. Wise	W.Wi.
Mrs L. Wharton	L.W.	Miss N.D. Wood	N.D.W.
Miss E. Whelan	E.Wh.	C. Woolf	C.W.
Mrs G. Whicker	G.Wh.		
Dr P.F. Yeo	P.F.Y.	A.J. Young	A.J.Y.
Mrs J.M. Yorston	J.M.Y.	A. Younger	A.Y.

(b) Groups and organisations

BRC	Biological Records Centre, Monks Wood Experimental Station.
BSBI	Field meeting of the Botanical Society of the British Isles
CFH	Lizard records of Messrs Coombe, Frost, & Hopkins
CRNHS	Field meeting of the Camborne-Redruth Natural History Society
LFC	Field meeting of the Lizard Field Club
CNT	Field meeting of the Cornwall Naturalists' Trust
NAAS	National Agricultural Advisory Service
NCS	Nature Conservancy Council survey
RNHS	Records from members of the Rye Natural History Society
WFS	Records from the Wild Flower Society

(c) **Herbaria**

   (i) National, municipal, and university

BIRM	University of Birmingham, Department of Botany
BM	British Museum (Natural History), London
CGE	Cambridge University, Botany School
E	Royal Botanic Garden, Edinburgh
K	Royal Botanic Gardens, Kew
KIEL	University of Kiel, Botanisches Institut
LTR	University of Leicester
LIV	Liverpool City Museum
LIVU	Liverpool University, Department of Botany
OXF	Oxford University, Department of Botany
RAMM	Royal Albert Memorial Museum, Exeter
SDN	Swindon Borough Museum
UCNW	University College of North Wales, Bangor, Department of Botany

   (ii) Personal and local

Herb. S. Bannister	Truro Museum (**TRU**)
Herb. F.H. Davey	Truro Museum (**TRU**)
Herb. J.E. Lousley	University of Reading (**RNG**)
Herb. Marl. Coll.	Marlborough College, Wiltshire (**MBH**)
Herb. F.H. Perrycoste	Truro Museum (**TRU**)
Herb. Tech. Coll.	Technical Coll., Pool, Camborne
Herb. E. Stackhouse	Truro Museum (**TRU**)
Herb. Willis	Communicated by the late Miss Janet C.N. Willis; and the herbarium is presumably that belonging either to her father, H.G. Willis, or to her grandfather, the Rev. H.M. Willis. We have failed to locate it.
Herb. W. Wise	Launceston Museum (**LAUS**)

(d) **Books and papers cited**

BRIGGS, T. Archer (1880). *Flora of Plymouth.* London.

COPE, T.A., & STACE, C.A., (1978). The Juncus bufonius L. aggregate in Western Europe, *Watsonia*, **12**: 113–128.

DANDY, J.E. (1958). *List of British Vascular Plants.* London.

DAVEY, F. Hamilton (1909). *Flora of Cornwall* ('Flora'). Penryn. Reprinted, with Supplement, 1978. Wakefield.

DONY, J.G., ROB, C.M., & PERRING, F.H. (1974). *English names of wild flowers.* London.

JERMY, A.C., ARNOLD, H.R., FARRELL, L., & PERRING, F.H. (1978). *Atlas of ferns of the British Isles.* London.

LOUSLEY, J.E. (1971). *The flora of the Isles of Scilly.* Newton Abbot.

MARSDEN-JONES, E.M., & TURRILL, W.B. (1954). *British Knapweeds.* London.

MARTIN, W. Keble, & FRASER, G.T. (1939). *Flora of Devon.* Arbroath.

PATON, J.A. (1968). *Wild flowers in Cornwall.* Truro.

PERRING, F.H. (1968). *Critical supplement to the atlas of the British flora.* London.

PERRING, F.H., & WALTERS, S.M. (1962). *Atlas of the British flora.* London.

PUGSLEY, H.W. (1948). A prodromus of the British Hieracia, *J.Linn.Soc.London,* 54: 1—356.

RICHARDS, A.J. (1972). The Taraxacum flora of the British Isles, supplement (pp. 1—141) to *Watsonia,* 9.

RICHARDS, A.J. (1981). New species of Taraxacum from the British Isles, *Watsonia,* 13: 185—193.

RILSTONE, F. (1927). Cornish Rubi, *J.roy.Inst.Cornwall,* 22: 269—280.

RILSTONE, F (1928). Cornish Rubi, *J.roy.Inst.Cornwall,* 22: 364—365.

RILSTONE, F. (1939). *Notes on Cornish Rubi,* MS in Truro Museum.

RILSTONE, F. (1940a). A new Rubus for Cornwall, *J. Bot. London,* 78: 13—14.

RILSTONE, F. (1940b). Three East Cornwall brambles, *J.Bot.London,* 78: 164—167.

RILSTONE, F. (1950). Some Cornish Rubi, *J.Linn.Soc. Bot.,* 53: 413—421.

RILSTONE, F. (1952). Rubi from Dartmoor to the Land's End, *Watsonia,* 2: 151—162.

STACE, C.A., ed. (1975). *Hybridization and the flora of the British Isles.* London.

THURSTON, E. (1928). Note on the Cornish flora, *J.roy. Inst.Cornwall,* 22: 350—363.

THURSTON, E. (1929a). Note on the Cornish flora, *J.roy. Inst.Cornwall,* 23: 74—86.

THURSTON, E. (1929b). The alien and British plants of Par and Charlestown harbours, Falmouth docks, and Eastern Green, Penzance, *J.roy.Inst.Cornwall:* 23: 137—205.

THURSTON, E. (1930). Note on the Cornish flora, *J.roy. Inst.Cornwall,* 23: 274—287.

THURSTON, E. (1935). Notes on the Cornish flora, 1930—1934, *J.roy.Inst.Cornwall,* 24: 240—286.

THURSTON, E. (1936). Note on the Cornish flora, 1935, *J.roy.Inst.Cornwall*, 24: 341—344.

THURSTON, E., & VIGURS, C.C. (1922). *A supplement to F. Hamilton Davey's flora of Cornwall* ('Suppt'). Truro.

THURSTON, E., & VIGURS, C.C. (1923). Note on the Cornish flora, *J.roy.Inst.Cornwall*, 21: 164—168.

THURSTON, E., & VIGURS, C.C. (1924). Note on the Cornish flora, *J.roy.Inst.Cornwall*, 21: 321—335.

THURSTON, E., & VIGURS, C.C. (1925). Note on the Cornish flora, *J.roy.Inst.Cornwall*, 21: 455—469.

THURSTON, E., & VIGURS, C.C. (1926). Note on the Cornish flora, *J.roy.Inst. Cornwall*, 22: 99—112.

THURSTON, E., & VIGURS, C.C. (1927). Note on the Cornish flora, *J.roy.Inst.Cornwall*, 22. 252—268.

TUTIN, T.G., HEYWOOD, V.H., BURGES, N.A., VALENTINE, D.H., WALTERS, S.M. & WEBB, D.A., eds (1964—80). *Flora europaea*, 5 volumes. Cambridge.

WATSON, W.C.R. (1958). *Handbook of the Rubi of Great Britain and Ireland.* Cambridge.

(e) Periodicals cited

Botanical Exchange Club of the British Isles: Reports 1879—1948 ('B.E.C.').

Botanical Society of the British Isles:
   News, 1972 — ('B.S.B.I. News')
   Proceedings, 1954—1969 ('Proc.B.S.B.I.')
   Watsonia, 1949—
   Year Book, 1949—1953 ('B.S.B.I. Year')

Cornishman, The, 1878— Penzance

Western Morning News, 1860— Plymouth

Note: The dates of the B.E.C. Reports and B.S.B.I. Year Books quoted are those on the title page and not the dates of publication, which are sometimes obscure. References are to the lists of New Records, unless otherwise indicated.

Signs   *   signifies new vice-county record since Thurston & Vigurs' Supplement 1922. For Scilly, it signifies a new record for the Isles since Lousley's *Flora* 1971.

         §   signifies that the plant is an introduced species.

         [ ]   square brackets mark errors that are to be removed from the Cornish list.

PTERIDOPHYTA

LYCOPODIACEAE
LYCOPODIUM L.

1/4   **L. clavatum L.**   Stag's-horn Clubmoss
Although there are plenty of suitable habitats, there are no recent records for the county.
East: 05, Starrick Moor, 1920, L.T.M. (Thurston & Vigurs 1923).

LYCOPODIELLA HOLUB = LEPIDOTIS BEAUV.

1/2   **L. inundata (L.)** Holub   Marsh Clubmoss
(Lycopodium inundatum L.)
Rare and local, but easily overlooked, and possibly elsewhere in the county.
East: 96, Goss Moor (Flora), still there, post—1950, J.A.P.; 05, Carbis Moor, J.A.P.; Carvear, St Blazey, L.T.M. (Thurston and Vigurs 1928); 06, in quantity, Retire Common, L.J.M.

HUPERZIA BERNH.

1/1   **H. selago (L.)** Bernh.ex Schrank & Mart.   Fir Clubmoss
(Lycopodium selago L.)
Very rare and local, but, like the last species, easily overlooked.
West: 71, Goonhilly Downs (Flora), persisted until 1966, D.E.C.
East: 18, Rough Tor, one plant, K.H.; 27, Kilmar Tor, M.L.

SELAGINELLACEAE
SELAGINELLA BEAUV.

2/2   § S. kraussiana (G. Kunze) A. Braun   Mossy Clubmoss
West: 42, Penzance, G.B.M.; 43, Trevaylor Woods, near Penzance, B.M.S.; Gulval churchyard, RNHS; 71, Landewednack (Suppt, as *S. denticulata Link*), still there, 1971, N.J.F.; 72, Glendurgan Gardens, B.E.M.G.; 73, Penjerrick, Falmouth, L.J.M.; Boslowick, Falmouth, L.J.M.; 83, Trelissick, B.E.M.G.
*East: 83, St Just churchyard, B.E.M.G.; 84 by old ruin, Trehane, near Truro, B.E.M.G.; 05, Porthpean, St Austell (B.E.C. 1927); 36, grounds of Newton Ferrers, E.Wh.
Scilly: Lousley 1971.

ISOETACEAE

ISOETES L.

3/2   **I. echinospora** Durieu = *I. setacea* auct. non Lam.

Spring Quillwort

In one station only.

*East: 17, Dozmary Pool, 1934, C.O. (Thurston 1936), still there, post—1950, R.W.D.

3/3   **I. histrix** Bory   Land Quillwort

This extremely small species has been recorded in the United Kingdom only from the Lizard and the Channel Isles.

West: 61, Caerthillian Valley (Suppt), still there, and in eight further stations, CFH; 71, now known in three stations, CFH.

EQUISETACEAE

EQUISETUM L.

Common species: 4/9 **E. arvense** L., Field Horsetail, and 4/6 **E. palustre** L., Marsh Horsetail (absent from Scilly).

4/4   **E. variegatum** Schleicher ex Weber & Mohr

Variegated Horsetail

Probably a fairly recent arrival in Cornwall. In both localities, the plants are referable to var. *arenarium* Newm.

*West: 53, Upton Towans, 1977, L.J.M.; 75, Penhale Sands, 1977, BSBI *(Watsonia*, **12**: 167).

4/5   **E. fluviatile** L.   Water Horsetail
(E. limosum L.)

More frequent and widespread than the records in the Flora and Supplement suggest.

West: 33, near Portheras Cove, J.A.P.; Bostraze, near St Just, J.A.P.; 42, near Kerris, Newlyn, B.M.S.; 43, Chy-an-dour, Penzance, J.R.P.; 53, St Erth, B.M.S.; 62, Gunwalloe Valley, L.J.M.; 63, Porkellis Moor, B.J. and E.J., and S.M.T.; 72, Maenporth Valley, L.J.M.; 73, Stithians Reservoir, L.J.M.; 74, Trewince Moor, Gwennap L.J.M.; 85, Newlyn East, CNT; 86, Mawgan Porth Valley, L.J.M.

East: 95, quarry near St Dennis, J.A.P.; 05, Pelyn

Wood, CNT; 06, Retire Common, L.J.M.; Red Moor, E.A. and L.J.M.; 08, Port Gaverne Valley; 16, NE of Cardinham, J.A.P.; 17, Whitebarrow Downs, St Neot, J.A.P.; 21, Tamar Lake, J.A.P.; 27, near Harrowbridge, Fowey Valley, S.M.

4/9 x5 **E. arvense x fluviatile** = *E.x litorale*   Kühlew. ex Rupr.
This hybrid is almost certainly under-recorded in Cornwall.

*West: 53, St Erth gravel-pits, CNT; 63, Newton Moor, L.J.M.; 64, Ashill Woods, R.J.M. and C.N.P.; 75, Penhale Sands, L.J.M.; 85, near old railway track, Newlyn East, CNT.

*East: 94, Caerhayes (B.E.C. 1941—2).

4/7 **E. sylvaticum** L.   Wood Horsetail
There are no recent records for this species, but it may still survive in the NE of the county.

*West: 62, Loe Pool, undated, but pre—1950, Herb. W. Harrison, LIV.

East: 29, near Week St Mary, R.O. (Thurston and Vigurs 1925); Week Ford (Thurston and Vigurs 1923). These two stations are an extension of the site in the Supplement 'between Ashbury and Berry Court.'

4/10 **E. telmateia** Ehrh.   Great Horsetail
(E. maximum Lam.)

Only in a very few scattered localities.

West: 71, Coverack (Flora), still there, 1950 onwards, various recorders; 72, Rosenithon, W.T. (Thurston 1928), still there, 1979, and in the adjacent Godrevy Cove (82), various recorders.

East: 95, by railway at St Dennis Junction, B.B.; 08, Bossiney (Flora), still there, 1966, J.A.P.; 47, Gunnislake, J.S.R.

OPHIOGLOSSACEAE
BOTRYCHIUM SW.
28/1 **B. lunaria** (L.) Swartz   Moonwort
Local and rare, and not refound in any of the old localities, but possibly overlooked.

West: 43, Trenowin Downs, Towednack, 1965, G.L.

East: 17, SW of Dozmary Pool, one plant, C.P.F. (Thurston and Vigurs 1927); 18, Crowdy Marsh, Bodmin Moor, 1973, E.A.

Scilly: Lousley 1971.

OPHIOGLOSSUM L.

29/Ia **O. vulgatum** L.   Adder's-tongue

Very local and rare. None of the older records have been refound.

West: 53, Phillack Towans, CRNHS; 75, Penhale Sands, L.J.M.; near the Gliding School, Perranporth, B.M.S.

East: 20, Efford Down, Bude, R.O. (Thurston and Vigurs 1925), still there, 1978, L.J.M.

Scilly: Lousley 1971; B, damp pasture, V.G.

29/Ib **O. azoricum** C. Presl
(O. vulgatum var. *polyphyllum* Braun.)

Only on the Isles of Scilly.
Scilly: Lousley 1971.

29/2 **O. lusitanicum** L.   Early Adder's-tongue

First found on St Agnes, Isles of Scilly, by J.E. Raven in 1950. An earlier record for the Land's End area was rejected by Davey (Flora), but it could have been correct, and the plant should be searched for.

Scilly: Lousley 1971; A, plentiful along cliff-path over Wingletang Downs, 1971, J.E.Lo.

OSMUNDACEAE

OSMUNDA L.

5/1 **O. regalis** L., Royal Fern, is still remarkably frequent in suitable habitats throughout the county, but is very scarce in the Lower Tamar area.

ADIANTACEAE

ADIANTUM L.

11/1 **A. capillus-veneris** L.   Maidenhair Fern

In a few scattered localities around the coasts as a native, but more frequent as an introduction.

West: 43, in six stations on walls, Penzance, G.B.M.; Chy-an-dour, near Penzance, B.M.S.; 53, Lelant (Flora), still there, 1956, J.B.; Carbis Bay (Flora), 1967, B.M.S.; 64, near Reskadinnick, Camborne, R.J.M.; 83, on wall, Trelissick, L.J.M.; 97, on brickwork of Padstow Station, L.J.M.

East: 83, wall at St Mawes, E.A.; 93, Camels Cove, Portloe (Suppt), still there, 1933, F.H.P.; 97, Ship Inn, Wadebridge, R.D.P.; Porthilly Cove, Camel Estuary, E.H.; Markham's Quay, Lundy Bay, R.W.D.; (98), in two places on Pentire Peninsula, R.W.D.; Port Isaac (Flora), 1968, L.B.; 08, Trebarwith (Flora), 1978, D.Ha.; 15, Lantic Bay, near Fowey, J.S.R.; 46, in old lime-kilns on Cotehele Quay, I.N.

Scilly: Lousley 1971; M, five plants, Hugh Town, V.G.

HYMENOPHYLLACEAE
HYMENOPHYLLUM SM.

7/1   **H. tunbrigense** (L.) Sm.   Tunbridge Filmy-fern

Still in a number of localities on granite outcrops, and in rocky streams.

West: 64, Carn Brea, Redruth, L.J.M.; 73, Kennall Wood, Ponsanooth (Flora), still there, 1980, CNT; College Wood, Penryn (Flora), still there, 1962, L.J.M.; near Budock Church, D.Sh.; Budock Bottom, L.J.M.

East: 05, Luxulyan Valley, R.D.P.; Prideaux Wood (Flora), 1966, R.D.P.; Pelyn Wood, M.L.; 07, De Lank Valley, J.A.P.; 17, near De Lank Bridge (Suppt), 1970, J.A.P.; 18, Rough Tor (Flora), 1960, E.A.; 19, Peters Wood, near Minster Church, E.A.; 25, near Sowdens Bridge, Looe Valley, J.A.P.; 26, Golitha Falls (Suppt), post—1950, E.A.; 27, woods W of Northill, J.A.P.; by R. Fowey, J.A.P.; Trewartha Tor, S.M.; Hawks Tor (Flora), 1971, S.M.

7/2   **H. wilsonii** Hook.   Wilson's Filmy-fern
(H. peltatum Desv.)

Only on the granite tors. Still in most of the old stations.

West: 43, Carn Galva (Flora), post—1950, B.M.S.

East: 17, Brown Willy, L.J.M.; 18, Rough Tor (Flora), 1959, E.A., 1979, K.H.; 27, Hawks Tor (Flora), 1970, J.Fo.; Sharp Tor, R.D.P.; Cheesewring (Flora), post—1950, Herb.Tech.Coll.

TRICHOMANES L.

6/1   **T. speciosum** Willd.   Killarney Fern

In a damp, shaded valley. This sole station was rejected by Davey (Flora), but the record was correct, and the plant is still to be found there.

East: 08, St Nectan's Kieve (Flora), confirmed *c* 1928, E.W.M., and refound, 1965, R.J.M.

POLYPODIACEAE

POLYPODIUM L.

25/1/1   **P. vulgare** Polypody, and   25/1/3   *   **P. interjectum** Shivas, Intermediate Polypody, are common and widespread species throughout the county.

25/I/2   **P. australe** Fée   Southern Polypody
(P. vulgare L., var. *serratum* Willd.)

In a few scattered localities in Cornwall, mainly in the SE, on walls, rarely on rock or trees.

West: 97, Padstow (Flora), frequent, 1972, M.R.   On rock as well as walls in this locality.

*East: 94, Tregoney, L.J.M.; 06, Lanhydrock Vicarage, B.G.; 15, luxuriant on wall behind the church, Fowey, L.J.M.; two plants, Polruan, L.J.M.; Lanreath, specimen in Herb. F.H. Perrycoste (TRU), still there, 1977, L.J.M.; 25, in small quantity, Looe, L.J.M.; 35, Port Eliot, St Germans, post—1950, BRC, frequent in the village, 1979, L.J.M.; on tree, St Germans Quay, L.J.M.; 45, frequent on walls, Saltash, L.J.M.; on sea-wall, Mt Edgecumbe, BSBI.

25/I/3   **P. interjectum x vulgare** = *P. x mantoniae* Rothm.

Almost certainly more frequent than these records indicate.

*West: 85, Trewalla, near Rejerrah, S of Newquay, 1964, L.J.M.; 86, Lane, near Newquay, 1964, L.J.M.
*East: 95, between Fraddon and Retew, 1964, L.J.M.

DENNSTAEDTIACEAE

PTERIDIUM SCOP.

8/1   **P. aquilinum** (L.) Kuhn, Bracken, is very common throughout the county.

THELYPTERIDACEAE
THELYPTERIS SCHMIDEL
24/2 **T. thelypteroides** Michx = *T. palustris* Schott
subsp. **glabra** Holub   Marsh Fern
A recent and interesting addition to the county flora.
*West: 42, Clodgy Moor, near Penzance, 1967, CNT.

PHEGOPTERIS (C.PRESL) FÉE
24/3 **P. connectilis** (Michx) Watt = *Thelypteris phegopteris*
(L.) Slosson   Beech Fern
(P. polypodioides Fée)

Very rare, and not seen in recent years.
East: 17, Brown Willy (Flora), refound *c* 1930,
E.W.M.; 18, Rough Tor, *c* 1930, E.W.M.

OREOPTERIS HOLUB
24/I **O. limbosperma** (All.) Holub = *Thelypteris limbosperma*
(All.) H.P. Fuchs
(Lastrea montana T. Moore)   Lemon-scented Fern

Still frequent on Bodmin Moor, rare elsewhere.
West: 63, Porkellis Valley, L.J.M.; 73, Penmarth,
Carnmenellis, L.J.M.; Tretheague Moor, Stithians,
L.J.M.; 74, Carn Marth, Redruth, L.J.M.
East: 95, Hensbarrow Downs, L.J.M.; near Biscovellet,
St Austell, L.J.M.; 96, Retire Common, R.W.D.; 16,
Cardinham Downs, E.A. and L.J.M.; 17, De Lank River,
from quarries to Bradford, E.A. and R.W.D.; near
Brown Willy, L.J.M.; near Temple Bridge, L.J.M.;
Redhill Marsh, R.Go. and L.J.M.; Smallacombe, Fowey
Valley, R.Go. and L.J.M.; 18, Bowithick, E.A.; Otter-
ham, L.J.M.; 27, Cheesewring, R.W.D. and L.J.M.

ASPLENIACEAE
ASPLENIUM L.
Common species: 14/1 **A. scolopendrium** L. *(Phyllitis
scolopendrium* Newm.), Hart's-tongue, 15/1 **A. adiantum
nigrum** L., Black Spleenwort, 15/4 **A. marinum** L., Sea
Spleenwort, and 15/5b **A. trichomanes** L., subsp.
quadrivalens D.E. Meyer, Maidenhair Spleenwort (rare
in Scilly).

15/4 **A. marinum L.**
var. acutum T. Moore
West: 86, near Newquay, specimen in Herb.E. Stackhouse **(TRU)**, is this variety, ? = Pentire Point East, 1979, L.J.M.

15/2 **A. billotii x scolopendrium** = *Asplenium x microdon*
x 14/1 (T. Moore) Lovis & Vida
(*A. lanceolatum* Huds. var. *microdon* T. Moore)
West: 42 or 43, near Penzance (Flora), 1856 (Thurston and Vigurs 1924). Not found since.

15/1 **A. adiantum-nigrum x scolopendrium** = *A. x jacksonii*
x 14/1 (Alston) Lawalrée
*West: 43, recorded for this square in Jermy et al, 1978.

[15/Ib **A. onopteris L.**
(*A. adiantum-nigrum* var. *acutum* Bory)
Davey (Flora) rejected this species, as requiring confirmation. In recent years a taxon has been found on the Lizard which approaches this, but an unequivocal voucher specimen is required before this species can be added to the Cornish list.]

[15/Ic **A. cuneifolium Viv.** Serpentine Black Spleenwort
In 1978 and 1979, plants were collected from parts of the Lizard which appeared to belong to this species. More recently, however, experimental work has shown that the Cornish plants thus named do not conform to European material. We, therefore, have no alternative but to remove this species from the Cornish list. We are indebted to Dr A. Sleep for alerting us to this situation.]

15/2 **A. billotii F.W. Schultz** Lanceolate Spleenwort
(*A. lanceolatum* Huds.)
This fern is still frequent in Cornwall, especially in the West. It is rarely present in quantity, however, and often goes unnoticed. The removal of old walls has no doubt contributed to a gradual decrease in numbers.
West: 32, Kelynack, B.M.S.; St Levan, K.H.; Sennen Cove (Flora), 1970, E.W.; 33, Cape Cornwall, L.J.M.; Kenidjack, L.J.M.; Cot Valley, St Just, M.C.; S of St Just, J.A.P.; Letcha Farm, St Just, G.B.M.; 42, Pen-

berth Cove, K.H.; Newlyn (Suppt), post—1950, B.M.S.; Wherry Town, Penzance, comm. G.B.M.; 43, Bosullow, S of Morvah, B.M.S.; Penzance, G.B.M.; around Gulval, B.M.S.; 52, St Michaels Mount (Flora), 1967, J.A.P.; Trewavas Head, J.A.P.; 53, Marazion, B.M.S.; Trencrom Hill, L.J.M.; 61, Predannack Wollas, J.A.P.; Rill Head, H.F.D. (Thurston 1928); 62, Porthleven, H.B.S.; Halsferran Cliff, L.C.F.; 64, near Portreath, L.J.M.; 71, near Coverack, L.C.F.; Hot Point, Lizard (Flora), 1959, J.Fo.; Housel Bay, R.H.; Black Head, Lizard, J.A.P.; 73, Stithians (Flora), Tregonning Moor, post— 1950, L.J.M.; Eathorne, near Constantine, L.J.M.; Treverva, Mabe, L.J.M.; Lanner, L.J.M.; 74, E of St Day, J.A.P.; 75, Bolingey, R.Go.; 83, Castle Drive, Falmouth, L.J.M.

East: 84, Pencalenick, C.J.; 93, The Jacka, Portloe, B.E.M.G.; 04, Trenarren, St Austell (Suppt), post— 1950, L.J.M.; 08, Port Gaverne, A.P.H.; Trebarwith, R.W.D. and L.J.M.; Tintagel (Flora), post—1950, E.A.; Rocky Valley (Flora), 1974, B.G. and R.J.M.; (09), Forrabury, Boscastle (Flora), post—1950, E.A.; 17, Blisland (Flora), 1978, L.J.M.; 19, Beeny Cliff, Boscastle, J.A.P.; 25, Polperro (Suppt), 1979, K.H.; 46, Calstock (Flora), 1974, I.N.; 47, Gunnislake, I.N. Scilly: common, Lousley 1971.

15/7 **A. ruta-muraria** L.   Wall-rue Spleenwort
Frequent in E Cornwall, but rather rare in the West. West: 42, Penzance, G.B.M.; 42 or 43, Penare, Penzance, E.A.R. (Thurston 1930); 43, two places in this part of Penzance, G.B.M.; Towednack, P.J.R.; 53, Angarrack, Hayle, J.S.R.; (54), St Ives, G.B.M.; 62, Porthleven, H.B.S., 62 or 63, Trannack, near Helston, H.B.S.; 63, Crowan (Flora), still there, 1968, J.B.; 71, Ruan Minor (Suppt), 1948, J.B.; 73, Budock Church, L.J.M.

East: Frequent and widespread.
*Scilly: Lousley 1971, with doubt; MN, wall, St Martins, 1979, D.W.L.

[15/8 **A. septentrionale** (L.) Hoffm.   Forked Spleenwort
An old record for Cornwall is rejected by Davey (Flora), and, in the absence of further records, we have no hesitation in doing the same.]

16/1   **A. ceterach** L.   Rustyback
(Ceterach officinarum Willd.)

Rare in W Cornwall, becoming more frequent in the East.

West: 33, St Just, M.C.; 43, Trevarrack, Penzance, B.M.S.; Gulval B.M.S. Madron (Flora), 1964, J.B.; 53 (54), Godrevy Hill, M.W.; 71, Poltesco, J.Fo.; 72, near St Anthony-in-Meneage, J.S.R.; 73, Stithians (Flora), post—1950, R.H.; Penryn, R.H.; 85, Trevemper Bridge, near Newquay, E.T. and L.T.M. (Thurston 1935); 97, railway between Padstow and Wadebridge, S.M.

East: widespread, especially in the Lower Tamar area.
Scilly: one station, Lousley 1971.

ATHYRIACEAE

ATHYRIUM ROTH

18/1   **A. filix-femina** (L.) Roth, Lady-fern, is common and widespread.

GYMNOCARPIUM NEWMAN

24/4   **G. dryopteris** (L.) Newman   Oak Fern
(Phegopteris dryopteris Fée)

Always very rare, this fern has not been seen in the county for many years.

East: 17, Brown Willy, *c* 1930, E.W.M.

CYSTOPTERIS BERNH.

19/1   **C. fragilis** (L.) Bernh.   Brittle Bladder-fern

Common in the N of England and in Scotland, this fern is of the utmost rarity in Cornwall.

West: 73, in fair quantity on wall at Penjerrick, Falmouth, 1961—1978, L.J.M.

East: 08, one plant on rock, Rocky Valley, 1973, B.G., now gone; 18, one plant on stone of Slaughter Bridge, 1957, R.W.D.; 46, on rock by Tamar, Landulph, C.P.H. (Thurston 1935).

ASPIDIACEAE
POLYSTICHUM ROTH.

22/2   **P. aculeatum** (L.) Roth   Hard Shield-fern
There are no reliable recent records, all material seen
being referable to extreme forms of the next species.
The following old records, however, appear to be
correct.
West: 63, Wendron, 1875, J. Cunnack, **K.**
East: 46, St Dominick, 1868, T.A. Briggs, **BM**; Carkeel,
near Saltash, T.A. Briggs, **BM.**

22/1   **P. setiferum** (Forsk.) Woynar   Soft Shield-fern
Widespread and locally common, but absent from a few
areas, and becoming rare in the extreme West, and in
Scilly. A form simulating the previous species is common
in shady places around the southern estuaries, and this
may well be the source of J.E. Lousley's record for
P. aculeatum.

DRYOPTERIS ADANSON
Common species: 21/1 D. filix-mas (L.) Schott *(Lastrea
filix-mas* Presl), Male-fern, 21/2 D. **pseudomas**
(Wollaston) Holub and Pouzar *(L. filix-mas* var. *paleacea*
T. Moore), Scaly Male-fern, and 21/7 D. **dilatata**
(Hoffm.) A. Gray *(L. aristata* Rendle and Britten),
Broad Buckler-fern.

21/1   **D. filix-mas x pseudomas =** *D. x tavelii* Rothm. von
x 2   Tavel's Male-fern.
     *East: 08, St Nectan's Glen, 1978, C.N.P.

21/8   **D. aemula** (Ait.) Kuntze   Hay-scented Buckler-fern
(Lastrea aemula Brackenridge)
Widespread throughout the county in woods and shady
lanes, but rarely in quantity.
West: 43, Dingdong, near Penzance, N.J.F.; Chysauster,
B.M.S.; Boskednan, B.M.S.; 53, Nanpusker Valley, near
Hayle, A.B.; 62, Methleigh, near Porthleven, H.B.S.;
63, near Crowan Vicarage, W.T. (Thurston and Vigurs
1927); Releath, L.J.M.; Treskillard, one plant, L.J.M.;
72, Polwheveral, Helford River, L.J.M.; near Maen-
porth, L.J.M.; St Martin Green, W.T. (Thurston and
Vigurs 1927); near Porth Navas, in quantity, L.J.M.;

73, Swanvale, Falmouth (Flora), post—1950, L.J.M.; Eathorne, near Constantine, L.J.M.; 74, Tregavethan, near Truro, L.J.M.; 84, St Clement Wood, Idless, L.J.M.; 85, St Allen, near Truro, L.J.M.; 86, Carnanton Woods, Vale of Lanherne, CNT.; 96, Black Cross, near St Columb Road, L.J.M.

East: 84, Lamorran Wood, L.J.M.; 05, Prideaux Wood, St Blazey, L.J.M.; 06, Hustyn Wood, St Breock, L.J.M.; Ruthernbridge, L.J.M.; Park Wood, Bodmin, L.J.M.; 16, Wood near Pelyne Farm, E.A.; 27, near Dozmary Pool, R.W.D.; 19, Peters Wood, Boscastle, L.J.M.; Tresparett Posts, R.W.D. and L.J.M.; near Marshgate, R.W.D. and L.J.M.; Dizzard Cliff, J.F.A.; 20, Hunthill Wood, near Stratton, J.A.P.; 21, Lee Wood, Coombe Valley, L.J.M.; 25, Sowdens Bridge, Looe Valley, L.J.M.; 28, near Treneglos, L.J.M.; 29, Week Ford, Week St Mary, L.J.M., 37, Luckett Wood, A.B.; Greenscombe Wood, Tamar Valley, S.M., 46, near Botusfleming, I.N. Scilly: not seen for many years, Lousley 1971.

21/6   **D. carthusiana** (Vill.) H.P.Fuchs   Narrow Buckler-fern
(Lastrea spinulosa Presl)

Rather local and rare, and mostly in the Bodmin Moor catchment area.

West: 43, near Lanyon Quoit, B.M.S.; 72, valley S of Helford, J.A.P.; 73, Budock Water, J.F.A. and R.Go.

East: 85, near Ladock, L.J.M.; 06, Hustyn Wood, St Breock, J.A.P., 16, Cabilla Wood, Fowey Valley, L.J.M.; 20, Hunthill Wood, near Stratton, J.A.P.; 26, near Treverbyn Bridge, Fowey Valley, J.A.P.; 27, N of Henwood, J.A.P.; 28, near Red Down, Egloskerry, J.A.P.

Scilly: not seen recently, Lousley 1971; but since found at M, lane to Watermill Cove, R. Stokoe.

21/7   D. dilatata x carthusiana = *D. x deweveri* (Jansen)
x 6   Jansen and Wachter.

*East: 17, recorded for this square in Jermy *et al.* 1978.

BLECHNACEAE
BLECHNUM L.

13/1   B. spicant (L.) Roth, Hard Fern, is frequent and wide-spread on the mainland of Cornwall, but thought to be extinct in Scilly, Lousley 1971, until recently found on MN, three plants near Lower Town, 1975, F.W.S.

The following ferns have all been recorded for Cornwall in the past, but were rejected by Davey (Flora), as unlikely to have occurred, and we support him in this view, especially as no further evidence has come to light.

[9/1   Cryptogramma crispa R.Br., Parsley Fern, 15/3, Asplenium fontanum (L.) Bernh., and 21/5 **Dryopteris cristata** (L.) A. Gray *(Lastrea cristata* Presl), Crested Buckler-fern.]

MARSILEACEAE
PILULARIA L.

26/1   **P. globulifera** L.   Pillwort

A rare plant of acid pools, old mine-workings, and wet heathland.

West: 53, between Penzance and Marazion (Flora), refound, post—1950, B.M.S.; 61, heath N of Penhale, the Lizard, J.A.P.; Ruan Pool (Suppt), 1961, J.Fo.; 63, Crowan Reservoir (Flora), refound, post—1950, B.M.S.; 71, Croft Pascoe Pool, L.J.M.; 72, near Traboe Cross, Goonhilly Downs, A.Br.

East: 95, quarry S of Goss Moor, L.J.M.; 96, Goss Moor (Flora), 1964, L.J.M.; 05, Molinnis Moor, near Bugle, W.T. (Thurston and Vigurs 1927); 06, Red Moor, Lanlivery, L.J.M.

AZOLLACEAE
AZOLLA LAM.

27/1   § **A. filiculoides** Lam.   Water Fern

An aquarists' throw-out that has only appeared in the county in recent years, now naturalised in a number of pools in the county.

*West: 43, Dingdong, near Penzance, 1971, B.M.S.; Penlee Park, Penzance, E.C., not deliberately introduced; Carfury, N of Penzance, B.M.S.; 74, Carn Marth, Redruth, R.J.M. *(Watsonia* 11: 151); 87 or 97, Guddna

Common, W of Padstow, B.B. and L.G.

*East: 07, Sladesbridge, B.B.; 45, Mt Edgcumbe Park, 1977, BSBI *(Watsonia,* 12: 62).

SPERMATOPHYTA
GYMNOSPERMAE

PINACEAE

PINUS L.

33/1 § **P. sylvestris** L., Scots Pine, is frequent and widely distributed as an introduced species (absent from Scilly).

§ **P. radiata** D.Don   Monterey Pine

A frequently planted tree in the SW, readily reproducing from seed in suitable habitats.

*West: 62, Porthleven, 1963, H.B.S.; 85, old railway near Shepherds, Newlyn East, G.A.

*East: 28, a great number of self-sown saplings on old railway track, Egloskerry, 1970, L.J.M.
Scilly: Lousley 1971.

CUPRESSACEAE

JUNIPERUS L.

34/1 **J. communis** L.   Juniper

Native only in one part of the Lizard, in a distinct form.
West: 61, Gew Graze (Flora), still surviving in small quantity, ten plants, 1977, D.E.C. Very dwarf and atypical, but apparently not referable to subsp. *nana* Syme; 64, Portreath square, post—1950, D.E.C. and F.H.P., probably introduced.

TAXACEAE

TAXUS L.

35/1 **T. baccata** L.   Yew

Frequent and widespread as an introduced tree, but nowhere as a native (absent from Scilly).

ANGIOSPERMAE: DICOTYLEDONES

SALICACEAE

SALIX L.

Common species: 343/12b S. **cinerea** L. subsp. **oleifolia**
Macreight, Common Sallow, 343/13 S. **aurita** L.,
Eared Willow, and 343/11 S. **caprea** L., Goat Willow.

343/4 **S. fragilis** L.   Crack Willow
Scattered in a few localities in the county.
West: 43, Heamoor, Penzance, E.A.R. (Thurston
1929a); between Madron and Tremithick Cross, B.M.S.;
53, Long Rock, B.M.S.; 73, swamp near Swanpool,
L.J.M.; Budock Bottom, L.J.M.; 74, Trevince Moor,
Gwennap, L.J.M.
East: 97, between Rock and St Enodoc, R.W.D.; 05,
near Par Station, J.A.P.; 08, Port Gaverne, L.J.M.; 35,
Seaton Valley (Flora), still there, post—1950, J.A.P.;
45, edge of car-park, Cawsand, L.J.M.
Scilly: Lousley 1971; M, Low Pool, D.E.A.; T, N of
Borough, D.E.A.

Var. **latifolia** Anderss.
West: 53, Long Rock, R.C.L.H.

343/2 S. **alba** x **fragilis** = *S. x rubens* Schrank
x 4   West: 62, Porthleven, H.B.S.

S. **decipiens** Hoffm.
Probably a derivative of *S. alba* and *S. fragilis*.
East: 38, by R. Tamar near Launceston, R.C.L.H.

343/2 S. **alba** L.   White Willow
Widely scattered in a few localities.
West: 42, near Chy-an-hal, Penzance, B.M.S.; 43,
Madron, B.M.S.; 63, Porkellis Moor, L.J.M.; 73, Swan-
vale, Falmouth, L.J.M.
East: 83, Pendower Valley, L.J.M.; 97, between Rock
and St Enodoc, R.W.D.; 20, Maer Marsh, Bude, L.J.M.

§ subsp. **vitellina** (L.) Arcangeli
West: 43, Tremithick Cross, near Penzance, R.C.L.H.;
61, Lizard, BRC.

343/5 **S. triandra** L.   Almond Willow
Very rare and local.
West: 53, Long Rock, B.M.S.; 62, Porthleven, H.B.S.
East: 20, between Red Post and Bridgerule, E.T.
(Thurston and Vigurs 1926); Bude Canal, R.O. (Thurston
and Vigurs 1925), still there, 1970, L.J.M.
Scilly: Lousley 1971

343/13 **S. aurita x repens** = *S. x ambigua* Ehrh.
x 16   Two localities (Flora), but there are no recent records.

343/13 **S. aurita x cinerea** subsp. **oleifolia** = *S. x multinervis*
x 12b   Doell
West: 75, Lambriggan, Perranzabuloe (B.E.C. 1938,
p. 200).
East: 18, near Hallworthy, J.E.L. (Thurston and
Vigurs 1926).

343/13 **S. aurita x viminalis** = *S. x fruticosa* Doell
x 9   West: 73, Menadue, near Rame, L.J.M.

343/   **S. cinerea** subsp. **oleifolia** x **viminalis** = *S. x smithiana*
12b x 9 Willd.
Scilly: Lousley 1971; T, end of Great Pool, D.E.A.

343/11 **S. caprea x cinerea** subsp. **oleifolia** = *S. reichardtii*
x 12b   A. Kerner
Scilly: Lousley 1971.

343/11 **S. caprea x viminalis** = *S. x laurina* Sm.
x 9   West: 62, Porthleven, H.B.S.
East.   17, between Hallworthy and Tredwen, J.E.L.
(Thurston and Vigurs 1926).

343/   **S. repens** L.   Creeping Willow
16a   The true plant is apparently rare in Cornwall, and the
following are the only reliable records.
West: 53, Marazion Marsh, L.J.M.; 75, Penhale Sands,
L.J.M.

343/   **S. repens/arenaria**   Creeping Willow
16a/   The common heathland plant is erect and intermediate
16b   between these two species. Material has been confirmed
from Cornwall by Mr R.C.L. Howitt.

West: 53, Marazion Marsh, L.J.M.; 74, Silverwell Moor, B.E.M.G. and L.J.M.; 75, Ventongimps Moor, B.E.M.G. and L.J.M.

East: 96, Goss Moor, CNT; 06, Retire Common, L.J.M.

343/ **S. arenaria** L.
16b *(S. repens* forma *argentea* Sm.)

West: 64, cliff-path, Porthtowan, L.J.M.; 71, Goonhilly (Flora), still there, D.E.C.; Croft Pascoe, L.J.M.; 72, Traboe Cross, L.J.M.; 75, Ventongimps Moor, B.E.M.G. and L.J.M.; Penhale Sands, R.W.D. and L.J.M.

343/9 **S. viminalis** L.   Osier
Frequent and widespread in marshy places and by streams.

West: 33, Cot Valley, St Just, M.C.; 53, Long Rock, B.M.S.; Tremelling, Hayle River, CNT; 62, Porthleven, H.B.S.; Loe Pool, L.J.M.; 72, Porthallow Valley, J.H. and L.J.M.; 73, Swanvale, Falmouth, L.J.M.; 75, Holywell Valley, A.B.; 83, Restronguet, L.J.M.

East: 08, Port Gaverne Valley, L.J.M.; 20, Bude Canal, L.J.M.; 35, Seaton Valley, J.A.P.; 45, between Penlee Point and Cawsand, L.J.M.

Scilly: Lousley 1971.

343/6 **S. purpurea** L.   Purple Willow
Extremely rare, and probably originally introduced.
*West: 53, St Erth, R.C.L.H.
*East: 18, recorded for this square, post—1950, R.W.D.

The following species are, we feel, correctly excluded by Davey (Flora), [343/10 § S. x **calodendron** Wimmer *(S. acuminata* Sm.), and 343/15 S. **phylicifolia** L., Tealeaved Willow. In addition, and in view of the great rarity of one of its parents, Davey's record for 343/6 x 9 S. **purpurea** x **viminalis** = *S. x rubra* Hudson, should also be rejected.]

POPULUS L.

342/1 § **P. alba** L. White Poplar

The following are additional records for this introduced tree.

West: 62, Porthleven, H.B.S.

East: 97, near Daymer Bay, J.A.P.; near St Enodoc Church, possibly the same station, R.W.D.; 45, Yonderberry Point and near Corbeile House, Torpoint, S.M. Scilly: Lousley 1971.

342/2 § **P. canescens** (Aiton) Sm. Grey Poplar

Almost certainly introduced into Cornwall.

West: 53, Copperhouse, Hayle, and Upton Towans, L.J.M.; 62, Gunwalloe Valley, CNT; 73, St Gluvias, Penryn, L.J.M.

*Scilly: T, Pool road, 1972, J.P.B.

343/3 **P. tremula** L. Aspen

Rare, except for the area between Bodmin Moor and the Tamar.

West: 53, Gurlyn Woods, near Relubbus, B.M.S.; 62, Porthleven, H.B.S.; 63, near Roseworthy, Camborne, L.J.M.; 64, by Tehidy Lake, R.J.M.; 71, Coverack cliffs, J.F.A.

East: 05, Luxulyan, B.Sh.; 27, near Trebartha, I.N.; near Treburland, Five Lanes, J.A.P.; 28, Badgall, Laneast, W.H.F. (Thurston and Vigurs 1923); by R. Inny, Trewen, I.N.; 35, Port Eliot, St Germans, I.N.; 36, S of Newbridge, Callington, J.A.P.; near Pillaton, I.N.; 37, Callington, I.N.; Stoke Climsland, I.N.; between Golberdon and Linkinhorne, I.N.; 45, Pillmere, and Trematon Castle, Saltash, I.N.; 46, Slimeford, Calstock, I.N.; 47, Gunnislake, I.N.

var. **villosa** (Lang) Wesm.

West: 74, Carrine Common, near Truro, R.J.M. and E.W.M.; 75, Carnkief, Perranzabuloe, W.T. (Thurston and Vigurs 1926).

[342/4 **P. nigra** L., Black Poplar, is recorded in the Flora from a number of places, but these are clearly mistakes for the next species. Davey's specimen from Ponsanooth, Herb. Davey (TRU), is certainly an error.]

342/5 § **P. x canadensis** Moench   Italian Poplar
Widely planted, in a number of clones. Davey's record
(Flora) for *P.deltoides* no doubt belongs here.
West: 53, Upton Towans, L.J.M.; Godrevy Bridge,
L.J.M.; 63, Merrymeeting, near Camborne, L.J.M.
East: 97, near St Enodoc's Church, R.W.D.; 16,
Glynn Bridge, L.J.M.; 25, St Martin's Wood, E Looe
River, S.M.; 26, Factory, Menheniot, S.M.; Deerpark
Wood, Herodsfoot, S.M.; 35, Seaton Valley, J.A.P.;
Wacker, near Antony, S.M.; 45, Wearde, near Saltash,
S.M.; Carbeile Mill, Torpoint, S.M.
Scilly: Lousley 1971; T, one tree, SW edge of Great
Pool, D.E.A.

MYRICACEAE

MYRICA L.

333/1 **M. gale** L.   Bog Myrtle
Frequent in wet heaths in Mid-Cornwall, very rare E of
Bodmin.
West: 61, near Penhale, the Lizard, L.C.F.; 64, Red
River Valley, R.J.M. and L.J.M.; 73, Pengreep (Flora),
still there, L.J.M.; 74, Trevince Moor, Gwennap (Flora),
still there, L.J.M.; Allet Common, G.A.; Silverwell
Moor, L.J.M.; 75, Carnkief, L.J.M.; Ventongimps,
R.W.D.; Goonhavern, R.W.D.; 85, Newlyn East Downs
(Flora), 1962, L.J.M.; Penhallow Moor, J.B.
East: 96, Goss Moor (Flora), 1964, L.J.M.; Rosenannon
Bog, R.W.D.; Hustyn Wood, St Breock, R.W.D. and
L.J.M.; 06, Retire Common, R.W.D.; 07, SW of
Hellandbridge, K.H.J.; 15, Lerryn, R.J.M.; 16, near
Middle Taphouse, J.A.P.

BETULACEAE

BETULA L.

335/1 **B. pendula** Roth *(B. alba* L.), Silver Birch, and
335/2 **B. pubescens** Ehrh. (*B. tomentosa* Reit. &
Abel), Downy Birch, are frequent and widespread in
the county (both absent from Scilly).

ALNUS MILLER

336/1 **A. glutinosa** (L.) Gaertner (*A. rotundifolia* Mill), Alder,
is common and widespread by rivers and streams (rare in
Scilly).

CORYLACEAE

CARPINUS L.

337/1 § **C. betulus** L.   Hornbeam

More frequent than indicated in the Flora, but nearly always originally planted.

West: 43, near Penzance, B.M.S.; near Madron, B.M.S.; 53, base of Trencrom Hill, L.J.M.; 64, Tehidy, L.J.M.; 74, near Mt Hawke, L.J.M.

East. 83, Trewince Creek, Roseland, L.J.M.; 05, Trenance, near St Austell, W.T. (Thurston and Vigurs 1927); 06, Pelyn Wood, E.A.; Washaway, Bodmin, L.J.M.; 07, near Helland, B.G.; 15, Lerryn, CNT; 21, Coombe Valley, R.D.; 26, St Pinnock, E.S.B.; Downpool, near Liskeard, E.S.B.; 29, Week St Mary, L.J.M.; 35, Wivelscombe Farm, I.N.; 36, Viverdon Down (Flora), still there, post—1950, R.W.D.; 38, Launceston (Flora), 1966, A.S.G.; Newchurches, W of St Stephens, I.N.; St. Stephens, G.L.K.; 45, near Trematon Castle, I.N.; Antony, S.M.; 46, Cotehele, I.N.

CORYLUS L.

338/1 **C. avellana** L., Hazel, is a common and widespread tree throughout the county, but strangely absent from Scilly.

FAGACEAE

FAGUS L.

339/1 **F. sylvatica** L., Beech, is frequent throughout Cornwall, but decidedly uncommon in the far west. Not listed by Lousley 1971, for Scilly, but subsequently found on T, two trees W of the abbey, 1972, J.P.B.

CASTANEA MILLER

340/1 § **C. sativa** Miller   Sweet Chestnut

Frequent as a planted tree, but also self-sown. The following records are additional to the Flora and Suppt.

West: 62, Porthleven, H.B.S.; 63, Clowance, L.J.M.; 64, near Reskadinnick, R.J.M.; Sparnon Gate, Redruth, L.J.M.; Nance Wood, Portreath, L.J.M.; 73, Devichoys Wood, Perranarworthal, R.Go.; 75, Carnkief Wood, L.J.M.; 86, Carnanton Woods, Vale of Lanherne, CNT.

East: 83, Turnaware Point, Fal Estuary, B.E.M.G.;

84, Lamorran Woods, G.A.; 05, Caruggatt Wood, Lanlivery, R.Go.; 06, Helland Wood, R.Go.; 07, Colquite Wood, R.Go.; 15, between Lostwithiel and Fowey, J.A.P.; 19, Peters Wood, Boscastle, J.F.A.; 27, W of Northill, J.A.P.; 36, near Pillaton, D.B.; S of Newbridge, J.A.P., 37, Luckett Wood, A.B.

Scilly: T, one tree W of abbey, 1972, J.P.B.

QUERCUS L.

341/2 § **Q. ilex** L., Evergreen Oak, and 341/1 § **Q. cerris** L., Turkey Oak, are widely planted and occasionally regenerate from seed. 341/4 **Q. petraea** (Mattuschka) Liebl. (*Q. robur* var. *sessiliflora* Salisb.), Sessile Oak (Scilly: T, N of abbey, 1972, J.P.B.), and 341/3 **Q. robur** L., Pedunculate Oak, are common and widely distributed native species.

ULMACEAE

ULMUS L.

A very complex genus, with many species and varieties named. Following *Flora Europaea*, we have taken a conservative view.

330/1 **U. glabra** Hudson   Wych Elm
Common and widely distributed in Cornwall, and probably the only native species.

var. **cornuta** (David) Rehd.
East: 05, Pelyn Wood, Lanlivery, CNT.

330/2 **U. procera** Salisb.   English Elm
(*U. campestris* L.)
Most of the Cornish records for this species refer to the hybrid listed below. Probably the genuine thing exists only as a planted tree.
West: 53, Gwithian, L.J.M.; 63, Upper Grillis, Treskillard, L.J.M.
East: 29, Week St Mary, L.J.M.
Scilly. Lousley 1971.

330/3 **U. minor** Miller
var. **cornubiensis** (Weston) Richens   Cornish Elm
(*U. campestris* var. *glabra* Mill.)

Common and widespread, but not listed by J.E. Lousley for Scilly.

330/1 **U. glabra x minor** var. **cornubiensis**
x 3 Frequent throughout the county, and probably our most common elm. It is usually recorded as *U. procera*, to which it admittedly bears a resemblance. The records in the Suppt for *U. major* probably belong here. Material has been confirmed for the following localities.

West: 64, Reskadinnick, Camborne, R.J.M.; Feadon Wood, Portreath, L.J.M. 71, Cadgwith, S.M.T. (this is the well-known Cadgwith Elmwood); Kennack Sands, S.M.T. et al; 75, Lambourne, F.R. (*B.S.B.I. Year* 1950, p.95); Carnkief Wood, L.J.M.

U. x hollandica Mill. Dutch Elm
(*U. glabra* var. *major* Sm.)
West: 75, Lambriggan, Perranzabuloe, 1950, F.R. Scilly: Lousley 1971.
There seems to be no respite at present from the ravages of the Dutch Elm Disease, *Ceratostomella ulmi*.

CANNABACEAE
HUMULUS L.
329/1 **H. lupulus** L., Hop, is frequent and widespread in Cornwall, though becoming rare in far West.

URTICACEAE
URTICA L.
328/2 **U. dioica** L., Common Nettle, is a common and widely distributed plant of hedges, woods, and waste places.

328/1 **U. urens** L. Small Nettle
This weed of cultivated ground is strangely rare in much of the East.
West: A frequent plant throughout the vice-county.
East: 94, near Caerhayes Castle, L.J.M.; 97, Amble Marshes, R.W.D.; 45, Wiggle, I.N.; Millbrook, I.N.; Whitsand Bay, I.N.
Scilly: Lousley 1971.

PARIETARIA L.

326/1 **P. judaica** L., Pellitory-of-the-wall, is frequent and wide-spread near the sea.

SOLEIROLIA GAUD-BEAUP.

327/1 § **S. soleirolii** (Req.) Dandy (Suppt as *Helxine soleirolii* Req.), Mind-your-own-business, has been steadily spreading since it was first found at St Just-in-Roseland *c* 1917, and is now a common plant of damp or shady walls.

LORANTHACEAE
VISCUM L.

263/1 **V. album** L.   Mistletoe

Now much decreased.   The following records refer mainly to garden or farm occurrences.

West: 73, Enys, near Penryn (Thurston 1929a); Perranwell Station (Thurston 1935); 74, near Scorrier, L.J.M.; 83, Falmouth (Flora), in three stations there (Thurston 1935), still in two gardens, 1962, L.J.M.; 84, near Kenwyn, Truro (Thurston 1928).

East: The following records, except the last, all appear in Thurston (1935).

93, Veryan; 94, Caerhayes; 07, near St Kew; 20, near Efford, Bude; 27, near Northill; 35, St Erney; 37; Halwell, near Linkinhorne; 45, on apple, Saltash, I.N.

POLYGONACEAE
POLYGONUM L.

Common species: 320/1/1 **P. aviculare** L., Knotgrass, 320/1/4   **P. arenastrum** Boreau, Knotgrass, 320/12 **P. hydropiper** L., Water-Pepper, 320/9   **P. persicaria** L., Redshank, and 320/10   **P. lapathifolium** L., Pale Persicaria.

320/3 **P. maritimum** L.   Sea Knotgrass

Often stated to be extinct on the mainland of Britain, this very rare plant still holds on in at least one Cornish station.

West: 61, Poldhu Cove, W.D.M. (Thurston and Vigurs 1927 and Thurston 1928); 62, Gunwalloe (Flora), in Church Cove, F.D. (Thurston and Vigurs 1927, and

Thurston 1935), refound 1966, B.M.S. et al.

East: 05, Par (Suppt), one plant, H.W.P. (Thurston 1935); 15, Lantic Bay, 1972, P.W. (*Watsonia* **10**: 87), 28 plants 1978, R.W.D. and L.J.M., two plants 1979, CNT.

Scilly: last record: 1909, Lousley 1971.

320/2   **P. oxyspermum** Meyer & Bunge ex Ledeb.

Ray's Knotgrass

subsp. **raii** (Bab.) D.A. Webb & Chater
(*P. raii* Bab.)

This species stands up well to human trampling, and is still fairly widespread.   It may be to some extent under-recorded.

West: 53, Marazion (Flora), 1948, S.B.; Hayle (Flora), 1966, J.A.P.; 61, Poldhu Cove, R.W.D.; 62, Porthleven, H.B.S.; Gunwalloe (Flora), still there, post—1950, R.H.; 64, Portreath, L.J.M.; Porthtowan (Flora), still there, post—1950, R.H.; 72, Maenporth (Flora), 1965, L.J.M.; (82), Godrevy Cove, St Keverne, J.H. and L.J.M.

East: 97, Rock, I.H.; 05, Polkerris, H.W.P. (Thurston 1935); Charlestown Quay, N.J.F.; 15, Lantic Bay, K.H.; 35, Seaton (Flora), post—1950, I.N.

Scilly: Lousley 1971.   Last recorded — 1909.

320/1/   **P. rurivagum** Jordan ex Boreau
3   West: No recent records.

East: 93, near Nare Hotel, the Roseland, B.E.M.G.; 45, St John's (Flora), still there 1967, S.M.

[320/   **P. nodosum** Pers. (*P. maculatum* Trim. & Dyer), has
11   been recorded from both vice-counties, and from Scilly, but Cornish material differs little from typical *P. lapathifolium*, and we have followed recent opinion in rejecting this as a species.]

320/8   **P. amphibium** L.   Amphibious Bistort

Rare in the East.   Scattered in the West, but often present in quantity.   The terrestrial form (var. *terrestre* Koch) is no more than a dry-ground state, occurring frequently in the summer.

West: 53, Marazion Marsh (Flora), 1949, J.B.; 61, Hayle Kimbro Pool (Suppt), 1950 onwards, LFC; 62, Loe Pool (Flora), 1978, L.J.M.; Gunwalloe (Flora),

1960, J.G.T.; Poldhu Marsh, LFC; 71, Kennack (Suppt), still there, post—1950, R.H.; 72, Porthallow, R.H.; 73, Stithians Reservoir, J.S.R.

East: 97, St Minver (Flora), 1979, R.W.D.; 26, near Liskeard, C.P.F. (Thurston and Vigurs 1927); 35, Seaton (Flora), still there, post—1950, I.N.

Scilly: Lousley 1971.

320/6 **P. bistorta** L.   Common Bistort

Only known now in E Cornwall, where it is local and rare.

East: 08, Lanteglos Churchyard, E.A.; 16, near Braddock Church, M.S.; 21, Coombe Valley, R.O. (Thurston and Vigurs 1925); 25, Portlooe, 1926, Herb. F.H. Perrycoste, (TRU); between Looe and Duloe Hill, J.L.; 25 or 26, Trewidland, St Keyne, S.M.; 26, Liskeard, J.L.; 36, near Pillaton, I.N.; 37, Trebullet, N.J.F.; 46, Botusfleming (Flora), still there, post—1950, I.N.; Calstock (Flora), wood near Calstock, 1977, E.G.

320/7 § **P. amplexicaule** D.Don   Red Bistort

An attractive introduction that may well increase.

*West: 33, Higher Boscaswell, L.J.M.; 53, Carbis Bay, 1971, B.M.S.

*East: 93, Veryan, 1964, B.Sh.

320/21 § **P. polystachyum** Wall. ex Meissner

Himalayan Knotweed

This introduced species has spread rapidly since c 1970, and is rampant in some places.

*West: 33, St Just, K.E.B.; 43, Madron Well, W.D.W. (Thurston and Vigurs 1926); 53, Troon, J.S.R.; Treskillard, L.J.M., 64, Pool, and Tolvaddon, J.S.R.; Reskadinnick road, Camborne, R.J.M.; Crane, and Rosewarne, both near Camborne, L.J.M.

*East: 05, Tregrehan Mills, B.E.M.G. and L.J.M.; 25, near Polperro, L.J.M.; Talland, S.M.; 27, Penhole, Coad's Green, E.Ca.; 35, Wacker, and Tregantle, S.M.; 36, S of Callington, J.A.P.; 45, Tregonhawke Cliffs, S.M.; Cawsand, S.M.; Torpoint, S.M.; St John's (B.E.C. 1935), 1967, S.M.

320/22 § **P. campanulatum** Hooker fil.   Lesser Knotweed
> A fairly recent garden escape that may spread.

> *West: 64, Trevingey, near Redruth, L.J.M.; 73, near
> Laity Moor, Stithians, 1965, L.J.M.

> *East: 93, Carne, near Veryan, 1972, B.E.M.G.

BILDERDYKIA DUMORT.

320/15 B. convolvulus (L.) Dumort. (*Polygonum convolvulus* L.);
> Black-bindweed, is a common weed of arable fields and
> waste places.

320/18 § **B. aubertii** (Louis Henry) Moldenke   Russian-Vine
> A rampant garden escape in a few places.

> *West: 33, near St Just, M.C.; 42, Chy-an-hal Moor,
> 1966, J.A.P.; Drift Reservoir, near Penzance, C.J.; 64,
> near Reskadinnick, R.J.M.

> *East: 93, Gwendra, near Pendower Beach, 1963,
> L.J.M.
> Scilly: Lousley 1971.

REYNOUTRIA HOUTT.

320/19 § **R. japonica** Houtt. (*Polygonum cuspidatum* Sieb. &
> Zucc.), Japenese Knotweed, is now abundant through-
> out Cornwall, mainly, but not exclusively, by roadsides.

320/20 § **R. sachalinensis** (Friedrich Schmidt Petrop.) Nakai
>   Giant Knotweed

> At present much less naturalised, but definitely on the
> increase.

> *West: 42, Chy-an-hal Moor, A.C.L. and R.B.

> *East: 97, Old Polzeath, extensively naturalised, 1950
> onwards, R.W.D.   37, South Hill, near Linkinhorne,
> N.J.F.,

FAGOPYRUM MILLER

321/1 § **F. esculentum** Moench   Buckwheat
> (*F. sagittatum* Gilib.)

> Now very rare, and casual only.

> West: 71, field at Lizard Town, E.G.; 73, Council tip,
> Falmouth, L.J.M.; 85, Council tip, Newlyn East, L.J.M.

> East: 04, Mevagissey, W.T. (Thurston 1935); 45,
> Antony House Nurseries, E.G.

> Scilly: Lousley 1971; T, one plant, E.G.

RUMEX L.

Common species: 325/1/1 **R. acetosella** L., Sheep's Sorrel, 325/2 **R. acetosa** L., Common Sorrel, 325/11 **R. crispus** L., Curled Dock, 325/15 **R. conglomeratus** Murray, Clustered Dock, 325/14 **R. sanguineus** L., Wood Dock, 325/13 **R. pulcher** L., Fiddle Dock, and 325/12 **R. obtusifolius** L., Broad-leaved Dock.

325/20 § **R. frutescens** Thouars   Argentine Dock
(Suppt as *R. magellanica* Griseb.)

West: 53, Phillack Towans (Suppt), still there in one spot, 1950—1979, various recorders.

325/4   **R. hydrolapathum** Hudson   Water Dock

Always rare in Cornwall, this Dock has further declined in recent years, but it is possibly overlooked.

West: 53, Marazion Marsh (Flora), 1949, J.B.; 62, Poldhu Marsh, L.J.M.; Gunwalloe (Flora), 1962, L.J.M.; 72, Maenporth (Flora), 1961, L.J.M.; 73, Swanpool (Flora), marsh above Swanpool, 1961, L.J.M.; 75, Ellenglaze, Penhale Sands (Flora), 1963, B.M.S. and L.J.M.

East: 08, Port Isaac, J.E.L. (Thurston and Vigurs 1926).

Scilly: Lousley 1971, last recorded 1877.

325/11 R. crispus x obtusifolius = *R. acutus* L.
x 12   Recorded in the Flora from many localities, but the following is the only recent one from the mainland.

West: 62, Porthleven, H.B.S.

Scilly: common, Lousley 1971.

325/4   **R. hydrolapathum** x **obtusifolius** = *R. x weberi* Fisch-
x 12   Benz.

(Flora, incorrectly, as *R. maximus* Schreber)

West, and East, there are no recent records.

Scilly: now extinct, Lousley 1971.

325/11 R. crispus x pulcher = *R. x pseudopulcher* Hausskn.
x 13   *East: 83 or 93, Pendower Cliffs, 1951, J.E.Lo.

Scilly: Lousley 1971.

325/15 R. conglomeratus x crispus = *R. x schulzei* Hausskn.
x 11   Recorded in the Suppt for Cornwall without locality.

*West: 75, waste ground near Penhale Camp, C.W.

325/15 R. conglomeratus x pulcher = *R. x muretii* Hausskn.

x 13   Scilly: Lousley 1971; W of Battery, Old Town Bay, J.P.B.

325/14 R. sanguineus L. var. **sanguineus**   Red-veined Dock

This distinct variety is probably overlooked.

West: 74, Parkhoskin Wood, near Mithian, G.A. and L.J.M.

East: 19, St Juliot's, near Boscastle, 1979, L.J.M.

325/16 R. rupestris Le Gall   Shore Dock

This rare Dock has much declined in the last 50 years in its known localities.

West: 75, Perranporth, F.R. (B.E.C. 1931, p.840); 87, Trevose Head and Constantine Bay, R.W.D.

East: 93, Pendower Beach (Flora), 1979, L.J.M.; 15, Lantivet Bay, 1925, F.H.P., still there, H.W.P. (Thurston 1935); 45 (44), Eastern end of Whitsand Bay (Flora), still there, 1966, I.N., 1979, E.G.

Scilly: frequent, Lousley 1971.

325/13 R. pulcher x sanguineus = *R. x mixtus* Lambert

x 14   *East: 84, Boscawen Park, Truro, 1951, J.E.Lo.

325/13 R. pulcher x rupestris = *R. x trimenii* Camus

x 16   *East: 45, Whitsand Bay, J.T., BM.

Scilly: Lousley 1971.

325/12 R. obtusifolius x pulcher = *R. x ogulinensis* Borbás

x 13   *West: 85, Council tip, Newlyn East, 1970, J.G.D.

Scilly: Lousley 1971.

MUEHLENBECKIA MEISSNER

323/1   § **M. complexa** (Cunn.) Meissn.   Wire Plant

This introduction from New Zealand soon becomes rampant once escaped from gardens.

*West: 71, lane near Lizard Town, 1959, J.Fo.

*East: 93, cliff near Camels Cove, Portloe, 1976, L.J.M.

Scilly: frequent, Lousley 1971.

CHENOPODIACEAE
BETA L.

155/1 **B. vulgaris** L., subsp. **maritima** (L.) Arcangeli (*B. maritima* L.), Sea Beet, is common and widespread near the sea.

CHENOPODIUM L.

154/4 **C. album** L., Fat-hen, is abundant in arable fields and on waste ground throughout the county.

154/1 § **C. bonus-henricus** L.   Good-King-Henry
Extremely rare and local now.
West: 42, near Lamorna, J.A.P.; 74, near Goodern, Baldhu, J.A.P.
East: 08, Delabole, J.E.L. (Thurston and Vigurs 1926); 38, St Stephens, Launceston, I.N.
Scilly: Lousley 1971.

154/16 § **C. glaucum** L.   Oak-leaved Goosefoot
Rejected by Davey (Flora), but included in the Suppt.
West: 53, Hayle, F.R. (Thurston and Vigurs 1924), refound, 1977, B.M.S.; 64, waste ground, Portreath, L.J.M.; 73, Council tip, Falmouth, B.E.M.G.; 75, Goonhavern, F.R. (B.E.C. 1923).

154/14 **C. rubrum** L.   Red Goosefoot
Waste ground and rubbish tips, probably frequent, but under-recorded.
West: 53, St Erth, L.J.M.; 61, Goonhilly Nature Reserve, S.M.T. *et al.*; 62, Council tip, Helston, R.W.D.; 64, waste ground, Portreath, L.J.M.; 75, Penhale Sands (Suppt), 1965, NCS; 85, Newlyn East, 1909, C.C.V. (B.E.C. 1931, p.571).
East: 04, Mevagissey, W.T. (Thurston 1935); 19, Crackington Haven, J.E.L. (Thurston and Vigurs 1926).
Scilly: Lousley 1971; TN, 1972, J.P.B.

154/2 **C. polyspermum** L.   Many-seeded Goosefoot
Not a common plant in Cornwall, but to some extent overlooked, like the majority of species in this genus.
West: 53, near Townshend, J.A.P.; Phillack Towans, B.M.S.; 72, Gweek, R.H.; 73, Penmere, Falmouth, L.J.M.; Council tip, Falmouth, L.J.M.; 83, near Swanpool, L.J.M.; old tip, Newham, Truro, L.J.M.

East: 83, garden, Philleigh, B.E.M.G.; 04, Trenarren, W.T. (Thurston and Vigurs 1928); 05, Tregrehan Mills, W.T. (Thurston and Vigurs 1926); Par Harbour, L.T.M. (Thurston and Vigurs 1927); 35, Trerulefoot, L.J.M.; 45, St John's, and between there and Antony, S.M.; 46, garden, Botusfleming, I.N.

Scilly: Lousley 1971; T, Pentle Bay, 1972, J.P.B.; W of Borough, 1975, D.E.A.

154/3 **C. vulvaria** L.   Stinking Goosefoot

Possibly now extinct in the county as a native, but recently found in gardens as a tan-bark alien.

West: 72, casual in garden, Helford Passage, 1974, L.J.M.; 83, in garden, Penpol House, Devoran, 1973, L.J.M.

Scilly: (Flora), but now rejected, Lousley 1971.

154/11 **C. murale** L.   Nettle-leaved Goosefoot

Now mainly as a casual in waste places and gardens.

West: 53, Marazion (Thurston 1928); 43, weed in nursery, Gulval, B.M.S.; 62, Council tip, Helston, L.J.M.; 85, Council tip, Newlyn East, L.J.M.; 86, Newquay, 1913, C.C.V., LIVU.

East: 83, garden, Philleigh, B.E.M.G.; 84, between Truro and Malpas, W.Bo. (Thurston 1935); 94, near Porthluney Beach, L.J.M.; 97 (98), near Portquin, R.W.D.; 35, Portwrinkle, B.E.M.G.; 45, Torpoint (Flora), Council tip, and elsewhere in Torpoint, S.M.

Scilly: common, Lousley 1971.

154/9 **C. ficifolium** Sm.   Fig-leaved Goosefoot

Often confused with forms of C. album, and possibly overlooked.

West: 53, near Gwithian Church, B.E.M.G. and J.A.P.; 74, Council tip, Bissoe, L.J.M.

ATRIPLEX L.

156/2 **A. patula** L., Common Orache, and   156/3 **A. hastata** L. (incl. **A. deltoidea** Bab.), Spear-leaved Orache, are both very common and widely distributed in the county.

156/5 **A. laciniata** L.   Frosted Orache
Rare and local.

West: 32, Gwenver Beach, near Sennen, M.C.; 53, Marazion (Flora), still there, B.M.S.; Phillack, B.M.S.; Lelant (Flora), Porthkidney and Lelant Beaches, 1960, J.B.; 62, Gunwalloe (Flora), post—1950, B.M.S.; 86 (76), Crantock, J.A.P.

East: 05, Par (Flora), still there, post—1950, J.A.P.
Scilly: common, Lousley 1971.

156/1 **A. littoralis** L.   Grass-leaved Orache
Now extremely rare, the following being the only recent record.

East: 05, Par (Flora and Suppt), refound 1966, J.A.P.

156/4 **A. glabriuscula** Edmondston   Babington's Orache
(*A. babingtonii* Woods)

In a few scattered stations round the coast, more frequent in Scilly.

West: 62, Porthleven, H.B.S.; Gunwalloe (Flora), 1949, J.B.; 71, Kennack Sands, E.D. (Thurston 1930); 72, Porthallow, R.H.; Rosemullion Head, J.A.P.

East: 83, near St Mawes, J.A.P.; Pendower Beach, J.A.P.; 97, Polzeath (Flora), 1946, R.W.D.; 15, Lantic Bay, J.C.D.; 35, Seaton (Flora), J.A.P.; 45, Torpoint, S.M.

Scilly: common, Lousley 1971.

var. **babingtonii** (Woods) Moss & Wilmott
West: 64, Porthtowan, L.J.M.

A. longipes Drejer
A taxon only recently recognised as occurring in Britain. *A. patula* var. *bracteata* Westerl. (Flora and Suppt) may belong here.

*East: 15, Penpol Creek, near Lerryn, 1977, P.M.T.

HALIMIONE AELLEN

157/1 **H. portulacoides** (L.) Aellen   Sea-purslane
(*Atriplex portulacoides* L.)

This is a species that seems to have increased considerably since Davey's day.

West: 62, Loe Bar, H.B.S.; 75, Holywell Bay, L.J.M.;

86 (76), Porth Joke, on cliffs; the Gannel, Newquay, K.M.S. (Thurston and Vigurs 1925), 1973, C.J.

East: 97, Amble Marshes, R.W.D.; Dinham Creek, C.J.; 05, Par Sands (Suppt), 1966, J.A.P.; 25, West Looe River, L.J.M.; between Looe and Sandplace (Flora), still there, post—1950, S.M.; 35, 45, and 46, frequent around the Tamar Estuary.

SALICORNIA L.

160/3 **S. europaea** L., Glasswort, is common throughout the county wherever estuarine conditions exist (absent from Scilly).

160/4 **S. ramosissima** J. Woods   Twiggy Glasswort
Rare, but possibly overlooked.

West: 73, between Devoran and Perranwharf (Flora), Devoran, 1965, L.J.M.; 83, Mylor Creek, W.T. (Thurston 1928, as *S. prostrata* Pallas).

East: 84, Pencalenick, L.J.M.; 05, Par Sands, H.W.P. (Thurston 1935); 35 or 45, River Lynher, S.M.

SUAEDA FORSKAL EX SCOP.

158/1 **S. maritima** (L.) Dumort.   Annual Sea-blite
Widespread in suitable habitats by the sea. The following records are additional to the Flora and Suppt.

West: 61, Kennack Sands, F.G.F.; 72, Maenporth, R.H.; Gweek, L.J.M.; 73, Bissom Creek, Penryn, L.J.M.; 83, Penarrow Point, Flushing, L.J.M.; 97, near Sea Mills, J.A.P.

East: 83, Froe Lake, Turnaware Creek, and St Just-in-Roseland, B.E.M.G.; 84, Tresillian, J.A.P.; Pencalenick, L.J.M.; 45, Forder, Coombe, and Wivelscombe, I.N.; 46, Landulph, I.N.

SALSOLA L.

159/1 **S. kali** L.   Prickly Saltwort
Apparently a decreasing species, except in Scilly.

West: 32, Gwenver Beach, Sennen, M.C.; 53, Lelant and Hayle (Flora), 1966, L.J.M.; Porthkidney Beach, abundant, 1958—1960, J.B.; 87, Constantine Bay, J.A.P.; 97, between Tregirls and Stepper Point, L.G.

East: 97, Rock (Flora), S of Brea Hill, 1951, R.W.D.;

20 Bude (Flora), still there, R.D.; 35, Downderry (Flora), 1966, I.N.
Scilly: frequent, Lousley 1971.

AIZOACEAE
CARPOBROTUS N.E.BR.
152/1 § **C. edulis** (L.) N.E.Br.   Hottentot-fig
Frequent and widespread around the coasts. The usual form has magenta flowers, but the yellow-flowered form also occurs in the West and East, and this is the common form in Scilly.

DISPHYMA N.E.BR.
§ **D. crassifolium** (L.) L. Bolus
This introduced succulent, though less frequent, is beginning to rival *Carpobrotus* as a cliff coloniser.
*West: 52, Rinsey Head, L.J.M.; several cliffs between Keneggy and Hoe Point, L.J.M.; Praa Sands, L.J.M.; 61, Kynance Cove, L.J.M., 62, Porthleven, 1969, L.J.M.; 64, Eastcliff, Porthtowan, L.J.M.; 71, Lizard Head, M.C.H.; Coverack, L.J.M., 87, low cliff, Constantine Bay, L.J.M.
Scilly: rare, Lousley 1971.

PORTULACACEAE
MONTIA L.
149/1 **M. fontana** L.   Blinks
Common and widespread in a variety of habitats.

149/   subsp. **variabilis** Walters
1d   (var. *major* All.)
West: 32, Lands End, 1901, H.H.Hs., 1925, **LTR.**
Scilly: Lousley 1971.

149/c   subsp. **amporitana** Sennen
West: 32, Lands End, E.B.W. (B.E.C. 1925).
East: 97, marsh SW of Pentire Farm, 1953, R.W.D., det. S.M.W.
Scilly: Lousley 1971.

subsp. **chondrosperma** (Fenzl) Walters
(var. *minor* All.)
West: 33, Carn Gloose, St Just, L.J.M.; 71, Poltesco, 1933, N.D.S.; Lizard Downs, 1911, A.M.G.

East: 04, Black Head, near St Austell, J.H.A.; 17, Bodmin Moor, G.G.G.; 25, Polperro, F.R.

149/2 **M. perfoliata** (Donn ex Willd.) Howell   Spring Beauty
West: 75, St Agnes, J.T.B. (Thurston 1935). This is the last record we have for the mainland of Cornwall. Scilly: abundant on the larger Isles, Lousley 1971.

149/3 **M. sibirica** (L.) Howell   Pink Purslane
Not known to Davey, and first recorded in the thirties, this plant is now frequent from the far East to the Lands End, but unknown in Scilly.
*West: 33, four stations around St Just, M.C.; 42, Lamorna, comm. G.B.M.; 43, Heamoor, Penzance, E.A.R. (Thurston 1935); Nancledra, S.B.; 53, Ludgvan, L.B.; below Trink Hill, L.J.M.; 62, Loe Pool, K.H.; 64, Chapel Porth, J.H.A., comm.R.Bu.; 71, W of Lizard Town, J.A.P.; 83, King Harry Ferry, B.E.M.G.
*East: 84, Nankilly, Probus, D.D. and J.G.; 93, Portloe, M.E.B.; near Carne, B.E.M.G.; 17, Blisland, B.B.; 25, Looe Valley, J.L.; 26, St Keynes Well, J.L.; 37, Inny Foot, L.J.M.; Greenscombe Wood, B.B.; between Luckett and Latchley, I.N.; 38, Wishworthy, near Lawhitton, S.M.; S of Greystone Bridge, J.A.P.; 46, between Cargreen and Salter Mill, I.N.; 47, near Morwell Rocks, I.N.

CARYOPHYLLACEAE
ARENARIA L.
141/1 **A. serpyllifolia** L. Thyme-leaved Sandwort, is common along the coasts in dry places.

141/6 § **A. balearica** L.   Mossy Sandwort
*West: 63, wall by Treslothan Church, Stennack, L.J.M.; 64, on wall, Portreath, C.C.T. (*Proc. B.S.B.I.*, **1**: 165); 83, hedge near Falmouth Hotel, 1923, W.T. (Thurston and Vigurs 1924).
*East: 94, Caerhayes, 1977, J.S.R.; 46, Cotehele, L.J.M.

141/1 **A. serpyllifolia** L.
subsp. **macrocarpa** (Lloyd) F.H. Perring & P.D. Sell (var. *macrocarpa* Lloyd)
West: 62, Loe Bar, R.O. (Thurston and Vigurs 1927).

141/2   **A. leptoclados** (Reichenb.) Guss.   Slender Sandwort
This taxon is probably frequent, but little attention has been paid to it in recent years, and the following are the only post—1922 records.

West: 32, Gwenver Cliff, Sennen, 1973, M.C.; 72, Dennis Head, Helford River, 1963, L.J.M.
*Scilly: T, W of Borough, 1975, D.E.A.

MOEHRINGIA L.

140/1   **M. trinervia** (L.) Clairv.   Three-nerved Sandwort
(*Arenaria trinervia* L.)

In hedges and woods, common and widespread, perhaps less so in the West, and absent from most of West Penwith and from Scilly.

MINUARTIA L.

137/1   **M. verna** (L.) Hiern   Spring Sandwort
(*Arenaria verna* L.)

Only on the W side of the Lizard.

West: 61, in numerous localities in this square.

HONKENYA EHRH.

139/1   **H. peploides** (L.) Ehrh., Sea Sandwort, is frequent and widespread in suitable habitats by the sea.

STELLARIA L.

Common species: 133/2 S. **media** (L.) Vill., Common Chickweed, 133/5 S. **holostea** L., Greater Stitchwort (probably now extinct in Scilly), 133/8 S. **uliginosa** Murr. (*S. alsine* Grimm), Bog Stitchwort, and 133/7 S. **graminea** L., Lesser Stitchwort, are all common and widely distributed.

133/4   S. **neglecta** Weihe   Greater Chickweed
Rather rare and local, and mainly in the shady lanes of the East.

West: 62, Loe Pool, T.M.; 72, The Hutches, Mawnan, L.J.M.; Gweek Drive, and near Mawgan Cross, R.H.; 83, Swanpool, R.H.; 84, near Truro School, A.S.

East: 83, Pendower Valley, L.J.M.; near Froe, St Anthony, L.J.M.; 06, near Grogley Halt, J.A.P.; 07, Rocksea Lane, St Mabyn, E.A.; Bishop's Wood, near Wadebridge, J.A.P.; 19, St Juliot, Boscastle, L.J.M.; 25,

W Looe Hill, L.J.M.; Talland, and Porthallow, L.J.M.; Polperro, Herb. F.H. Perrycoste, (TRU), as *S. nemorum;* 26, Merrymeet, near Liskeard, D.B.; 35, Seaton Valley, J.A.P.; 36, near St Ive, D.B.; between Hatt and Trematon, D.B.
Scilly: Lousley 1971.

133/3 **S. pallida** (Dumort.) Piré   Lesser Chickweed
(*S. apetala* Ucria)

West: 53, between Marazion and Penzance (Suppt), 1971, L.J.M.; 62, Gunwalloe, L.J.M.; 71, between Kennack Sands and Eastern Cliff, J.H. and L.J.M.; 75, Perranporth (Suppt), Penhale Sands, post—1950, L.J.M.; Holywell Bay (Flora), 1977, L.J.M.; 87, Constantine Bay, L.J.M.

East: 83, Pendower Beach, L.J.M.; 94, Porthluney Beach, L.J.M.; 05, Carlyon Bay, J.A.P.; 36, S of Newbridge, J.A.P.
Scilly: Lousley 1971.

CERASTIUM L.

Common species: 131/3 *§ **C. tomentosum** L., Snow-in-Summer (absent from Scilly), 131/7 **C. fontanum** Baumg., subsp. **triviale** (Link) Jalas (*C. vulgatum* L.), Common Mouse-ear, 131/8 **C. glomeratum** Thuill., (*C. viscosum* L.), Sticky Mouse-ear, and 131/10 **C. diffusum** Pers. (*C. tetrandrum* Curt.), Sea Mouse-ear, are all common and widespread.

131/12 **C. semidecandrum** L.   Little Mouse-ear

Virtually confined to sand-dunes, where it is often abundant.

West: 33, Kenidjack Quarry, Carn Gloose Point, and Carn Leskeys, all near St Just, M.C.; 53, Lelant, Gwithian, and Phillack (Flora), still frequent all the way from Lelant to (54) Godrevy, L.J.M.; 75, Perranporth (Suppt), Penhale Sands, 1962, L.J.M.; 86 (76), Porth Joke, L.J.M.; 87, Constantine Bay, W.G.

East: 83, Pendower Beach, L.J.M.; 97 St Enodoc golf links, 1950—1979, R.W.D.; 05, Par Sands, L.J.M.

MOENCHIA EHRH.

135/1 **M. erecta** (L.) P. Gaertner, B. Meyer, & Scherb.

Upright Chickweed

This small and inconspicuous plant is still present in a number of coastal areas, but, in view of its general decline in Britain, all extant stations are listed here.

West: 32, near Logan Rock (Flora), 1977, M.G. and L.J.M.; 33, Carn Gloose Point, M.C.; Kelynack, B.M.S.; 43, Boskednan, B.M.S.; Morvah, B.M.S.; Bosigran, G.L.; 52, Praa Sands, R.H.; Rinsey Head, RNHS; Kings Cove Quarry, S.M.T. and B.J. and E.J.; 53, Gwithian Towans, G.L.; Trenow Cove, Perranuthnoe, B.M.S.; Marazion, B.M.S.; Trencrom Hill, M.G. and L.J.M.; (54), Godrevy Towans, L.J.M.; 61, Mullion (Flora), 1966, J.A.P.; Predannack Wollas, L.C.F., J.H., and M.M.; Kynance, D.E.V.; 62, Porthleven, H.B.S.; 71, Lizard and Kennack, R.H.; Eastern Cliff, J.A.P.; 72, Dennis Head, W.T (Thurston 1930); Durgan, and Rosemullion Head, L.J.M.; 83, Pennance Point, near Falmouth, L.J.M.

East: 97, Miniver Hill, and Pentire Head, New Polzeath, R.W.D.; 04, Trenarren (Suppt), 1976, B.E.M.G.; 08, Treknow Cliff, Trebarwith, R.W.D. and L.J.M.; 25, Polperro (Flora), 1945, D.E.V.; 35, Tregantle Cliff, L.J.M.; 45, Mt Edgcumbe Park (Flora), still there, post—1950, I.N.; near Cawsand, I.N.; (44), Rame Head (Flora), post—1950, I.N.

Scilly: rejected, Lousley, 1971.

SAGINA L.

Common species: 136/9 **S. subulata** (Swartz) C. Presl, Heath Pearlwort (absent from Scilly), 136/4 **S. procumbens** L., Procumbent Pearlwort, 136/1 **S. apetala** Ard., subsp. **erecta** (Hornem.) F. Hermann, Annual Pearlwort, and 136/3 **S. maritima** G. Don, Sea Pearlwort, are all widespread in dry places.

136/10 **S. nodosa** (L.) Fenzl   Knotted Pearlwort

Very local and rare; damp sandy places, especially near the sea.

West: 61, Pentreath, the Lizard, J.Fo.; Kynance (Flora), 1963, D.S.D.; heath N of Penhale, the Lizard, J.A.P.; 62, Porthleven, H.B.S.; Carminowe, Loe Pool,

R.H.; 71, Goonhilly Downs (Flora), 1966, J.A.P.; 75, Perranporth (Flora), 1965, J.B.

East: 95, clayworks NE of Nanpean, J.A.P.; 97, Rock Sandhills (Flora), 1979, R.W.D.

136/2 **S. apetala** Ard., subsp. **apetala**   Fringed Pearlwort
(*S. ciliata* Fr.)

West: 52, King's Cove Quarry, R.J.M.; 53, Hayle, L.J.M.; (54), near Godrevy, J.S.R.; 61, Lizard Cliffs, J.S.R.; 62, Gunwalloe, R.H.; 63, Drym, near Camborne, J.S.R.; near Penponds, Camborne, J.S.R.; 64, Porthtowan, J.S.R.; 71, Lizard (Flora), 1959, D.E.V.; 84, Idless, near Truro, 1910 E.D. and H.D. (B.E.C. 1928, p.798); 97, near Hawkers Cove, Padstow, R.W.D.

East: 04 (03), near Dodman Point, J.S.R.; 15, St Catherine's Point, Fowey, L.J.M.; 25, near Plaidy, Looe, L.J.M.; E of Millandreath, Looe, J.A.P.

Scilly: common, Lousley 1971.

SCLERANTHUS L.

148/
1/1
S. annuus L., subsp. **annuus**   Annual Knawel

Rare, and only in a few scattered localities.

West: 43, Carnaquidden Downs, Nancledra, B.M.S.; 63, near Four Lanes, L.J.M.; Porkellis Moor, R.H.; 71, Kennack, specimen in Herb. Tech. Coll.; Erisey, Goonhilly, E.J.P. (Thurston and Vigurs 1927), still there, post—1950, R.H.; 72, Constantine, R.H.; 73, Penryn, R.H.; Rame, R.H.

East: 95, near St Austell, L.J.M.; 96, Castle-an-Dinas, L.J.M.; 16, Cardinham, B.E.M.G.; 18, Davidstow, J.E.L. (Thurston and Vigurs 1926); 26, near Liskeard, C.P.F. (Thurston and Vigurs 1927); 27, near Trebartha, I.N.

Scilly: no recent records, Lousley 1971.

CORRIGIOLA L.

145/1 **C. litoralis** L.   Strapwort

Probably now extinct in Cornwall.

West: 62, Loe Pool (Flora), where it was stated to have been last seen in 1904. There is, however, a specimen in BM labelled 'Lizard, 1931, R. Meinertzhagen' and this may refer to Loe Pool. Further, Martin and Fraser (1939), affirm that the plant was refound in Cornwall, in 1936, which could be a misquoted repeat of Meinertzhagen's record. We have no further information, and, at present, believe that the plant is unlikely still to occur.

Scilly: a further specimen in BM, again collected by R. Meinertzhagen, is labelled Tresco, 1929. J.E. Lousley rejected this record as unlikely, and we are bound to do the same.

HERNIARIA L.

[146/1 **H. glabra** L., Smooth Rupturewort, is a rare plant of Eastern England, which was rightly rejected by Davey (Flora).]

146/2 **H. ciliolata** Melderis   Fringed Rupturewort
(*H. ciliata* Bab.)

Only on the Lizard, where it is locally common.

West: 61, in numerous stations; 71, numerous stations; 72, near Traboe Cross, J.H.

ILLECEBRUM L.

147/1 **I. verticillatum** L.   Coral-necklace

This very local plant has declined further in the last fifty years for reasons that are not easy to find, as there are still plenty of suitable habitats.

West: 32, near Porthgwarra, E.G.; 33, Bostraze Moor, G.B.M.; 43, Mulfra, BRC; Lanyon Farm, G.L.; Zennor (Flora), 1948, J.B.; Towednack (Flora), still there, post—1950, B.M.S.; 52, near Trink Hill, B.M.S.; near Halse Town (Flora), 1950, BRC; Marazion Marsh (Flora), 1924, E.A.R.; 63, Crowan Reservoir, J.B.; 71, Croft Pascoe Plantation, LFC; 73, Tretheague Moor, Stithians (Flora), 1960, L.J.M.; Polmarth Bog, Carnmenellis, L.J.M.

East: 96, Retire Common, Withiel, R.W.D.; 17, De Lank Valley at Bradford Bridge (Flora), 1976, CNT; Bedrawle, E.A.; near Rose, J.A.P.

POLYCARPON LOEFL.

144/1 **P. tetraphyllum** (L.) L.   Four-leaved Allseed

Only certainly native on the Lizard, where it has not been seen since 1934. Otherwise a very rare casual, except in Scilly, where it is common.

West: 71, Cadgwith (Flora), last seen there c 1934, BRC.

East: 45, garden weed, Wearde Quay, Saltash, I.N., still there, 1975, R.B. and A.C.L.

Scilly: common on all the larger islands, Lousley 1971.

SPERGULA L.

142/1 **S. arvensis** L. Corn Spurrey

In arable land, and in waste places, very common and widely distributed. The type and the var. *sativa* (Boenn.) Mert. & Koch both occur.

SPERGULARIA (PERS.) J. & C. PRESL

Common species: 143/3 S. **rupicola** Lebel, Rock Sea-spurrey, and 143/1 S. **rubra** (L.) J. & C. Presl, Sand Spurrey.

143/4 **S. maritima** (All.) Chiov. Greater Sea-spurrey
(*S. marginata* Kittel)

Rather local, but present in most of the larger salt-marsh areas.

West: 32, Gazzick, Nanquidno, M.C.; 33, Penamver, St Just, M.C.; 72, Manaccan, R.H.; Gweek, R.H.; 83, near Mylor Church, R.H.; 84, Calenick Creek, near Truro, L.J.M.; 86, Gannel, Newquay (Flora), still there, post—1950, Herb. Tech. Coll.; 97, near Sea Mills, J.A.P.

East: 83, Turnaware Creek, B.E.M.G.; 84, Ruan Lanihorne (Suppt), 1963, D.R.; between Tresillian and Malpas, L.J.M.; 97, Trevilling, Wadebridge, N.J.F.; Amble Marshes, R.W.D.; 25, Trenant, Looe, S.M.; 35, St Germans, J.A.P.; Grove, S of Trematon, J.A.P.; 45, Coombe Creek (Flora), still there, post—1950, I.N.; 46, Landulph, I.N.; Halton Quay, J.A.P.

143/5 **S. marina** (L.) Griseb. Lesser Sea-spurrey
(*S. salina* Presl)

Not uncommon in salt-marshes. Too common in the Tamar Estuary for listing of stations there.

West: 53, Hayle, J.B.; 62, Porthleven, H.B.S.; 72, Gweek, R.H.; 73, Devoran (Flora), still there, post—1950, R.H.; 86, Gannel (Flora), 1976, C.J.

East: 84, Lamorran, L.J.M.; 97, Trevilling, Wadebridge, N.J.F.; 05, Par Sands (Suppt), still there, F.R. (Thurston

1930); 21, Duckpool, N of Bude, J.A.P.; 25, Sandplace and Looe (Flora), between the two, J.A.P.; 35, 45, and 46, still frequent in the Tamar Estuary, various recorders. Scilly: rare, Lousley 1971.

145 x 3   **S. marina x rupicola**
*West: 53, St Michael's Mount, 1974, B.M.S.
*East: 05, Par Harbour, 1959 (*Proc. B.S.B.I.* 5: 25).

143/2   **S. bocconii** (Scheele) Ascherson & Graebner
                                          Greek Sand Spurrey
(Suppt as *S. atheniensis* Aschers. & Schweinfurth) Extremely rare and local. Status unknown, but probably introduced originally.
*West: 32, Lands End, 1974, P.D.S.; 53, Marazion, 1959, BRC; about 30 plants, St Michael's Mount, 1975, R.B. and A.C.L.; 62, Porthleven, W.T. (Thurston 1930); 73, Penryn Quay, 1957, R.H.
East: 83, St Mawes (Thurston 1930); 05, Par (Suppt), refound, 1950 onwards, R.W.D., still there in 1975, various recorders.
*Scilly: one station in 1953, Lousley 1971.

143/2 x 5   **S. bocconii x marina**
*East: 05, Par, J.E.Lo. (B.E.C. 1935).

LYCHNIS L.

124/3   **L. flos-cuculi** L., Ragged Robin, is common and widespread in marshes throughout the county.

AGROSTEMMA L.

125/1   **A. githago** L.   Corncockle
(*Lychnis githago* Scop.)
Formerly a familiar cornfield weed, 'locally plentiful' in the Flora, now virtually extinct except as the merest casual.
West: 42, in a field between Lamorna and Mousehole, J.R.P.; 74, Tywarnhayle, R.Go.
East: 05, St Austell, B.Sh.; 20, Sandymouth, N of Bude, till 1949, D.H.; 36 or 37, weed in garden, Harrowbarrow, near Callington, J.M.W.; 45, weed in garden, Coombe, Saltash, I.N.
Scilly: now extinct, Lousley 1971.

SILENE L.

All the following are reasonably common throughout the county:

123/1 S. **vulgaris** (Moench) Garcke, subsp. **vulgaris** (*S. latifolia* Rendle & Britten), Bladder Campion (rejected for Scilly, Lousley 1971), 123/2 S. **vulgaris** subsp. **maritima** (With.) A. & D. Löve (*S. maritima* With.), Sea Campion, 123/14 S. **alba** (Miller) E.H.L. Krause (*Lychnis alba* Mill.), White Campion, 123/13 S. **dioica** (L.) Clairv. (*Lychnis dioica* L.), Red Campion, and 123/6 S. **gallica** L., var. **anglica** (L.) Mert. & Koch (*S. anglica* L.), Small-flowered Catchfly.

123/2 **S. vulgaris** subsp. **maritima** x subsp. **vulgaris**
x 1   Plants intermediate between the two subspecies have been found at:

*West: 53 (54), Gwealavellan, near Godrevy, 1971, R.J.M.; 87, Trevone Head, A.B.

123/12 S. **noctiflora** L.   Night-flowering Catchfly

Always rare in the county, this arable weed has further decreased in recent years.

West: 61, Mullion, W.B. (Thurston 1930); 62, Helston, R.O. (Thurston and Vigurs 1925).

East: 97, cornfields, Trebetherick, 1951, R.W.D.; 05, Par (Suppt), 1928, F.H.P.; Crinnis, W.T. (Thurston 1935); 45, Coombe Farn, Saltash, 1952—54, I.N.

123/14 **S. alba x dioica**
x 13   West: 53, Upton Towans, N.J.F.; Copperhouse, Hayle, L.J.M.; St Erth, L.J.M.; 63, Treskillard, L.J.M.; 64, Bridge Moor, near Portreath, S.B.; below Carn Brea, L.J.M.; Barncoose, Redruth, L.J.M.; 75, Holywell Bay, A.B.

East: 94, and 29, recorded post—1950 for these squares, BRC.

Scilly: Lousley 1971.

123/6+ **S. gallica** L. var. **gallica**
       West: 53, Phillack Towans, R.O. (Thurston and Vigurs 1925).

Scilly: in several stations, Lousley 1971.

var. **quinquevulnera** (L.) Koch

West: 53, Ludgvan (Suppt), 1930, Herb. F.H. Perry-coste, (TRU).

Scilly: Lousley 1971; M, near Waterworks and Tremellan, 1973, L.A.H.

SAPONARIA L.

129/1 **S. officinalis** L., Soapwort, is an ancient introduction, with every appearance of a native plant. Frequent and widespread, in both single and double-flowered forms.

DIANTHUS L.

127/1 **D. armeria** L.   Deptford Pink

Local and rare, but still present in four localities.

West: 53, Copperhouse, Hayle, B.M.S., still there in 1967, G.A. and L.J.M.; 64, many plants by footpath above Portreath, 1966, L.J.M.; one plant, top of Light-house Hill, Portreath, L.J.M.

East: 05, Charlestown, W.T. (Thurston and Vigurs 1926); 35, Wiveliscombe (Flora), three plants, 1979, E.G.; 45, Wearde Quay, Saltash, I.N., still there, 1978, E.G.; Saltash Goods Yard, I.N., still there, plentifully, 1972, E.R.

NYMPHAEACEAE

NYMPHAEA L.

55/1 **N. alba** L. (*Castalia alba* Wood)   White Water-lily

Rare in Cornwall, and mostly an introduction.

West: 32, near Sennen, G.H.; 42, Chy-an-hal Moor (Flora), 1949, J.B.; 62, Loe Pool (Flora), still there, 1950 onwards, various recorders; 63, Pendarves Lake, S.M.T.; 97, quarry near Sea Mills, Camel Estuary, J.A.P.

East: 96, Goss Moor (Flora), 1950 onwards, various recorders; 05, Walden Pond, W of St Blazey, J.A.P.; 26 or 27, near Westerlake Farm, Upper Fowey Valley, E.G.

NUPHAR SM.

56/1 **N. lutea** (L.) Sibth, & Sm.   Yellow Water-lily

Only where originally introduced, see note (Thurston and Vigurs 1924, p. 322).

*West: 43, pool near Trengwainton, Penzance, P.J.R.

East: 96, Goss Moor (Flora), 1950 onwards, various recorders; 27, one plant in moorland pool near Great Gimble, Minions, W.C., 1970, L.J.M.

CERATOPHYLLACEAE
CERATOPHYLLUM L.
57/1 **C. demersum** L. Rigid Hornwort
Extremely local, but usually in quantity where it does occur.

West: No recent records.

*East: 20, plentiful in Bude Canal, L.J.M.; 21, Tamar Lake, J.A.P.; River Tamar, near Kilkhampton, post— 1950, D.H.

RANUNCULACEAE
HELLEBORUS L.
38/2 **H. viridis** L., subsp. **occidentalis** (Reuter) Schiffner
Green Hellebore

West: 71, Hendra Farm, Ruan Major (Suppt), 1968, R.B.G.; 72, Trelowarren Mills, E.A.

East: 84, Mellingoose Woods, Ruan Lanihorne, C.J.; 97, Hay Wood, St Breock, R.W.D.; 07, Colquite, Helland, E.W.M., (Thurston 1928); in old orchard near Helland Bridge, K.H.J.; 20, near Wooda Farm, Stratton, R.O. (Thurston and Vigurs 1925); 21, Scadghill Farm, Stibb, R.D.; Coombe Valley, R.D.

CALTHA L.
36/1 **C. palustris** L. Marsh-marigold
Frequent in Mid and East Cornwall, becoming rare in the West, and absent from the extreme West and from Scilly (as a native).

ACONITUM L.
40/1 **A. napellus** L. Monk's-hood
Nearly all the records refer to garden cultivars. In the Coombe Valley, N of Bude, it may, however, be native.

West: 62, Nancemerrin, near Helston, D.M.S.; 63, woodland, Clowance, J.B.; 64, Porthtowan, L.J.M.; 72, Tregidden, S of Manaccan, R.H.

East: 21, near Morwenstow, J.S.R.; Coombe Valley

(Flora), still there, 1950 onwards, various recorders; 26, rubbish tip, St Cleer, I.N.; 36, wood near Smeaton Farm, Pillaton, E.G.

ANEMONE L.

43/1   **A. nemorosa** L.   Wood Anemone

Frequent and widespread, except in the extreme West and Scilly, mainly in woodland, but also associated with granite tors.

var. caerulea DC.

West: 43, between St Ives and Zennor (Flora), still there, post—1950, M.B.; 53, below Trink Hill, L.J.M.; 73, Kennall Valley (Flora), Ponsanooth, I.M.R. (Thurston 1935).

East: 84, Tresillian (Flora), C.N. (Thurston 1935); 97, Hawkes Wood, Wadebridge, E.A.; 05, Luxulyan Valley (Flora), six plants, E.A.; 27, Northill, W.H.F. (Thurston 1929a).

CLEMATIS L.

45/1   **C. vitalba** L., Traveller's-joy, is common and widely distributed along the coasts, rarely far inland.   An introduction in Scilly.

RANUNCULUS L.

Common species: 46/2 **R. repens** L., Creeping Buttercup, 46/1 **R. acris** L., Meadow Buttercup (very rare in Scilly), 46/3 **R. bulbosus** L., Bulbous Buttercup, 46/16 **R. hederaceus** L., Ivy-leaved Crowfoot, and   46/17 **R. omiophyllus** Ten., Round-leaved Crowfoot (absent from Scilly).

46/7   **R. sardous** Crantz   Hairy Buttercup

Frequent in sandy areas near the coast, rarely inland. West: 43, Gulval, B.M.S.; 53, Gwithian, S.B.; 61, Kynance, L.A.B.; Mullion, B.Sh.; 62, Gunwalloe (Flora), 1963, D.S.D.; Carminowe, Loe Pool, R.H.; 64, near Carn Brea Station, L.J.M.; Porthtowan, J.A.P.; 71, Lizard (Flora), 1959—77, J.Fo.; Downas Valley, the Lizard, CNT; 72, Rosemullion, J.A.P.; St Martin, R.H.; 73, Devoran Quay, R.H.; 86, Mawgan Porth, J.A.P.; 87, Trevone, J.A.P.

East: 93, Nare Head, J.A.P.; 97, near Com Head, Pentire Peninsula, R.W.D.; 35, Tideford (Flora), still there, I.N.; Shevoick, 1966, now gone, S.M.
Scilly: Lousley 1971.

46/8 § **R. marginatus** D'Urv. St Martin's Buttercup
A colonist at present restricted to one locality in St Martins, and one in St Mary's.
*Scilly: Lousley 1971; M, Parting Carn, 1979, D.W.L.

46/6 §- **R. muricatus** L. Scilly Buttercup
A common bulb-field weed in Scilly that has now spread to the mainland.
*West: 43, Gulval, S.B.; ?=between Trevarrick and Gulval, 1968, B.M.S.; 71, near Poltesco, the Lizard, 1951 (Lousley 1971).
*Scilly: common, Lousley 1971.

46/5 **R. arvensis** L. Corn Buttercup
Now extinct as a cornfield weed, and only occurring as a very rare casual.
West: 53, Copperhouse, Hayle, R.O. (Thurston and Vigurs 1925); 72, weed in garden, Mawnan Smith, R.B.G.
East: 84, St Clement, W.H.F. (Thurston and Vigurs 1926); 94, weed in garden, Grampound, S.S.; 25, garden weed, Polperro, M.M.P. (Thurston 1928); 26, one plant, Trevillis, Liskeard, C.P.F. (Thurston and Vigurs 1927); 36, N of Trematon, D.B.
Scilly: Lousley 1971.

46/9 **R. parviflorus** L. Small-flowered Buttercup
Frequent in the West, but rather rare in the East of the county.
West: Too many stations to merit listing.
East: 94, Porthluney Beach, L.J.M.; 97, Pentire Peninsula, R.W.D.; 04, Pentwean, Herb. Tech. Coll.; 21, Stanbury Mouth, N of Bude, J.A.P.; 35, Seaton, J.A.P.; Downderry (Flora), 1966, J.A.P.; Wivelscombe, I.N.; 36, Viverdon Down, near Callington, R.W.D.; 45, Saltash (Flora), still there, post—1950, I.N.; Empacombe, near Cremyll, J.A.P.
Scilly: common, Lousley 1971.

46/10 R. auricomus L.   Goldilocks Buttercup

Very rare in Cornwall, as it has always been.

West: 72, Gweek (Flora), Merthen Wood, 1968, J.F.A.

East: 21, roadside near Coombe, R.O. (Thurston and Vigurs 1925), 1967, J.A.P.; 36, Pillaton Mill (Flora), site destroyed in 1964, I.N.; 37, Tamar Valley S of Greystone Bridge, J.A.P.

46/15 R. sceleratus L.   Celery-leaved Buttercup

Rather local and rare and usually in small quantity.

West: 53, Hayle Causeway, T.J.P. (Thurston 1929a), 1956, J.B.; Copperhouse, Hayle, B.M.S.; W of St Erth, J.A.P.; Marazion Marsh (Flora), still there, 1965, J.B.; 75, nursery weed, Zelah, L.J.M.; 83, Mylor Bridge, W.H.F. (Thurston 1935); 86, Gannel, Newquay, L.J.M.

East: 84, Ardevora, near Lamorran, K.H.; St Clements (Flora), 1950 onwards, J.B.; 97, Amble Marshes (Flora), still there, post—1950, R.W.D.; 04, London Apprentice, A.B.; 05, Lampetho Marsh, near Tywardreath, W.T. (Thurston and Vigurs 1927), at lower end of marsh, 1967, B.G.; 38, in two places near Launceston, G.L.K.; 46, Saltash (Flora), 1966, I.N.; Landulph, I.N.; Haye Farm near Cargreen, I.N.; Halton Quay (Flora), 1966, J.A.P.

46/24 R. ficaria L.   Lesser Celandine
subsp. **ficaria**

Abundant and widespread throughout the county.

var. **albiflora** Druce

West: 42, Penzance, G.B.M.; 62, Helston, R.K. (Thurston 1935).

subsp. **bulbifer** Lawalrée

*West: 43, Penlee Park, Penzance, B.M.S.; 63, old tip, Treskillard, L.J.M.; 75, Zelah Nurseries, 1970, L.J.M.; 83, Penpol House, Devoran, L.J.M.; garden, Falmouth, L.J.M.; 84, Truro, J.Be.

East: 05, Charlestown, W.T.; Tregrehan, Carvear, Par, and St Blazey, all L.T.M. (Thurston 1935); 06, Bodmin, and Lanhydrock, E.A.; 07, St Breward, E.A.; 15, Golant (Thurston 1935); frequent around Lostwithiel, E.A.; 16, Restormel road, Lostwithiel, E.T. and L.T.M. (Thurston 1935); 25, Polperro, F.R. (Thurston 1935).

46/12 **R. flammula** L.   Lesser Spearwort
       subsp. flammula
       Abundant in wet places throughout the county.

    var. **natans** Pers.
    West: 75, St Agnes, W.T. (Thurston and Vigurs 1924).

    var. **ovatus** Pers.
    East: 96, near Indian Queens, E.Ch.

    var. **radicans** Noltke
    West: 74, Silverwell Moor, B.E.M.G. and L.J.M.; 75,
    Penhale Sands, L.J.M.

46/11 **R. lingua** L.   Greater Spearwort
       Very rare, but still present in two localities.
       West: 42, pool in lane near Paul, E.A.R. (Thurston and
       Vigurs 1925), 1948, S.B. and J.B., probably now gone;
       Chy-an-hal Moor, G.L.; 62, Gunwalloe Valley (Flora),
       still plentiful, 1968, CNT.
       East: 97, St. Enodoc marsh, A.J.Y. (Thurston and
       Vigurs 1925), 1970, J.A.P.

46/17 **R. omiophyllus x peltatus** Schrank
x 22b *East: 84, Tresillian, 1908, H.D. (Thurston 1929a).

46/18 **R. tripartitus** DC.   Three-lobed Crowfoot
       (incl. *R. lutarius* (Revel) Bouvet)
       On acid soils throughout Cornwall, but very local and
       rare. Probably more frequent on the Lizard than else-
       where in Britain.
       West: 32, ditch E of Sennen, J.A.P.; 42, Kerris Moor
       (Flora), 1949, J.B.; Chy-an-hal Moor (Flora), 1949, J.B.;
       43, near Lanyon Farm, Morvah, J.A.P.; Nancledra,
       B.M.S.; 61, in a number of stations; 63, Porkellis Moor,
       J.A.P.; 71, four stations, various recorders; 72, one
       station, L.C.F. and M.M.
       East: 95, near Burngullow Station, W.T. (Thurston
       1935); 17, Bradford, near Blisland, R.W.D.; Dozmary
       Pool (Thurston 1928); 27, near Minions, J.A.P.; 29,
       Greena Moor (Flora), 1953 and 1954, R.W.D.
       Scilly: extinct, Lousley 1971.

46/23 R. baudotii Godron   Brackish Water-crowfoot
This species is surprisingly rare for a maritime county.
West: 62, Loe Pool, Herb. Tech. Coll.; 71, near Grade
Church, J.E.Lo. (Thurston 1935); 75, Penhale Sands,
NCS.
Scilly: common, Lousley 1971.

46/22b R. peltatus Schrank   Common Water-crowfoot
The true species seems to be almost confined to the
Lizard, where it is frequent.
West: 53, Retallack Ponds, Relubbus, J.B.; 61, Hayle
Kimbro Pool, J.H.; Goonhilly Reserve, J.H.; Kynance,
J.H.; 71, Croft Pascoe Pool, J.H.; Carn Barrow, J.H.;
small pool near Crousa Downs, L.J.M.; 72, pool at
Croftnoweth, J.H.
Scilly: recorded in Flora, (but rejected by J.E. Lousley,
1971), under *R. aquatilis* L.

46/22c R. penicillatus (Dumort.) Bab.
(*R. peltatus* var. *penicillatus* Hiern)
Only in the extreme E of the county.
East: 36, Heskyn Mill, near Tideford (Flora), 1966,
S.M.; 37, R. Tamar near Luckett, I.N.; 39, R. Tamar
near N Tamerton, L.J.M.

46/22a R. aquatilis L.
(*R. heterophyllus* Weber)
Earlier records may refer to other species. The following
is the only recent record, *sensu stricto:*
East: 20, Mere Marsh, near Bude, 1978, L.J.M.
Scilly: rejected, Lousley 1971.

46/21 R. trichophyllus Chaix   Thread-leaved Water-crowfoot
(incl. *R. drouetii* F. Schultz)
In Cornwall this species is characteristic of slow streams
in sand-dune areas.
West: 75, Trebisken Moor (Flora), another name for
the Ellenglaze Valley, which runs into Holywell Bay, still
there, post—1950, Herb. Tech. Coll.; near Mount
(Flora), 1977, L.J.M.; 87, Constantine Sandhills (Flora),
1964, L.J.M.; Towan Green, near Constantine Bay,
1967, L.J.M.

East: 97, stream on path from St Enodoc to Rock, R.W.D.

Scilly: not confirmed, Lousley 1971.

[46/19 **R. fluitans** Lam., River Water-crowfoot, is a plant of Central and Eastern England, and most unlikely to occur. Davey's rejection of this species must be upheld.]

MYOSURUS L.

48/1   **M. minimus** L.   Mousetail

Probably only sporadic here.

*East: 20, near Maer, Bude, 1941, J.H.D. (B.E.C. 1941–42).

AQUILEGIA L.

49/1   **A. vulgaris** L.   Columbine

Frequent and widespread, but rarely in quantity. A long-standing introduction in most places, but possibly native in some of the wooded valleys of E Cornwall.

THALICTRUM L.

50/3   **T. minus** L., subsp. **minus**   Lesser Meadow-rue
(incl. subsp. *majus* (Crantz) Rouy & Fouc.)

The Lizard plants are very variable, and many names have been applied to them. Pending further investigation of these taxa, we have grouped them under one name. Probably introduced outside the Lizard area.

West: 53, near Loggans Moor, B.M.S.; Carnsew Spit, Hayle, P.J.R.; 61, in three loaclities, various recorders; 63, Brea Valley, near Carn Brea, L.J.M.; near Troon, L.J.M.; 64, Tregajorran, near Carn Brea, L.J.M.; Tolvaddon, near Camborne, R.J.M. and L.J.M.; 71, in six localities, comm. J.H.; 72, in three localities, comm. J.H.

Scilly: one station, Lousley 1971.

BERBERIDACEAE

BERBERIS L.

53/1   **B. vulgaris** L.   Barberry

Formerly widespread as an introduced plant, now rare. West: 43, Tremithick Cross, J.A.P.; N of Heamoor, Penzance, B.M.S.; Trengwainton Carn (Suppt), 1960, J.B.; 72, near Maenporth, L.J.M.

East: 35, Trevollard (Flora), Trevollard House, post—
1950, I.N.; Wivelscombe, I.N.; 45, Thanckes, Torpoint,
S.M.

PAPAVERACEAE

PAPAVER L.

58/1   **P. rhoeas** L., Common Poppy, is still frequent in the
county, on waste ground, especially near the coast, less
frequently than formerly in cultivated land.

58/6   § **P. somniferum** L.   Opium Poppy
Frequent as a casual, sometimes in quantity.

West: 53, Marazion, G.C.D. (Thurston 1935); Lelant,
S.M.; Phillack Towans, CRNHS; (54), near Godrevy,
abundant, J.S.R.; 61, Goonhilly Reserve, D.E.C. *et al;*
63, near Redruth, L.J.M.; 64, near Porthtowan, J.G.T.;
75, Goonhavern, C.K.C.; 83, Swanpool, Falmouth,
L.J.M.

East: 84, Pencalenick, L.J.M.; 20, Bude (Flora),
1972, L.J.M.; 35, Seaton, S.M.; Portwrinkle, S.M.; 45,
in four places around Torpoint and Saltash, S.M.

58/2   **P. dubium** L.   Long-headed Poppy
West: frequent and widespread.

East: 97, St Minver (Flora), Stoptide, and Trebetherick,
R.W.D.; 05, Par (Flora), 1969, L.J.M.; 20, Bude (Flora),
1972, L.J.M.; 25, W Looe, L.J.M.; 26, St Cleer, I.N.;
35, Seaton,, N.J.F.; Downderry (Flora), post—1950,
S.M.; 45, in three places near Torpoint, S.M.; South-
down Quarry, J.A.P.; 46, Clifton Farm, N of Cargreen,
I.N.
Scilly: common, Lousley 1971.

58/3   **P. lecoqii** Lamotte   Yellow-juiced Poppy
A very rare casual, now almost extinct.

West: 73, in two waste spots in Falmouth, 1962,
L.J.M.
Scilly: rejected, Lousley 1971.

58/5   **P. argemone** L.   Prickly Poppy
Like the next species, this plant is confined to sandy
coastal habitats, in a few places only.

West: 32, near Sennen (Flora), E.B. (Thurston and

Vigurs 1926); 53, Marazion, G.C.D. (Thurston 1935); between Hayle and Gwithian, L.J.M.; 61, Mullion Cove, (Suppt), E.J.P. (Thurston and Vigurs 1927); 75 Gear Sands, Perranporth, J.A.P.; 86 (76), Porth Joke, J.A.P.; 87, Harlyn Bay (Flora), 1965, J.A.P.; St Merryn (Flora), Constantine Bay, 1977, L.J.M.

East: 97, St Minver (Flora), Trebetherick, post— 1950, R.W.D.

58/4 **P. hybridum** L. Rough Poppy

Still surviving in many of its old stations.

West: 32, Sennen (Flora), E.B. (Thurston and Vigurs 1924); 53, Marazion, G.C.D. (Thurston 1935); Connor Downs (Flora), post—1950, B.M.S.; arable field near the Navocks, L.J.M.; Phillack, L.J.M.; (54), Gwithian, J.A.P.; 61, near Mullion (Flora), W.B. (Thurston 1935); 75, Rose, Perranporth, B.M.S.; Holywell Bay, W.D.M. (Thurston and Vigurs 1927); 86 (76), West Pentire, Newquay, L.J.M.; 87, Harlyn Bay (Flora), 1968, J.A.P.; St Merryn (Flora), Constantine Bay, 1977, L.J.M.

East: 83, Porthcurnick, Gerrans, L.J.M.; 97, St. Minver, and Polzeath (Flora), Trebetherick, 1952, R.W.D.; near Lundy Bay, R.W.D.

MECONOPSIS VIG.

59/1 **M. cambrica** (L.) Vig. Welsh Poppy

Now frequent as a garden escape, especially in the East. It could be native in Carthamartha Wood, which is adjacent to Dunterton in Devon, where it has long been regarded as native.

West: 42 or 43, Penzance, B.M.S.; 86, one plant, Vale of Lanherne, St Mawgan, L.G.

East: 25, Polvean, Looe, L.J.M.; 27, Northill village, E.A.; Trebartha, K.P.; Rilla Mill, N.J.F.; St Cleer, S.M.; Upton Cross, R.F.W.; 28, Polyphant, and Lewannick, L.J.M.; Altarnun (Flora), 1979, L.J.M.; Egloskerry, L.J.M.; 37, Carthamartha Wood, Tamar Valley (Suppt), 1970, L.J.M.

GLAUCIUM MILLER

61/1 **G. flavum** Crantz Yellow Horned-poppy

A distinctly rare plant, considering the number of suitable habitats in the county. but common in Scilly.

West: 43, between Penzance and Marazion (Flora), 1971, B.M.S.; 53, Marazion, L.J.M.; Upton Towans, J.R.P.; 62, Loe Bar (Flora), still there, 1978, J.S.R.; 71, Kennack Sands (Suppt), 1950 onwards, R.H.; 72, St Anthony, and Mawnan, Helford River, R.H.; Gillan Creek, L.A.B.; 75, Perranporth (Flora), 1966, J.A.P.; 87, Constantine Bay, L.J.M.; Trevose Head, J.A.P.

East: 05, Par (Flora), 1950, R.D.P.

Scilly: common, Lousley, 1971.

CHELIDONIUM L.

62/1 **C. majus** L., Greater Celandine, is frequent in hedges, usually not far from houses, over the whole county, except for Scilly.

CORYDALIS VENT.

65/3 **C. claviculata** (L.) DC.   Climbing Corydalis

Rare in the West, less so, but still rather local, in E Cornwall.

West: 42, Lamorna Cove (Flora), between there and Mousehole, post—1950, various recorders; 53, Trencrom Hill, R.B.G.

East: 05, Pelyn Tor, E.A.; Luxulyan Valley (Suppt), 1950 onwards, several recorders; 06, Red Moor, E.A. and L.J.M.; Helmentor, J.A.P.; 07, railway cutting, Sladesbridge, L.J.M.; 15, Lantivet Bay, K.H.; 17, De Lank Valley (Flora), 1963, E.A.; 18, Rough Tor, K.H.; 19, Lesnewth, Boscastle, E.A.; 27, Trewortha Tor, E.G.; Siblyback Reservoir, R.F.W.; Cheesewring, R.W.D.; 36, woods by R. Lynher N of Newbridge, E.G.

65/4 §- **C. lutea** (L.) DC.   Yellow Corydalis

A rather persistent wall-colonist, originally introduced.

West: 53 (54), between St Ives and Clodgy Point, L.B.; 72 (82), Rosenithon, St Keverne, J.H. and L.J.M.; 83, Pendennis Point, Falmouth, L.J.M.; Greenbank, Falmouth, L.J.M.

East: Frequent throughout the vice-county.

FUMARIA L.

Common species: 66/4 **F. bastardii** Boreau, Tall Ramping-fumitory, 66/6b **F. muralis** Sonder ex Koch, subsp. **boraei** (Jordan) Pugsley, Common Ramping-fumitory, and 66/8 **F. officinalis** L., Common Fumitory.

66/1   **F. occidentalis** Pugsley   Western Fumitory

Frequent and widespread in West Cornwall, very rare in the East. As its world distribution is restricted to Cornwall, we have felt it advisable to list all records additional to those in the Flora and Suppt.

West: 32, Lands End, BRC; 42, Mousehole, J.M.M.; 53, Lelant Church, L.J.M.; Phillack, L.J.M.; Upton Towans, B.E.M.G. and J.A.P.; near Gwithian Church, J.A.P.; Connor Downs, A.C.L.; St Erth, J.A.P.; (54), Godrevy, J.S.R.; 61, Mullion, BRC; 62, Gunwalloe, CNT; Porthleven, H.B.S.; 63, Piece, Carnkie, L.J.M.; Penponds, and Trevoole, near Camborne, J.S.R.; 64, Porthtowan, D.E.C.; 71, Ruan Minor, BRC; Housel Bay, E.S.T. (Thurston and Vigurs 1925); Lizard Town, D.E.C.; Cadgwith Bay, BRC; 72, Main Dale, BRC; 75, Zelah Nurseries, L.J.M.; Lambourne, Perranzabuloe, (B.E.C. 1927, p.562); 85, N of Zelah, L.J.M.; Gwills, near Newquay, L.J.M.; Newlyn East, L.J.M.; 86, Newquay (Flora), still frequent around the town; Watergate Bay, L.J.M.; Bedruthan Steps, BRC; 87, St Ervan, L.J.M.; 95, S of Fraddon, J.A.P.; 96, Winnards Perch, R.J.M. and L.J.M.; 97, Padstow, L.J.M.

East: 96, Winnards Perch, L.J.M.; 97, Rock (Flora), 1976, R.P.

Scilly: Lousley 1971; A, 1967, J.A.P.

66/2   **F. capreolata** L.   White Ramping-fumitory

Very local in the county, but often persistent in any one station.

West: Additional localities: 32, Sennen, J.B.; 42, Mousehole, J.R.P.; 52, Praa Sands, J.R.P.; 53, Carbis Bay, J.A.P.; Lelant, J.B.; (54), between St Ives and Clodgy Point, L.B.; Gwithian, J.A.P.; 62, Helston Station, R.W.D.; 64, near Camborne waterworks, L.J.M.; 73, Roscarrock, Budock, L.J.M.; 74, Council tip, Bissoe, B.E.M.G.; 75, near Perranporth, J.A.P.; 83, Swanpool, Falmouth, L.J.M.; 97, Stepper Point, J.A.P.

East: 83, St Mawes, L.J.M.; 25, Polperro, M.M.P.
(Thurston 1930); 45, Torpoint, S.M.
Scilly: Lousley 1971.

66/3 **F. purpurea** Pugsley   Purple Ramping-fumitory
Very rare and sporadic, but fairly constant in the Hayle
area.
West: 53, near Lelant Church, L.J.M.; edge of Hayle
Saltings, J.M.M., L.J.M. and R.P.; cultivated field,
Hayle, CRNHS; Phillack Towans, G.A. and L.J.M.; (54),
St Ives (Suppt), 1949, J.B.; Godrevy Towans, J.S.R.;
62, Council tip, Helston, R.W.D.; 64, Tregea Hill,
Portreath, J.S.R.; Tehidy, and Illogan, J.S.R.; 75,
weed, Zelah Nurseries, L.J.M.; Cubert (Suppt), abundant,
1977, L.J.M.; 87, Harlyn Bay, A.B.
  *East: 83, St Anthony-in-Roseland, L.J.M.; 84, between
Truro and Malpas (det. E.F. Warburg), 1956, R.W.D.

66/5 **F. martinii** Clavaud
(Suppt as *F. major* Badarro)
Often stated to be extinct in Britain, it may reappear at
Pulla Cross after ploughing.
West: 62, Helston car-park, BRC; 73, Gilly Tresamble,
near Perranwell Station (Suppt), it has been known in
one field at nearby Pulla Cross by various recorders
until 1974, when seen there by J.Fr.

66/6a **F. muralis** subsp. **muralis**
var. **cornubiensis** Pugsley
East: 94, near Tregony, 1922, E.S.T. (Thurston and
Vigurs 1925).

66/6c subsp. **neglecta** Pugsley
(Suppt as *F. neglecta* Pugsley)
East: 84, between Truro and Malpas (Suppt), 1956,
R.W.D.

CRUCIFERAE
SISYMBRIUM L.
108/1 **S. officinale** (L.) Scop., Hedge Mustard, is a common
and widespread weed of waste places.

108/2 § **S. irio** L.   London-rocket
Only ever casual, and now probably gone from the county.

West: 43 or 53, railway between Marazion and Penzance, E.A.R.; 53, near the ferry, Lelant, E.A.R. (both in Thurston and Vigurs 1925); Copperhouse, Hayle, E.A.R. (Thurston and Vigurs 1926).

108/5 § **S. altissimum** L. Tall Rocket
Purely casual and sporadic.
West: 42, Chy-an-hal, Penzance, G.L.; 53, Copperhouse, Hayle, R.O. (Thurston and Vigurs 1925).
East: 05, Porthpean, and St Austell, W.T. (Thurston 1928); 20, Bude, E.T. (Thurston and Vigurs 1926).

108/4 § **S. orientale** L. Eastern Rocket
This species is slowly increasing as an introduction.
West: 53, Hayle (Flora), 1966, L.J.M.; Phillack, L.J.M.; 64, Camborne, J.S.R.; 73, Lanner, R.L.S. and W.D.W. (Thurston and Vigurs 1925); 83, Falmouth (Flora), W.T. (Thurston 1929a).
East: 84, near Boscawen Park, Truro, W.Bo. (Thurston and Vigurs 1923); 97, Rock, R.W.D.; 05, St Austell, W.T. (Thurston 1928); Crinnis, W.T. (Thurston and Vigurs 1926); 20, Bude, D.H.; Bude Canal, 1979, B.E.M.G.; 26, garden, Liskeard, C.P.F. (Thurston and Vigurs 1927).
Scilly: Lousley 1971.

ALLIARIA SCOP.

107/1 **A. petiolata** (Bieb.) Cavara & Grande (*Sisymbrium alliaria* Scop.), Garlic Mustard, is common and widespread in E Cornwall, less so in the West, and absent from Scilly.

ARABIDOPSIS (DC.) HEYNH.

109/1 **A. thaliana** (L.) Heynh. Thale Cress
(*Sisymbrium thalianum* Gay)
Stated in the Flora to be rather rare, this species has increased gradually, and is now too frequent and widespread for listing of records, but it is rare in Scilly.

ERYSIMUM L.

105/1 § **E. cheiranthoides** L. Treacle Mustard
Rare, as it has always been.
West: 32, fields near Penberth, and St Buryan, J.R.P.

East: 15, Lostwithiel (Suppt), 1971, L.J.M.; 36,
plentiful in Holwood Quarry, Pillaton, E.G.; 45, two
plants in field near Polhawn Cove, E.G.; (44), field
near Rame Church, S.M.

HESPERIS L.

104/1 § **H. matronalis** L., Dame's-violet, is widespread and
increasing as a garden escape.
*Scilly. M, N of Porthloo, 1963, J.R.P.

CHEIRANTHUS L.

106/1 § **C. cheiri** L. Wallflower
Long-naturalised, mainly on cliffs.
West: 62, Porthleven, H.B.S.; 75, Perranporth, J.S.R.;
83, Falmouth Docks (Flora), quarry, Falmouth, 1967,
L.J.M.; Feock, J.S.R.; 86, Newquay (Flora), 1967,
L.J.M.; Watergate Bay, L.J.M.
East: 08, Trebarwith, R.L.G.L.; (09), Forrabury,
Boscastle, L.J.M.; 15, Fowey Harbour, B.B.; 19, Crack-
ington Haven, J.A.P.; 38, Launceston (Flora), on the
town gate, 1971, L.J.M.; 45, Torpoint (Flora), 1966,
S.M.

MATTHIOLA R.BR.

103/1 § **M. incana** (L.) R.Br. Hoary Stock
Increasing as a garden escape near the sea, and often
on cliffs. The cultivars found are those generally
known as 'Brompton Stock'.
West: 53, Phillack, L.J.M.; Marazion, L.J.M.; 61,
Lizard Point, J.Fo.; 64, Portreath, L.J.M.; 86, Newquay
(Flora), 1954, J.B.; Watergate Bay, L.J.M.
East: 83, St Anthony lighthouse, B.E.M.G.; St Mawes
Castle, L.J.M.; 93, Carne, the Roseland, B.E.M.G.; 97,
Polzeath, A.P.H.; 35, Downderry, L.J.M.; 45, Kingsand,
L.J.M.
Scilly: Lousley 1971.

103/2 **M. sinuata** (L.) R.Br. Sea Stock
'Long disappeared from Cornwall' (Flora).
West: 83, two plants on cliff at Falmouth, introduced
(Thurston 1935). Not seen since, and the species is
probably extinct, both as a native, and as an introduction.
Scilly: an old record is rejected, as a mistake for *M.
incana*, Lousley, 1971.

BARBAREA R.BR.

98/1 **B. vulgaris** R.Br., Winter-cress, and 98/4 § **B. verna** (Miller) Ascherson, American Winter-cress, are frequent and widespread.

98/1 **B. vulgaris**
var. **arcuata** (Opiz) Fr.
West: 73, Treluswell, near Penryn, L.J.M.
East: 95, Nanpean, E.T. (Thurston and Vigurs 1925); 36, N of Tilland Farm, Tideford, J.A.P.
Scilly: Lousley 1971.

98/3 § **B. intermedia** Boreau   Medium-flowered Winter-cress
Slowly increasing in the county.
West: 33, Tregaseal, St Just, M.C.; 53, Ludgvan, B.M.S.; 61, Ruan Pool, WFS; 63, Praze-an-Beeble, R.H.; S of Camborne, J.S.R.; 64, Tolvaddon, near Camborne, J.S.R.; near Carn Brea Station, L.J.M.; 72, near Mawnan Church, L.J.M.; 73, Stithians, J.S.R.; 74, Redruth (*Watsonia*, 1949—50).
East: 05, Par (Flora), 1971, N.J.F.
Scilly: Lousley 1971.

RORIPPA SCOP.

102/3 **R. sylvestris** (L.) Besser   Creeping Yellow-cress
(*Radicula sylvestris* Druce)
Still very rare and local.
East: 05, Par, 1925, Herb. F.H. Perrycoste **(TRU)**; 07, R. Camel above Egloshayle, J.A.P.; 27, Upton Cross, N.J.F.; 25, Looe, 1928, Herb. F.H. Perrycoste **(TRU)**; 37, R. Tamar above Horsebridge, J.A.P.; 38, St Stephens, Launceston (Suppt), T.N.S.P. (Thurston 1935); railway W of Launceston, G.L.K.; Polson Bridge, Launceston, L.J.M.; 45, Council tip and nursery, Saltash, E.G.; 47, R. Tamar, at Weir Head, I.N.

102/4 **R. islandica** (Oeder) Borbás   Marsh Yellow-cress
(*Radicula palustris* Moench)
Extremely rare, and mainly casual.
West: 33, casual in garden, St Just, M.C.; 73, Stithians Reservoir, J.S.R.; weed in arable field, Chyvogue, Perranwell Station, L.J.M.
East: 15, Lostwithiel (Flora), still there, 1967, L.J.M.

ARMORACIA GILIB.

96/1 § **A. rusticana** P. Gaertner, B. Meyer & Scherb.

Horse-radish

Probably more frequent than the records show.

West: 52, Perranuthnoe, J.A.P.; 53, Hayle (Flora), 1970, J.A.P.; Upton Towans, L.J.M.; 62, Porthleven, H.B.S.; 63, Treskillard, L.J.M.; 64, Tuckingmill (Flora), Tolvaddon, J.S.R.; 75, Cubert, B.B.; 83, Falmouth (Flora), 1972, L.J.M.; 97, Wadebridge (Flora), 1979 B.E.M.G. and L.J.M.

East: 08 (09), Boscastle (Suppt), 1979, L.J.M.; 15, Lostwithiel, L.J.M.; Lansallos, J.A.P.; 20, Bude, J.A.P.; (10), Widemouth Bay, L.J.M.; 46, Cargreen, J.A.P. Scilly: Lousley 1971.

NASTURTIUM R.BR.

102/1 **N. officinale** R.Br., (*Radicula nasturtium-aquaticum* Rendle & Britten), Water-cress, is a common and widespread plant of ditches and streams.

102/2 **N. microphyllum** (Boenn.) Reichenb.

One-rowed Water-cress

(var. *microphylla* Druce)

Probably unrecognised and thus under-recorded.

West: 62, Helston, 1900 (Thurston 1930); 75, Penhale Sands (Flora), 1978, L.J.M.

*East: 93, Camels Cove, Portloe, L.J.M.; 36, near Pillaton Church, 1974, I.N.; 46, Morden Mill, near Cotehele, I.N.

102/2 **N. microphyllum x officinale** = *Rorippa x sterilis* Airy
x 1 Shaw

*West: 33, Portheras, L.J.M.; 53, pool near Hayle River, L.J.M.; 61, Predannack Head, C.J.; 64, Porthtowan Valley, L.J.M.; 75, Lambourne, Perranzabuloe (*B.S.B.I. Year* 1951).

*East: 94, stream, Caerhayes, 1963, L.J.M.

CARDAMINE L.

Common species: 97/1 **C. pratensis** L., Cuckooflower, 97/4 **Č. flexuosa** With., Wavy Bitter-cress, and 97/5 **C. hirsuta** L., Hairy Bitter-cress.

C. palustris (Wimmer & Grab.) Peterm.
(*C. pratensis* L., var. *palustris* Peterm.)
Recorded for two localities (Flora). They may be correct, but this taxon needs further investigation in Britain. Plants that may be this, with violet flowers and stalked cauline leaflets have been found recently in
East: 18, Kittows Moor, Treneglos, L.J.M.

[97/2 **C. amara** L., Large Bitter-cress, and 97/3 **C. impatiens** L., Narrow-leaved Bitter-cress, have both, in the past, been recorded for Cornwall, (Flora), but there are no specimens to support these claims, and we have no hesitation in removing them from the Cornish list.]

ARABIS L.

100/4   **A. hirsuta** (L.) Scop.   Hairy Rock-cress
Very local, and confined to fixed dunes, but often abundant there.
West: 32, Sennen (Flora), still there, post—1950, B.M.S.; Bosanketh, B.M.S.; 53, Phillack, and Gwithian (Flora), still from Phillack to (54), Godrevy, 1950 onwards, various recorders; 75, Penhale Sands (Suppt), Reen Sands, 1966, and near Mount, 1976, L.J.M.
East: 97, Rock (Flora), still there, various recorders.

LUNARIA L.

L. annua L.   Honesty
An increasing garden escape, but rarely persisting.
West: 32, Numphra, SW of St Just, M.C.; 33, Carn Gloose, M.C.; St Just, M.C.; 63, Trevarno, near Crowan, L.J.M.; 74, between Truro and Chacewater, L.J.M.
East: 97, St Endellion, R.W.D. and L.J.M.; 28, Lewannick, L.J.M.; 35, Downderry, S.M.; 45, Torpoint, Antony, and St John, S.M.
Scilly: Lousley 1971.

LOBULARIA DESV.

92/1   **L. maritima** (L.) Desv.   Sweet Alison
Rather frequent as a garden escape, usually near the sea.
West: 53, Hayle (Suppt), 1971, B.M.S.; Marazion, E.A.R. (Thurston 1935); 71, Coverack, B.B.; 73, Penryn, W.T. (Thurston 1928).

East: 97, Rock, J.E.L. (Thurston and Vigurs 1926), 1978, R.W.D.; 20, Bude (Flora), 1959, B.Sh.; 45, Torpoint, S.M.

Scilly: Lousley 1971.

DRABA L.

94/4 **D. muralis** L. Wall Whitlow-grass

A rare introduction, rejected by Davey (Flora), but found subsequently as a garden weed.

West: 72, garden weed, Bosahan, Helford, C.V. (Thurston 1935); abundant in garden near Porth Navas, L.J.M.; 84, Treseder's Nursery, Truro (B.E.C. 1937, p.651), still there, post—1950, B.E.M.G.

*East: 83, Philleigh, garden weed, 1972, B.E.M.G.

EROPHILA DC.

95/1 E. verna (L.) Chevall., *sensu lato* Common Whitlow-grass

West: 62, Loe Pool, K.H.; 74, St Agnes Station, L.J.M.

East: 97, St Minver (Flora), Rock, R.W.D.; (98), Lundy Bay, N.J.F.; 05, Charlestown, W.T. (Thurston 1935); 20, Bude (Flora), 1966, J.A.P.; 26, near Moorswater, Liskeard, D.B.; 45, Wearde, Saltash, I.N.

Scilly: rejected, Lousley 1971.

subsp. **verna**

Rather rare over much of the county, but frequent on the Lizard.

West: 61, Caerthillian Cove, R.W.D. and L.J.M.; 71, near Lizard Lighthouse, R.W.D. and L.J.M.; between Kennack and Eastern Cliff, J.H. and L.J.M.; 73, arable field, Chyvogue, Perranwell Station, L.J.M.

subsp. **spathulata** (A.F. Lang)Walters

Round-podded Whitlow-grass

Mainly on dunes. The records for *E. praecox* DC in the Flora and Suppt belong here.

West: 53, Lelant Towans (Suppt), and Gwithian Towans (Flora), still plentiful on dunes from Lelant to (54), Godrevy, 1950 onwards, L.J.M.; 64, Porthtowan, L.J.M., 75, Penhale Sands (Suppt), 1961, L.J.M.; 86 (76), Porth Joke, L.J.M.; 87, Constantine Bay, L.J.M.

East: 45, Torpoint (Flora), 1973, S.M.; Mt Edgcumbe, 1979, L.J.M.

COCHLEARIA L.

88/5 **C. danica** L., Danish Scurvygrass, and   88/1 **C. officinalis** L., Common Scurvygrass, are common species along the entire coastline.

88/6   **C. anglica** L.   English Scurvygrass
Frequent only in the salt-marshes of the East.
West: 86, Newquay (Flora), Gannel, 1977, B.B.
East: 97, Wadebridge (Flora), Camel Estuary, 1966, J.A.P.; Amble Marshes, 1950 onwards, R.W.D.; 25, W Looe Estuary, J.A.P.; 35, 45, and 46, in many places around the Tamar Estuary, 1950 onwards, various recorders.

[88/4   **C. scotica** Druce (*C. groenlandica* L.), Scottish Scurvy-grass was rejected by Davey (Flora) as an obvious mistake, which it undoubtedly is.]

CAMELINA CRANTZ

110/1 **C. sativa** (L.) Crantz   Gold-of-pleasure
Now only as an infrequent casual.
West: 62, Council tip, Helston, R.W.D.; 73, Penryn, W.T. (Thurston 1928); Council tip, Falmouth, L.J.M.; 84, near the old County Hall, W.Bo. (Thurston and Vigurs 1925); 85, Council tip, Newlyn East, L.J.M.
East: 05, Tregorrick, near St Austell, W.T. (Thurston 1928); 19, near Boscastle, J.A.P.

CAPSELLA MEDICUS

86/1   **C. bursa-pastoris** (L.) Medic., *sensu lato*, Shepherd's-purse, is an abundant weed of waste places and cultivated ground.   The following segregates were recorded by G.C. Druce:

C. batavorum E.At.
*West: 42 or 43, Penzance, G.C.D. (Thurston 1935).

C. laevigata E.At.
*West: 53, Hayle, G.C.D. (Thurston 1935).

C. patagonica E.At.
*West: 42 or 43, Penzance, G.C.D. (Thurston 1935).

86/2 § **C. rubella** Reuter

Known for several years from one station, but now gone.

*West: 32, roadside, Sennen, 1970—78, B.M.S.

TEESDALIA R.BR.

85/1 **T. nudicaulis** (L.)R.Br. Shepherd's Cress

Very local, but still in most of its old localities.

West: 42, Chy-an-hal (Flora), still there, post—1950, B.M.S.; 52, Rinsey Head, H.B.S., 1978, R.G.; 62, Tregonning Hill, Breage, R.J.M.; 73, walls near Rame, L.J.M.; Penmarth, near Carnmenellis (Flora), 1965—79, L.J.M.

East: 93, The Jacka, Portloe, B.E.M.G.; Nare Head, B.E.M.G.; 04 (03), Dodman Point, K.H.; 04, Trenarren (Suppt), 1973, L.J.M.; Pentewan (Flora), 1966, L.J.M.; 05, Trethurgy, St Blazey, B.Sh.; 06, Helmentor (Flora), Breney Common, B.B.; 17, Bedrawle, and between Whiteheads and Bradford, E.A.; near Bolventor, E.G.; near Redhill Marsh, E.G.; 27, Upper Fowey Valley (Flora), 1950 onwards, various recorders; 45, Rame Head (Flora), post—1950, J.A.P.

THLASPI L.

84/1 **T. arvense** L. Field Penny-cress

Considerably increased since the Flora.

West: Widespread throughout this vice-county, but rather local.

East: 97, Com Head, Pentire Peninsula, R.W.D.; 05, St Blazey, St Austell, and Crinnis, W.T. (Thurston 1928); 08 (09), Boscastle, E.A.; 26, near Liskeard, C.P.F. (Thurston and Vigurs 1927); SE of Liskeard, D.B.; 35, Trevollard (Flora), Trevollard Green, post—1950, I.N.; 38, Launceston (Flora), 1960, B.Sh.; 45, near Ince Castle, I.N.; Saltash (Flora), still there, post—1950, I.N.; 46, Landulph, I.N.

Scilly: common, Lousley 1971.

LEPIDIUM L.

79/3 **L. heterophyllum** Bentham, Smith's Pepperwort, is frequent and widely distributed throughout the county.

79/2   **L. campestre** (L.) R.Br.   Field Pepperwort

Now very rare, and mostly casual.

West: 62, Breage, H.B.S.; 63, Treskillard, L.J.M. East: 35, Polbathic, S.M.; 37, roadside between Callington and Gunnislake, L.J.M.; 38, Launceston (Flora), 1970, G.L.K.; 45, Torpoint (Flora), 1966—72, S.M.

Scilly: rejected, Lousley 1971.

79/4   § **L. ruderale** L.   Narrow-leaved Pepperwort

Formerly frequent in some places, now virtually extinct.

West: 97, Wadebridge, 1950, R.W.D.

79/6   §- **L. latifolium** L.   Dittander

A recent introduction in E Cornwall.

*East: 94, beach near Portholland, planted, comm. M.E.B.; Hemmick Beach, near Dodman Point, 1961, B.Sh., still there, 1979, L.J.M.

CARDARIA DESV.

81/1   §- **C. draba** (L.) Desv.   Hoary Cress
(*Lepidium draba* L.)

Possibly slightly increasing, and under-recorded.

West: 42, Newlyn, J.S.R.; 53, Hayle (Flora), 1977, J.S.R.; Upton Towans, B.M.S.; (54), Gwithian, J.S.R.; 64, Tolvaddon, J.S.R.; Portreath, H.H. (Thurston 1935); 64 or 74, railway bank, Redruth, W.D.W. (Thurston and Vigurs 1926); 75, Perranporth (Suppt), 1965, L.J.M.; 84, Truro (Flora), 1965, J.A.P.; 86, Newquay (Flora), 1966, J.A.P.

East: 83, St Anthony, W.T. (Thurston 1930).

81/2   § subsp. **chalepensis** (L.) O.E. Schulz

East: 05, Par Sands (Suppt), 1967, B.M.S.

CORONOPUS HALLER

80/1 **C. squamatus** (Forskål) Ascherson, Swine-cress, and 80/2 **C. didymus** (L.) Sm., Lesser Swine-cress, are both common and widespread in the county.

DIPLOTAXIS DC.

72/2 § **D. tenuifolia** (L.) DC.   Perennial Wall-rocket
Now the merest casual.

West: 61, Mullion, E.J.P. (Thurston and Vigurs 1926);
73, waste ground, Devoran, 1961, L.J.M.

East: 05, Par Sands, N.D.S.; 25, garden weed, Polperro,
F.H.P. (Thurston 1928).

Scilly: very rare, Lousley 1971.

72/1 § **D. muralis** (L.) DC.   Annual Wall-rocket
Considerably increased in the West, but absent from
much of Mid-Cornwall.

West: 32, between St Levan and Porthcurno, G.H.; 33,
St Just, and Trewellard, M.C.; 43, Zennor, L.J.M.; 52,
Praa Sands, J.A.P.; 53, Marazion, K.P.; Phillack, L.J.M.;
62, Porthleven, H.B.S.; Helston, L.J.M.; 64, Tolvaddon,
Camborne, R.J.M. and L.J.M.; Portreath, and Porth-
towan, L.J.M.; 75, Perranporth (Suppt), 1965, L.J.M.;
83, Falmouth (Flora), 1960, L.J.M.; 84, Truro (Flora),
1967, J.A.P.; 86, Newquay (Flora), 1966, J.A.P.;
Mawgan Porth, J.A.P.; 87, Constantine Bay, L.J.M.;
Trevone, J.A.P.

East: 05, London Apprentice, L.J.M.; 15, Fowey,
L.J.M.; 20, Bude, J.A.P.; 45, Saltash, I.N.; Torpoint
(Flora), 1971, S.M.

Scilly: Lousley 1971.

BRASSICA L.

Common species: 67/2 **B. napus** L. (incl. *B. rutabaga*
(DC.) Briggs), Rape, 67/3 **B. rapa** L., Wild Turnip, and
67/4 **B. nigra** (L.) Koch, Black Mustard.

67/1 **B. oleracea** L.   Wild Cabbage
Very local, but often plentiful where it does occur.

West: 52, Kings Cove, Kenneggy (Flora), 1970, B.M.S.;
Bessy's Cove, L.J.M.; 53, St Ives (Flora), 1964, L.J.M.;
71, Lizard (Flora) between the lighthouse and Landewednack, 1954, R.W.D.

East: 04, Pentewan, W.T. (Thurston and Vigurs 1927);
05, Gwendra Beach, Charlestown, W.T. (Thurston and
Vigurs 1927); Par (Flora), J.A.P.; 15, Fowey, and

Polruan (Flora), 1966, J.A.P.; 25, Looe (Flora), 1966, J.A.P.; 35, one plant, Portwrinkle, S.M.; 38, casual, Launceston, G.L.K.

SINAPIS L.

70/1 **S. arvensis** L. (*Brassica arvensis* O. Kuntze), Charlock, is common and widely distributed as a weed of cultivated land and waste places.

70/2 § **S. alba** L. White Mustard
(*B. alba* Boiss.)
A rare relic of cultivation.
West: 53, Hayle, E.A.R. (Thurston and Vigurs 1927); 64, Portreath, J.S.R.; 73, Penryn, W.T. (Thurston 1935).
East: 05, Par Sands, N.J.F.
Scilly: Lousley 1971.

RHYNCHOSINAPIS HAYEK

69/3 § **R. cheiranthos** (Vill.) Dandy Wallflower Cabbage
A long-standing introduction in Cornwall.
East: 04, Pentewan (Flora), still there, 1954, J.B.; 05, Par (Flora), still plentiful, 1954, J.B.

CAKILE MILLER

77/1 **C. maritima** Scop. Sea Rocket
Still frequent and widespread on sandy beaches.
West: 32, Sennen (Flora), 1972, M.C.; 43, Eastern Green, Penzance (Flora), 1971, B.M.S.; 53, Marazion (Flora), 1967, J.B.; Lelant (Flora), still there, post—1950, R.H.; Hayle Causeway, L.J.M.; (54), Gwithian, R.H.; 62, Gunwalloe (Flora), still there, post—1950, R.H.; 72 (82), Godrevy Cove, St Keverne, J.H. and L.J.M.; Porthoustock, R.H.; Maenporth (Flora), still there, post—1950, R.H.; 86, Newquay (Flora), 1966, J.A.P.; Mawgan Porth, B.B.; 87, Constantine Bay (Flora), 1956, W.G.
East: 83, Pendower Beach (Suppt), 1963, L.J.M.; 94, Porthluney Beach (Flora), 1963, L.J.M.; 97, Polzeath (Flora), 1951, R.W.D.; 04, Vault Beach, Gorranhaven, L.J.M.; 15, Polridmouth, J.B.; Lantic Bay, J.C.D.; 35, Seaton (Flora), 1966, L.J.M.; Portwrinkle, and Tregantle (Flora), 1966, S.M.
Scilly: Lousley 1971.

CRAMBE L.

75/1 **C. maritima** L. Sea-kale

Very rare and sporadic, as it has always been.

West: 43, Eastern Green, Penzance (Suppt), one plant, post—1950, G.B.M.; 52, Perranuthnoe (Flora), 1971, B.M.S.; 53, Long Rock (Flora), 1967, J.A.P.; 61, Polurrian, and Poldhu Coves, E.J.P. (Thurston and Vigurs 1926); 62, Loe Bar, H.B.S.; 86, Newquay, J.A.P.

East: 83, Porthbean Beach, Portscatho, B.E.M.G.; 15, Lantic Bay, J.C.D., in plenty there, 1978, R.W.D.; and L.J.M.

Scilly: Lousley 1971; MN, small bay near Higher Town, 1975, F.W.S.; Rushy Bay, one plant, 1975, F.W.S.; A, one plant, Gugh, F.W.S.

RAPHANUS L.

74/1 **R. raphanistrum** L., subsp. **raphanistrum** Wild Radish

Frequent throughout the county in cultivated fields and waste places, especially near the sea. Much increased since the Flora.

var. **raphanistrum**

West: 53, Phillack; 63, near Troon; 64, cornfield, Reskajeague Downs; Redruth by-pass; 73, near Falmouth reservoir; 75, Wheal Kitty, St Agnes, all L.J.M.

Scilly: Lousley 1971; M, near Maypole, Tremelethan, 1975, D.E.A.

var. **flavus** Schub. & Mart.

West: 32, Gwenver, Sennen, M.C.; 33, Tregaseal, M.C.; 53, Phillack, L.J.M.; 64, cornfield, Reskajeague Downs, L.J.M.; Redruth by-pass, L.J.M.; 73, near Falmouth Reservoir, L.J.M.; 75, Wheal Kitty, St Agnes, L.J.M.; Penhale Sands, L.J.M.; 83, Loe Beach, Feock, B.E.M.G.

East: 84 or 94, between Ruan Lanihorne and Ruan High Lanes, B.E.M.G.; 95, near St Dennis Junction, L.J.M.

Scilly: M, near Maypole, Tremelethan, 1975, D.E.A.

var. **aureus** Wilmott

Scilly: Lousley 1971.

74/2   subsp. **maritimus** (Sm.) Thell.   Sea Radish
         (*R. maritimus* Sm.)
         This species has clearly increased since the Flora, but
         it is still rare in the East and North.
         West: 43, between Marazion and Penzance (Flora),
         1971, B.M.S.; 52, Praa Sands, B.B.; 53, Marazion,
         B.M.S.; (54), Gwithian, R.H.; Godrevy Bridge, L.J.M.;
         71, Lizard (Flora), 1959—77, J.Fo.; 72, Kennack,
         H.B.S.; Maenporth (Flora), still there, post—1950, R.H.;
         73, Newporth Head, L.J.M.; 83, Falmouth (Flora),
         1977, J.S.R.; 86 (76), Porth Joke, L.J.M.; Vugga Bay,
         A.B.; 86, Mawgan Porth, L.J.M.; (76), near Crantock,
         K.H.
         East: 83, St Anthony (Flora), K.H.; 84, Ruan
         Lanihorne, L.J.M.; 93, Pendower Beach (Flora), 1967,
         L.J.M.; Camels Cove, L.J.M.; 97, New Polzeath, R.W.D.;
         04, Pentewan (Flora), 1962, L.J.M.; 08 (09), Boscastle
         Harbour, H.W.P. (Thurston 1935); 15, Lantic Bay,
         J.C.D.; 35, Downderry, J.A.P.; Tregantle, S.M.
         Scilly: Lousley 1971.

         var. **albus** Druce
         West: 53, Godrevy Bridge, L.J.M.
         Scilly: Lousley 1971.

RESEDACEAE
                          RESEDA L.
112/1   **R. luteola** L., Weld, is widely distributed and often
         common in Cornwall, on waste ground, dunes, and old
         mining ground (now probably extinct in Scilly).

112/3   § **R. alba** L.   White Mignonette
         Always rare, this species can now only be reliably seen
         in one station on the mainland.
         West: 53, about 30 plants by railway, Angarrack,
         Hayle, 1975—78, L.J.M.; 64, Portreath (Flora), one
         plant surviving, 1978, L.J.M.
         East: 20, Bude, two plants, J.H.A. (Thurston 1935),
         1966, J.A.P.; 24 plants by old railway station, 1973,
         L.J.M.
         Scilly: Lousley 1971; M, found at Porth Mellin, 1954,
         S.C.H.

112/2 **R. lutea** L.   Wild Mignonette
Rather rare and local, and mainly in dune areas. Probably slightly more widespread than our records show.
West: 53, Lelant, and Porthkidney (Flora), 1967, J.B.; Upton Towans, G.B.M.; (54), Gwithian (Suppt), still there, post—1950, R.H.; 61, Kynance, Herb. Tech. Coll.; 62, Gunwalloe, R.H.; 63, Gwinear Road, R.H.; 64, Portreath (Flora), 1966, L.J.M.; 74, on old tin-workings, Bissoe, R.H.; 86 (76), Porth Joke, L.J.M.; 87, Constantine Bay, L.J.M.
East: 95, Trerice, St Dennis, L.G.; 97, St Minver (Flora), still there, BRC; 05, Par (Flora), still there, BRC; 20, Bude, BRC.
Scilly: very rare, Lousley 1971.

DROSERACEAE
DROSERA L.
247/1 **D. rotundifolia** L.   Round-leaved Sundew
Still common on wet heaths and bogs throughout the county, but absent from Scilly, and very rare in the Lower Tamar area.

247/2 **D. anglica** Hudson   Great Sundew
Now on the borderline of extinction in its sole extant station.
West: 75, Ventongimps Moor (Flora), seen several times in small quantity since 1950, but not in the last few years.

247/3 **D. intermedia** Hayne   Oblong-leaved Sundew
A decreasing species that is still present in a number of localities, mainly on Bodmin Moor.
West: 42, Chy-an-hal (Flora), 1948, J.B.; 43, Towednack, B.M.S.; N of Mulfra Hill, B.M.S.; 53, Marazion (Flora), Long Rock, B.M.S.; 63, Black Rock, J.B.; 73, Polmarth, Carnmenellis, L.J.M.; 74, Silverwell Moor, B.M.S.; 75, Ventongimps, 1926, Herb. F.H. Perrycoste, (TRU).
East: 95, Goss Moor (Flora), 1954, J.B.; 96 Retire Common, R.W.D.; Rosenannon Bog, J.A.P.; 06, E arm of Retire Common, L.J.M.; 18, Crowdy Marsh, R.Go. and L.J.M.; Bowithick, J.A.P.; 27, Smallacombe, Fowey

Valley, R.Go. and L.J.M.; Lamelgate, Fowey Valley, L.G.; near Hawks Tor, C.B., R.J.M., and L.J.M.; Fox Tor Bog, E.G.

CRASSULACEAE
UMBILICUS DC.

238/1 U. **rupestris** (Salisb.) Dandy (*Cotyledon umbilicus-veneris* L.), Navelwort, is a common plant of rocky places and walls.

SEDUM L.

Common species: 235/8 **S. acre** L., Biting Stonecrop, 235/6 § **S. album** L., White Stonecrop, and 235/5 **S. anglicum** Hudson, English Stonecrop.

235/2 **S. telephium** L. Orpine
Frequent in hedges and on waste ground. Possibly native in a few maritime stations.

Sensu lato:
West: 32, near the Logan Rock, G.H.; 71, Black Head, near Coverack, O.R.; 85, near Carland Cross, J.N. East: 08, Tregardock Beach, near Delabole, K.H.; 19, lane at Marshgate, R.W.D. and L.J.M.; Tresparett Posts, R.W.D.; 26, Liskeard (Flora), in four places, post—1950, D.B.; St Cleer (Flora), post—1950, J.A.P.; 27, Northill, E.A.; Rilla Mill, N.J.F.; 35, Denabole, Sheviock, S.M.; 45, Saltash (Flora), Castle Farm, I.N.; 46, Cargreen, I.N. Landulph (Flora), still there, post—1950, I.N.

subsp. **telephium**
West: 63, old mine near Troon, L.J.M.; 73, near Rame, L.J.M.; Penhalveor, near Stithians, L.J.M.; 75, Lanteague, Goonhavern, L.J.M.; 85, Newlyn East, 1968, L.J.M. East: 95, St Dennis, L.J.M.; 05, St Austell, B.Sh.; 25, near St Keyne, J.L.; 38, W of Launceston, G.L.K.

subsp. **fabaria** (Koch) Kirschleger (*S. purpureum* Tausch) East: 95, New Mills, Ladock, L.J.M.; between Grampound Road and St Stephen, L.J.M.; 25, near Sowdens Bridge, J.A.P.; 26, Coombe, Liskeard, L.J.M.; 27, Henwood, R.W.D.

235/11 § **S. reflexum** L.   Reflexed Stonecrop
An old introduction, occurring in a number of localities scattered throughout Cornwall.

West: 33, in two places near St Just, M.C.; 53, Ludgvan, G.B.M.; 63, Killivose Lane, Camborne, R.J.M.; 74, near Goonbell, St Agnes, L.J.M.; 75, Perranporth, J.A.P.

East: 95, Retew, St Dennis, L.G.; 97, St Endellion, R.W.D.; 08, Trebarwith, R.W.D.; 25, Looe (Flora), 1969, L.J.M.; 26, near Menheniot, S.M.; 35, Seaton, S.M.; Polbathic, S.M.; St Germans, 1939, J.B.; 36, Budge's Shop, S.M.; Tideford (Flora), in two places, S.M.; 38, Launceston, B.Sh.; 45, Saltash (Flora), still there, post—1950, I.N.; 46, Halton Quay, N.J.F.; 47, Gunnislake, I.N.

235/10 § **S. forsteranum** Sm.   Rock Stonecrop
(*S. rupestre* L.)

Increasingly recorded as an introduction on Cornish hedges.

West: 63, Copper Hill, Stennack, R.J.M. and L.J.M.; Troon, L.J.M.; 64, Carn Brea, L.J.M.; 73, Barncoose, near Redruth, L.J.M.; 75, old railway track, Perranporth, L.J.M.

East: 20, Stratton, L.J.M.; 37, Kellybray, N of Callington, J.A.P.; Luckett, J.A.P.

235/6b § **S. album** L., subsp. **micranthum** (Bast.) Syme
*East: 97, wall, Pentireglaze, 1972, B.E.M.G.; 08, wall, St Nectan's Glen, B.E.M.G.

SAXIFRAGACEAE
SAXIFRAGA L.

[239/2 S. **stellaris** L., Starry Saxifrage, was rejected by Davey (Flora), as it is a most unlikely species for Cornwall.]

239/5   § **S. x urbium** D.A. Webb = *S. spathularis x umbrosa*
x 4   Londonpride
Increasingly reported as a garden throw-out, sometimes forming large masses.

West: 63, Killivose Lane, Camborne, R.J.M.; Four Lanes, L.J.M.; 73, Swanvale, Falmouth, L.J.M.

East: 16, Braddock Church, C.J.; by river, St Neot, L.J.M.; 18, Wilsey Down Plantation, L.J.M.; Otterham Station, R.D.; near Marshgate, R.W.D. and L.J.M.; 19, abundant in Minster churchyard, E.A. and L.J.M.

239/8 **S. tridactylites** L.   Rue-leaved Saxifrage
Now absent from the West, rare in Mid-Cornwall, but frequent in the Tamar Estuary.
East: 94, Tregony (Flora), 1968, L.J.M.; 97, Wade-bridge (Flora), 1975, E.A.; 05, Charlestown, W.T. (Thurston 1935); 15, Golant (Suppt), one plant, 1971, L.J.M.; 20, Bude, R.O. (Thurston and Vigurs 1925); 35, 'hundreds of plants', Trematon village, E.G.; 38, Launceston (Flora), one plant, 1970, N.J.F.; 45, Saltash (Flora), in four places, post—1950, I.N.; Millbrook (Flora), still there, post—1950, I.N.; Antony House, B.E.M.G.; Mt Edgcumbe, L.J.M.; Cawsand, E.G.; 46, Carkeel, Saltash, E.G.; Cargreen, I.N.

TOLMIEA TORREY & A. GRAY
241/1 § **T. menziesii** (Pursh) Torrey & A. Gray
Pick-a-back-plant
*East: 07, by R. Camel below Hellandbridge, 1956, B.G.; in two places near Keybridge, and in Shell Woods, B.G.

CHRYSOSPLENIUM L.
242/1 **C. oppositifolium** L., Opposite-leaved Golden-saxifrage, is frequent and widespread in damp, shady places (absent from Scilly).

ESCALLONIACEAE
ESCALLONIA MUTIS EX L.FIL.
245/1 §- **E. macrantha** Hooker & Arnott   Gum Box
Increasing as a garden escape, frequently on railway banks.
*West: 32, Porthgwarra, S.M.; 42, Kemyl Crease Wood, near Lamorna, R.W.D. and L.J.M.; 43, Zennor, S.M.; Trythal, N of Madron, B.M.S.; Chy-an-dour, Penzance, B.M.S.; 53 (54), St Ives, J.S.R.; 63, Camborne, J.S.R.; 64, Portreath, J.S.R.; 74, N of Mt Hawke, L.J.M.; 75, St Agnes, J.A.P.; 83, Falmouth, J.S.R.; Swanpool, Falmouth, 1964, B.Sh.

*East: 93, near Camels Cove, 1967, L.J.M.; 35, Down-
derry, N.J.F.
Scilly: Lousley 1971.

GROSSULARIACEAE
RIBES L.
246/1 § **R. rubrum** L.   Red Currant
Originally introduced. Rather local.

West: 43, between Heamoor and Tremethick Cross,
B.M.S.; 62, Porthleven, H.B.S.; 63, Clowance Woods,
L.J.M.; Pendarves Wood (Flora), 1963, L.J.M.; 64,
Nance Wood, J.S.R.; Tehidy Woods, L.J.M.; 74, Bissoe
Valley, L.J.M.

East: 06, near Grogley Halt, J.A.P.; Fletchers Bridge,
E.A. and L.J.M.; 07, Allen Valley below Kellygreen,
St Tudy, J.A.P.; 15, Fowey, N.J.F.; 16, S of St Neot,
J.A.P.; 26, W of Menheniot, J.A.P.

246/3 § **R. nigrum** L.   Black Currant
Only as an introduction, mainly in woods.

West: 63, Porkellis, L.J.M.; 64, near Kehelland, J.S.R.;
71, NE of Ruan Minor, J.S.R.; 72, near Mawnan, L.J.M.;
75, Ellenglaze Valley, B.M.S. and L.J.M.; Holywell Bay,
A.B.; below Polgoda Downs, J.A.P.; 85, Penhallow
Moor, CNT; 86, near Trevemper Bridge, L.J.M.; 86
(76), Porth Joke Valley, J.A.P.

East: 84, Lamorran, L.J.M.; 97, Trebetherick, J.A.P.;
19, between Dizzard and Dizzard Point, J.A.P.; 26, two
places near Liskeard, C.P.F. (Thurston and Vigurs 1927).

246/6 § **R. uva-crispa** L.   Gooseberry
(*R. grossularia* L.)

An ancient introduction, often in woods.

West: 43, between Heamoor and Tremethick Cross,
B.M.S.; 62, Nancemerrin, Culdrose, CNT; 63, S of
Camborne, J.A.P.; near Praze Station, L.J.M.; 64,
Tehidy Woods, L.J.M.; Nance Wood, L.J.M.; 72, wood
E of Mawgan-in-Meneage, J.A.P.; 75, Penwartha
Coombe, Perranporth, B.B.; near Carnkief, J.A.P.

East: 84, Malpas, L.J.M.; 97, old garden, Trebetherick,
J.A.P.; 21, Morwenstow, J.A.P.; 25, near Talland
Church, L.J.M.; 28, Altarnun (Flora), 1979, L.J.M.;

35, valley below Freathy Farm, S.M.; 37, Linkinhorne, N.J.F.

ROSACEAE
SPIRAEA L.

209/1 § **S. salicifolia** L. Bridewort

An increasing garden throw-out.

West: 32, Porthcurno, K.E.H.; 83, Swanpool, Falmouth, L.J.M.

East: 95, Carbis Moor, Roche, B.E.M.G. and L.J.M.; 15, Lostwithiel, L.J.M.; 18, Rough Tor Farm, E.A.; 19, Otterham village, C.H.W.; 25, between Looe and Polperro (Thurston and Vigurs 1925); 37, Bray Shop, N.J.F.; 38, Launceston (Flora), post—1950, B.Sh.

FILIPENDULA MILLER

210/2 **F. ulmaria** (L.) Maxim. Meadowsweet
(*Spiraea ulmaria* L.)
subsp. **ulmaria**

Common and widespread in damp places.

subsp. **denudata** (J. & C. Presl) Hayek
(var. *denudata* Boenn.)

Recorded in the Flora from West and East, and no doubt it still occurs, but there are no recent records.

210/1 **F. vulgaris** Moench Dropwort
(*Spiraea filipendula* L.)

A characteristic plant of the Lizard, rare elsewhere, and apparently now absent from the East.

West: 61, 62, 71, and 72, frequent and sometimes abundant on the Lizard; 63, one plant on hedgebank, Treskillard, Redruth, L.J.M.; 64, Connor Downs (Flora), still a few plants 1967—79, L.J.M.; 73, hedgebank, Penryn, W.T. (Thurston 1935); 74, one plant on hedgebank, Cusgarne, J.G.D.; 75, one plant, Penhale Sands, L.J.M.

RUBUS L.

211/6 **R. idaeus** L. Raspberry

Doubtful as a native, except perhaps in a few places in E Cornwall.

West: 43, Heamoor (Flora), between Tremethick Cross and Heamoor, B.M.S.; 63, Nine Maidens, near Crowan, L.J.M.; 64, Seligan, near Redruth, L.J.M.; 74, Mt Hawke, L.J.M.

East: 05, Charlestown Wood, W.T. (Thurston and Vigurs 1926); 18, near Wilsey Down, J.E.L. (Thurston and Vigurs 1926); 20, N of Marhamchurch, J.A.P.; 27, E of Bolventor, F.R. and E.T. (Rilstone 1928); 28, valley E of Lewannick, J.A.P.; 36, S of Newbridge, J.A.P.; 38, Launceston (Flora), 1971, N.J.F.

Scilly: Lousley 1971.

211/8 § **R. spectabilis** Pursh   Salmonberry

A rather rare introduction that suckers readily, and spreads into extensive stands.

*West: 43, Penzance, 1972, B.M.S.; 64, Pendarves Wood, post—1950, various recorders; 73, Penmarth, Carmenellis, R.J.M. and E.W.M.

211/9 **R. caesius** L.   Dewberry

'Locally common, especially near the sea' (Rilstone 1939). This species is easily confused with members of the Sect. Triviales of *R. fruticosus*, and is probably quite rare in Cornwall.

West: 42, Kerris, B.M.S.; 53, St Erth, B.M.S.; (54), Gwithian, R.H.; 71, Lizard (Flora), Kennack, post— 1950, R.H.; 72, Flushing, near Helford, R.H.; 75, Perranporth (Flora), 1968, L.J.M.; Newquay, J.A.P.

East: 97, Wadebridge (Flora), 1971, N.J.F.; 45, Torpoint (Flora), 1967, S.M.

Scilly: Lousley 1971.

211/ 11/— **R. fruticosus** L.   Blackberry

The following account of the species of blackberry to be found in Cornwall owes much to the early encouragement and advice of E.S. Edees, who has named much of our material, and, latterly, to A. Newton. We also acknowledge here the pioneer work of the late Francis Rilstone in elucidating the Cornish species, and in describing many new taxa. As most of these are not mentioned in *Flora Europaea*, we are here following the arrangement given in Dandy 1958, with updated nomenclature by Edees and Newton. All records are those of L.J.M. unless otherwise credited.

Section Suberecti

211/ **R. nessensis** W. Hall
11/1 (*R. suberectus* Anders.)

Rare and very local in Cornwall.

East: 16, wood, Restormel Road, Lostwithiel; 21, plentiful in ride, Coombe Valley; 28, near Laneast.

2 **R. scissus** W.C.R. Watson

East: 06, Margate Wood, near Bodmin (Flora, as *R. fissus*), 1925, F.R. and E.T. (Rilstone 1939).

4 **R. bertramii** G. Braun

*East: 06, Racecourse Downs, near Bodmin, 1978.

5 **R. plicatus** Weihe and Nees

Rare, but sometimes present in quantity. The plants from Colbiggan Down and Helmentor represent a distinct dwarf form.

East: 95, Goss Moor (Flora), 1977; 95 or 96, near Roche (Rilstone 1927); 06, Colbiggan Down, Withiel (Flora), still there, 1977; Helmentor (Rilstone 1952), refound, 1978, E.A.; 36, St Mellion (Flora), still there, 1926 (Rilstone 1927).

7 **R. fissus** Lindley

*East: 06, Bodmin G.C.D., as *R. rogersii* (B.E.C. 1930); 36, near Cadsonbury, E.S.E.

9 **R. affinis** Weihe and Nees

*East: 84 or 94, Probus, comm. A.N.; 36, near Clapperbridge, Pillaton, 1923, F.R. (Rilstone 1927).

10 **R. briggsianus** (Rogers) Rogers

'Locally common . . . . . . throughout most of Cornwall' (Rilstone 1952). The records for *R. affinis* in the Flora and Suppt belong here.

West: 75, near Carnkief Pond (Rilstone 1927).

East: 36, near Cadsonbury (Rilstone 1927).

12 **R. divaricatus** P.J. Mueller

Rejected by F.R. (Rilstone 1939), but recently recorded by E.S. Edees.

East: 36, near Cadsonbury, 1974, E.S.E.

Section Triviales

14 **R. conjungens** (Bab.) Warren
(*R. corylifolius* var. *cyclophyllus* Lindeb.)
Probably not common, but precise distribution not known owing to confusion with related taxa. The following records are correct, however:
West: 53, Upton Towans, 1977; 64, Connor Downs, 1977.

17 **R. sublustris** Lees
(*R. corylifoius* var. *sublustris* Lees)
'Of fairly common occurrence' (Rilstone 1939), but there are no recent records.

21 **R. balfourianus** Bloxham ex Bab.
'Chiefly in the Tamar Valley' (Rilstone 1939). There are no recent records.

27 **R. tuberculatus** Bab.
The remarks about *R. conjungens* apply equally here. F.R. said (Rilstone 1952) that he had never seen it in the county. The only recent records are as follows:
West: 75, railway, Goonhavern, 1974, E.S.E.
Scilly: Lousley 1971; M, in four stations, 1975, D.E.A.

Section Sylvatici

34 **R. gratus** Focke
Uncommon in Cornwall, and mainly in the East.
East: 96, Retire Common; 05, Par Sands (Rilstone 1927); Par Station (Rilstone 1939); 06, Racecourse Downs, near Bodmin; 16, Bodmin Road, F.R. (Rilstone 1939).

52 **R. nemoralis** P.J. Mueller
(*R. selmeri* Lindeb.)
'Most frequent in the East of the county' (Rilstone 1939).
East: 16, between Bodmin Road and Glynn Bridge, F.R. (Rilstone 1927); 36, Cadsonbury (Rilstone 1927), still there, 1974, E.S.E.

53 **R. questieri** P.J. Mueller & Lefevre
Mainly in E Cornwall.
*West: 84, St Clement Wood, near Truro, 1979.
*East: 06 or 16, Lanhydrock to Bodmin Road (Rilstone 1927); 25, Trelawne Mill, near Looe, F.R. and E.T. (Rilstone 1928); Longcoombe, Polperro (Rilstone 1927).

54 § **R. laciniatus** Willd.   Cut-leaved Blackberry
'Sometimes found as an escape' (Rilstone 1939).
West: 43 (44), near Trowan, St Ives, 1972, A.G.
East: 38, Launceston, 1891, W.Wi., Herb. W. Wise, **LAUS.**

59 **R. lindleianus** Lees
'Commoner in the East of the county than in the West' (Rilstone 1939).
East: 25, Polperro Valley, F.R. (Rilstone 1928); 26, Castle Hill, Liskeard (Rilstone 1927).

60c **R. plymensis** (Focke) Edees & Newton
*East: 25, Trelawne Mill, near Looe (Rilstone 1939).

77 **R. amplificatus** Lees
West: Recorded in the Flora as requiring confirmation, but subsequently accepted, comm. A.N. Not found since.

80 **R. pyramidalis** Kaltenb.
Probably very rare, and not seen by Rilstone.
East: 06, Retire Common, 1977.

81 **R. albionis** W.C.R. Watson
Possibly an under-recorded species.
*West: 63, Porkellis Moor, 1977.

90a **R. daveyi** Rilstone (1950)
*West: Common and widespread.
*East: 96, Goss Moor, 1974; 21, Wrasford Moor; West Youlston, near Kilkhampton.

R. viridescens (Rogers) T.A.W. Davis
(Suppt as *R. thysoideus* var. *viridescens*)
Rather local, but widespread, especially in the West.

West: 61, Mullion Cliff (Flora), still there, 1977; Hayle Kimbro; 64, Connor Downs; Porthtowan; Mt Hermon, Lizard; Main Dale, Lizard, J.H. and L.J.M.; 73, near Penryn; Rame Common; 74, Silverwell Moor (Rilstone 1927); 75, Lambourne Hill (Rilstone 1927); near St Agnes Beacon (Rilstone 1927); Goonhavern (Flora), still there, 1977.

East: 95, St Stephens; 97, Pentire Peninsula; 25, Polperro (Rilstone 1927).

92   **R. ramosus** Bloxam ex Briggs

Rather local. Davey's specimens, **TRU**, from Ponsanooth, are clearly *R. carnkiefensis*.

West: 64, Tehidy Woods, Camborne; 72, Gweek, E.S.E.; 73, Frogpool; near Perranwell Station; 75, near Perranzabuloe Church, 1923, F.R.; 84, Playing Place Wood, Kea (Flora), still there, 1974.

100   **R. stanneus** Barton & Riddelsd.

Locally frequent in the West, rare in the East. The records in the Flora for *R. latifolius* belong here.

*West: 42, Penberth Cove; 43, Men-an-tol, near Penzance; 63, Nine Maidens; Porkellis Moor; Nancegollan, W.T. (Suppt), still there, 1975; 63 and 64, in numerous stations around Carn Brea; 73, Rame Common; 74, Silverwell Moor; 75, Lambourne, F.R. (B.E.C. 1953); Ventongimps Moor; Carnkief Pond; 84, Killiow, near Truro.

*East: 96, Goss Moor; 06, Grogley Halt; 26, near Trekeivesteps, Bodmin Moor.

103   **R. incurvatus** Bab.

Recorded in three stations in the Flora, but not found since.

R. 'villicaulis'

This distinct bramble, with deep pink flowers, is not the true plant of Koehler, but an unnamed taxon, due to be described soon, as a new species, by A. Newton.

East: 95, Goss Moor (Rilstone 1927); Hensbarrow (Rilstone 1939); 05, Carbis Moor, B.E.M.G. and L.J.M.; St Austell to Roche (Rilstone 1927); 06, Conce Moor (Rilstone 1927); 27, below Caradon Hill (Rilstone 1927).

108   **R. riddelsdellii** Rilstone (1950)

*A frequent plant throughout the county.
Scilly: Lousley 1971.

113   **R. polyanthemus** Lindeb.
(*R. pulcherrimus* Neum.)
Locally frequent.   Easily confused with *R. pydarensis.*
West: 33, Crookhorn, near St Just, E.S.E.; 43, Men-an-tol, near Penzance; 61, Hayle Kimbro, Lizard; 63, near Bolenowe, Troon; 72, Lizard Downs (Flora), Traboe Cross, 1979; Porthallow, J.H. and L.J.M.; 73, Laity Moor, Stithians.
East: 96, Roche (Rilstone 1927); 16, downs N of St Neot (Rilstone 1927); 17, Harpus Downs, Bodmin Moor; near Bolventor (Rilstone 1927); 25, near Polperro (Rilstone 1927); 27, Caradon (Rilstone 1927); 36, St Mellion (Flora), between there and Callington (Rilstone 1927).

114   **R. rubritinctus** W.C.R. Watson = *R. cryptadenes* Sudre, non Dumort.
(*R. argenteus* Weihe & Nees)
Very common and widespread throughout the county, but not recorded from Scilly.

117   **R. prolongatus** Boulay & Letendre
*Throughout the county — 'one of the commonest Cornish brambles' (Rilstone 1952).
*Scilly: M, in four stations, 1975, D.E.A.

124a   **R. dumnoniensis** Bab.
Common and widespread, often near the sea.
*Scilly: M, in three stations, 1975, D.E.A.

124   **R. altiarcuatus** Barton and Riddelsd.
Many of the records for *R. leucandrus* Focke (especially those of Rilstone) belong here, *fide* A. Newton.
*East: 16, near Lostwithiel; 26, Liskeard; 27, Caradon Hill; 36, Callington (all Rilstone 1939).

127   **R. imbricatus** Hort
Recorded for three stations in the East (Flora), but not found since.

Section Discolores

129 **R. ulmifolius** Schott
(*R. rusticanus* Merc.)
Abundant and widespread throughout the county in a number of distinct forms.
White-fruited variety:
West: 87, near Trevone Farm (Thurston 1929a).

133a **R. lamburnensis** Rilstone (1950)
A variable species, probably more widespread than Rilstone thought.
*West: 64, Connor Downs; 72, Main Dale, Lizard, J.H. and L.J.M.; 73, College Wood, Penryn; Cot Wood, Ponsanooth; near Mabe Quarry; 75, Rose, near Perranporth; Lambourne, Perranzabuloe, 1949, F.R.; Ventongimps, 1938, F.R.; 85, N of Zelah.

133b **R. carnkiefensis** Rilstone (1950)
A very local species, apparently confined to an area from near Perranporth to S of Truro.
*West: 73, Ponsanooth; 74, Silverwell Moor; 75, Mill Downs, F.R.; Ventongimps, F.R.; Lambourne, Perranzabuloe, 1949, F.R.; 84, Idless Valley, F.R., still there, in St Clement Wood, 1979.

133c **R. pydarensis** Rilstone (1940a)
'From Lands End and the Lizard to about 40 miles Eastward' (Rilstone 1939).
*West: 64, Connor Downs: 75, Ventonvaise, 1952, F.R.; Lambourne Hill, 1938, F.R.; 85, Newlyn East Downs.

137 **R. cornubiensis** (Rogers & Riddelsd.) Rilstone
*One of the most common brambles in W Cornwall, less so in the East, and becoming rare in the Lower Tamar area.
Scilly: Lousley 1971; T, in two stations, 1975, D.E.A.

137a **R. tresidderi** Rilstone (1950)
Very local and apparently restricted to a small area.
*West: 75, Lambourne, 1946, F.R.; near Perranzabuloe Church, 1950, F.R.

139 § **R. procerus** P.J. Mueller

The familiar garden blackberry, now widely naturalised.

*West: 61, Goonhilly Reserve; 62, Penrose Walk, Loe Pool; 63, Newton Moor, Troon, 1975; 71, Kennack Sands; 83, Falmouth; Devoran; 84, Truro; 97, Wadebridge, B.E.M.G. and L.J.M.; Padstow.

East: 95, railway track, St Dennis; 06, railway near Grogley; 36, Callington; 45, Saltash.

Section Sprengeliani

146 **R. sprengelii** Weihe

Very rare in Cornwall, except in Scilly.

*West: 43, Men-an-tol, near Penzance, F.R. (Rilstone 1939), refound 1978.

East: 85, moor near Carland Cross, 1979.

*Scilly: M, near Bants Carn, 1966, M.M.W.; Innisidgen, D.E.A.; T, in three stations, D.E.A.

Section Appendiculati

158 **R. cinerosiformis** Rilstone (1940b)

'Widely but sparingly distributed in Cornwall' (Rilstone 1952). Most of Davey's records for *R. podophyllus* belong here.

*East: 15, Langreek, near Polperro, F.R.; 25, about Polperro (Rilstone 1927).

160a **R. thurstonii** Rilstone (1950)

'Locally frequent in Cornwall along the borders of the hills' (Rilstone 1952).

*West: 63, Brea Valley, Redruth; Treskillard; 75, Perranzabuloe (Rilstone 1939).

*East: 95, Woon, near Roche; 96, Retire Common; 05, Lanlivery (Rilstone 1939); 36, Callington, F.R. and E.T., 1923 (Rilstone 1939).

161 **R. orbus** W.C.R. Watson = *R. iricus* var. *minor* Rogers & Riddelsd.

'Common in East Cornwall from Roche eastward' (Rilstone 1952).

*West: 71, Mt Hermon, the Lizard, 1978.

*East: 95, Roche Rock (Rilstone 1927); Stepaside,

St Stephens; 04, Pentewan (Rilstone 1927); 15, Bocaddon, Lanreath (Rilstone 1927); 21, Coombe Valley, N of Bude; 25, Polperro (Rilstone 1927); 27, between Trebartha and Five Lanes (Rilstone 1928); 28, Kennards House, near Launceston; 36, near Newbridge, Callington (Rilstone 1927).

170 **R. adscitus** Genev.

A characteristic bramble of the East of the county.

*West: 63, Porkellis Moor, 1977.

*East: Common throughout this vice-county.

191 **R. leyanus** Rogers

(*R. drejeri* var. *leyanus* Rogers)

Local and rare.

West: 73, Ponsanooth (Flora), still there, 1979; 84, Idless, near Truro (Rilstone 1939), still there, in St Clement Wood, 1979.

East: 04, Mevagissey, and Pentewan (Rilstone 1927); 05 St Austell and Luxulyan Valley (Rilstone 1927); 16, N of St Neot (Rilstone 1928); 35, Tregantle, near Torpoint (Rilstone 1939).

R. 'metallus'

Almost certainly an undescribed species, locally common in the old mining area around Carn Brea.

*West. 43, Men-an-tol, near Penzance; 63, Troon; Porkellis Moor; Nine Maidens; Carnkie; Treskillard; 64, Bosleake, Carn Brea, 1974; 73, Penmarth, Carnmenellis; Polmarth Moor; Stithians Reservoir.

197 **R. dentatifolius** (Briggs) W.C.R. Watson

(*R. borreri sensu* Rogers, *non* Bell Salter)

Frequent and widespread in Cornwall, but rather rare in the West.

West. 62, Trenethick, near Helston; 63, Porkellis Moor; 64, Tehidy Woods, Camborne; 73, Rame Common, and Stithians Reservoir; Buller Downs, Redruth; 85, Newlyn East Downs.

East: Too frequent for listing of localities.

204 **R. radula** Weihe x Boenn
Possibly an overlooked species. Most Cornish material is not typical, but represents a dwarf form.
West: 75, Lambourne Hill, Perranzabuloe, 1923, F.R.

212 **R. echinatus** Lindley
Very rare in Cornwall, and not seen by Rilstone.
*West: 32, above Gwenver Beach, Sennen, 1974, E.S.E.; 33, Crookhorn, St Just, 1974, E.S.E.
East: 97 (98), Roscarrock Hill, Port Isaac (as *R. pseudadenanthus*), *in litt.*, A.N.

223 **R. flexuosus** P.J. Mueller & Lefevre
Apparently very rare in the county.
East: 36, Cadsonbury, Callington, 1974, E.S.E.

243 **R. pallidus** Weihe & Nees
*East: 35, Polbathic Wood, 1980, BSBI, det. E.S.E.

247 **R. coombensis** Rilstone (1950)
A local plant, frequent around Liskeard.
*East: 04, Pentewan Valley (Rilstone 1927); 26, Coombe, Liskeard, 1927, F.R. and E.T.; near Coombe Junction, 1926, F.R., still there, 1979; Trevelmond, Liskeard (Rilstone 1927).

263 **R. scaber** Weihe and Nees
Extremely rare in the county.
East: 21, Coombe Valley, N of Bude, 1975.

269 **R. longithyrsiger** Lees ex Bak.
'Mainly in E Cornwall' (Rilstone 1939).
West: 75, near Penhallow (Rilstone 1927).
East: 15, St Catherines Point, Fowey (Flora), still there, 1980; 25, Looe, H.J.R. (B.E.C. 1924, p. 718); Polperro, H.J.R. (B.E.C. 1924, p. 718); Woolwashing, near Polperro (Rilstone 1927); 46, Cotehele (Rilstone 1928).

271 **R. peninsulae** Rilstone (1950)
'From the Tamar to the Lands End' (Rilstone 1939).
*West: 43, Men-an-tol, near Penzance, 1930, F.R., still there, 1978.

*East: 05, between Luxulyan and St Blazey, 1926, F.R. and E.T.; 15, Bury Down; 16, Restormel, Lostwithiel, 1920, F.R. and E.T.; 28, Kennards House, near Launceston; 36, Newbridge, Callington, 1924, F.R. and H.J.R.; 46, near Carkeel, Saltash, W.B.L.

278 **R. botryeros** (Focke ex Rogers) Rogers
Probably widespread but overlooked, and confused with other species.
East: 85, by pool, top of Newlyn East Downs, 1977.

289 **R. fuscoviridis** Rilstone (1940b)
'Frequent in Polperro valleys' (Rilstone 1927)
*East: 25, Polperro, 1919, F.R.; frequent around Polperro, F.R. (Rilstone 1927), still there, 1979.

292 **R. newbouldianus** Rilstone (1950)
*Frequent and widely distributed throughout the county, but unrecorded for Scilly.

295 **R. micans** Gren. & Godron
(*R. anglosaxonicus* Gelert)
Confined to one station, where it was found by Moyle Rogers in 1886.
East: 20, near Red Post, between Stratton and Bridgerule (Flora), still there, F.R. (Rilstone 1939).

296 **R. heterobelus** Sudre = *R. penhallowensis* Rilstone (1950)
Only in a small area of Perranzabuloe parish, according to Rilstone.
*West: 75, Callestick, 1925, F.R.; field near Penhallow, 1950, F.R.; Lambourne Hill, 1949, F.R., still there, 1979.

310 **R. leightonii** Lees ex Leighton
(*R. radula* var. *anglicanus* Rogers)
'Not uncommon in the extreme East of the county from Callington to Stratton' (Rilstone 1939).
West: 74, Tregavethan, near Truro (Flora), F.R. (Rilstone 1939); 75, about Chyverton, Perranzabuloe (Rilstone 1939).
East: 20, Launcells (Flora), F.R. and W.T. (Rilstone 1928).

322a **R. hiernii** Riddelsd.

(*R. hirtus* var. *rotundifolius* Bab.)

'In Cornwall only in the extreme East' (Rilstone 1952). Recorded in the Flora from Stratton. There are no recent records.

325 **R. hastiformis** W.C.R. Watson

(*R. thyrsiger* Bab., non Banning and Focke)

A recently recognised species, this bramble may be more common than the few records show.

*West: 64, Tehidy Woods, 1975; 73, College Wood, Penryn; 84, St Clement Wood, Idless, Truro.

*East: 83, Turnaware Point, Fal Estuary, 1976, B.E.M.G. and L.J.M.

Scilly: Lousley 1971.

329 **R. rilstonei** Barton & Riddelsd.

*Very common and widespread in W Cornwall, becoming infrequent in the extreme East. The records in the Flora for *R. plinthostylus* belong here.

*Scilly: M, The Garrison, 1975, D.E.A.; T, common, 1975, D.E.A.

Section Hystrices

330 **R. murrayi** Sudre

Found by J. Ralfs near Penzance, Herb. Briggs, teste Moyle Rogers, (Flora). Not found since.

342 **R. tumulorum** Rilstone (1940b)

'Rather frequent about Looe and Polperro, and for some miles inland' (Rilstone 1952).

*East: 15, Bury Down, near Lanreath, F.R. (Rilstone 1927); Bocaddon (Rilstone 1939); Langreek, near Polperro; 25, Looe, and Polperro (Rilstone 1939).

348 **R. hylocharis** W.C.R. Watson

(*R. rosaceus* var. *silvestris* R.P. Murray)

Recorded by Watson for both vice-counties, but the following is the only localised record:

*West: 43, Madron, near Penzance, 1879, E.F.L. (Watson 1958).

349   **R. scabripes** Genev. (*R. rosaceus* Wh. & N of Flora)
Rather local in Cornwall, but frequent in the area
around Perranporth. Mainly in light woodland.
  *West: 42, Chy-an-hal Moor (Rilstone 1927); 64,
Tehidy Woods, Camborne, E.S.E.; between Porth-
towan and Nancekuke; Nance Wood, Portreath; 74,
Silverwell Moor (Rilstone 1927), still there, 1976;
Manor Parsley, Mt Hawke; 75, Wheal Butson, St Agnes
(Rilstone 1927); Pendale, near Perranporth (Flora),
still there, 1979; Lambourne Hill, F.R.; Ventongimps
Moor, E.S.E.
  *East: 25, Keyne Ridge, Polperro (Rilstone 1927).

350   **R. vigursii** Rilstone (1950).
'Fairly common in the southern valleys of Cornwall
from the R. Lynher to the R. Fal' (Rilstone 1939).
  *West: 33, Cot Valley, St Just, E.S.E.; 64, near Tehidy
Woods, Camborne, E.S.E.; 73, near Carclew, Penryn,
F.R. (Rilstone 1939); 75, Ventongimps, Perranzabuloe,
F.R. (Rilstone 1939).
  *East: 04, Pentewan Valley, F.R. (Rilstone 1939); 25,
about Looe and Polperro, 1919, F.R.; 35, below Hessen-
ford, Seaton Valley, F.R. (Rilstone 1939); 36,
Cadsonbury, Callington, 1924, F.R., still there, 1974,
E.S.E.

[225   **R. pseudadenanthus** W.C.R. Watson was recorded from
Scilly (Lousley 1971), but A. Newton has shown
(*Watsonia*, 8 (1971): 374—5) that the name cannot be
upheld.]

Twenty-two other species within this aggregate were
recorded in Flora, but F. Rilstone has shown (Rilstone
1952), that they have no place in the Cornish list, and
they are therefore omitted from this account.

ROSA L.

Common species: 225/1 **R. arvensis** Hudson, Field Rose
(absent from Scilly), 225/4 **R. pimpinellifolia** L. (*R.
spinosissima* L.), Burnet Rose (absent from Scilly),
and 225/8 **R. canina** L.

225/5 § **R. rugosa** Thunb.   Japanese Rose
An increasing garden introduction, forming large masses
in sandy areas.

*West: 43, Zennor, L.J.M.; 53, Marazion, 1965, L.J.M.; 63, Filtrick, near Four Lanes, L.J.M.; near Porkellis Moor, L.J.M.; 64, Portreath, L.J.M.; 73, near Budock, Falmouth, L.J.M.

*East: 93, Pendower Beach, B.E.M.G.; 96, lane W of Retire Common, J.A.P.; 97, Rock, 1931, W.W.M. (Thurston 1935); (98), Port Isaac, L.B.; 05, Crinnis Beach, 1922, L.T.M. (Thurston and Vigurs 1923), still there, 1961, B.Sh., abundant, 1980, L.J.M.; Par Beach, L.J.M.

225/7 **R. stylosa** Desv.

This species is possibly more frequent in the extreme East of the county, but in all probability some of Davey's records refer to forms of *R. canina*.

West: 53 (54), Pennance, Gwithian, L.J.M.; 62, near Loe Pool, T.M. and L.J.M.; 83, Goon Piper, Feock, L.J.M.

East: 83, King Harry Ferry, Philleigh side, B.E.M.G.; 84, Pencalenick, R.M.

var. **garroutei** (Pug. & Rip.) Rouy
East: 84, near Lamorran Bridge, 1964, L.J.M.

225/9 **R. canina** L.
var. **dumalis** Bechst.
West: 53, Crowlas, E.S.T. (Thurston 1935); 73, Devoran, E.S.T. (Thurston 1935).

R. andegavensis Bast. (*R. canina* var. *andegavensis* Bast.), 22/10 **R. obtusifolia** Desv. (*R. borreri* Woods), **R. corymbifera** Borkh. (*R. dumetorum* Thuill.), and **R. scabriuscula** Sm. (incl. *R. andrzejowskii* Steven), were all recorded in the Flora, but there have been no subsequent records, and while there is a possibility of their occurrence, further work is desirable to establish their presence in the county.

[225/ **R. mollis** Sm., and **R. agrestis** Savi were both rejected by
17 Davey (Flora) as unlikely records, and we support him
225/13 in this view.]

225/12 **R. sherardii** Davies   Downy Rose
(incl. *R. omissa* Déséglise)
This is the common Downy Rose of Cornwall. The
records in the Flora for *R. tomentosa* may be taken to
refer to this species.
West: 62, Skyburriowe, the Lizard, R.B.G.; 63, near
Crowan Reservoir, L.J.M.; 72, Gweek, and Mawnan,
R.B.G.; Tregidden, St Martin, and between Newton
and Manaccan, R.B.G.; 74, Silverwell Moor, L.J.M.;
Baldhu, L.J.M.; 85, Penhallow Moor, Newlyn East,
L.J.M.
East: 95, New Mills, Ladock, L.J.M.; 97, Amble, near
Trewornan, R.W.D.; 16, Cardinham, L.J.M.; Goonzion
Downs, St Neot, L.J.M.; 19, valley E of Boscastle,
J.A.P.; 21, near Wrasford Moor, J.A.P.; 25, near Polperro,
L.J.M.; 27, Coads Green, E.G.; 28, Altarnun, E.G.; 36,
Cadsonbury, L.J.M.; 37, Bray Shop, E.G.; Kelly Bray,
E.G.; Luckett Reserve, L.J.M.; 46, near Carkeel, Saltash,
L.J.M.

225/14 **R. rubiginosa** L.   Sweet Briar
Now very rare or overlooked, but some of the records in
the Flora may refer to the next species.
West: 53, one bush, Copperhouse, Hayle, L.J.M.; 63,
one bush, an obvious garden throw-out, on Council tip,
Treskillard, Redruth, L.J.M.; 86, Trevemper Bridge
(Flora), still there, 1976, L.J.M.
East: 97, St Enodoc golf-course, R.W.D.
Scilly: rare, Lousley 1971; M, Garrison, 1975, D.E.A.;
T, Gimble Porth, 1975, D.E.A.

225/15 **R. micrantha** Borrer ex Sm.   Small-flowered Sweer Briar
Like most of the roses, this species is under-recorded,
and the following records do not fully illustrate its true
frequency.
West: 63, Clowance, near Praze-an-Beeble, L.J.M.; 64,
Goonzoyle, Red River Valley, R.J.M. and L.J.M.; North
Cliffs, near Portreath, L.J.M.; 75, Lambourne, Perran-
zabuloe (B.E.C. 1930, p. 514); 83, Trefusis Point,
Flushing, L.J.M.; 85, Penhallow Moor, Newlyn East,
L.J.M.
East: 83, lane to Turnaware Point, Fal Estuary,
B.E.M.G. and L.J.M.; Percuil, near Gerrans, L.J.M.; 84,

Pencalenick, near Truro, L.J.M.; 97, Chapel Amble, E.A.; Porthilly, and St Enodoc golf-course, R.W.D.; 06, Washaway, near Bodmin, L.J.M.; 07, old railway, Saldesbridge, L.J.M.; 16, Fletchers Bridge, near Bodmin, E.A. and L.J.M.; 25, near Polperro, L.J.M.; 35, Wacker, near Antony, S.M.; 46, Halton Quay, N.J.F.

*Scilly: not listed by Lousley 1971; M, Garrison Farm, 1974, J.P.B.; SW of Holy Vale, 1972, J.P.B.; T, between Appletree Banks and Abbey Hill, 1972, J.P.B.

AGRIMONIA L.

218/1 **A. eupatoria** L., Agrimony, is frequent and widespread in the county.

*Scilly: not listed, Lousley 1971; M, one plant, between church and Peninnis, 1975, A.V.L.

218/2 **A. procera** Wallr.   Fragrant Agrimony
(*A. odorata* Mill.)

Frequent only in the Tamar Estuary, rare elsewhere. West: 71, Mt Hermon, the Lizard, L.J.M.; 75, wood by Carnkief Pond, L.J.M.

East: 07, St Tudy (Flora), still there, E.A.; 25, W of Looe, I.N.; 35, Seaton Valley, J.A.P.; Poldrissick, Landrake, I.N.; Wivelscombe Farm, near Saltash, I.N.; 36, S of Newbridge, Callington, J.A.P.; near St Mellion, I.N.; Pillaton (Flora), still there, post—1950, I.N.; Quethiock (Flora), near Hepwell Bridge, I.N.; 37, near South Hill, I.N.; 38, St Stephens, Launceston, I.N.; 45, near Shillingham Farm, Saltash, I.N.; near Wearde, Saltash, I.N.; Southdown Quarry, Millbrook, J.A.P.

SANGUISORBA L.

222/1 **S. officinalis** L.   Great Burnet
(*Poterium officinale* A. Gray)

West: 61, 62, 71, and 72, recorded for all the Lizard squares, and frequent to common, especially in 61 and 71.

East: 94, near Hemmick Beach, the Roseland, C.C.; 05, Duporth, near St Austell (Suppt), 1965, R.D.P.; 06, Tredinnick, near Lanhydrock (B.E.C. 1941); 16, Bofarnel, N of Lostwithiel, C.C.; 46, a few plants by the Tamar near Slimeford, E.G.

223/1 S. minor Scop., subsp. **minor**   Salad Burnet
       (*Poterium sanguisorba* L.)
       Frequent to common in coastal area, except on the
       granite, and probably still in most of its old localities.
       The following are additional records:
       West: 53, Angarrack, Hayle, B.M.S.; (54), Godrevy,
       and Gwithian, L.J.M.; 71, Cadgwith, N.C.S.; 72,
       Trethewey, St Martin, W.T. (Thurston 1935); 86 (76),
       Crantock, R.H.
       East: 83, Turnaware, Fal Estuary, B.E.M.G.; 84,
       Lamorran, L.J.M.; 97, Daymer Bay, E.A.; Pentire
       Peninsula, R.W.D.; 07, Sladesbridge, L.J.M.; 15, Lantic
       Bay, K.H.; 35, Whitsand Bay, at Tregantle, and between
       Sharrow and Freathy, S.M.; 45, Wearde, Saltash, S.M.

223/2 subsp. **muricata** Briq.   Fodder Burnet
       (*Poterium polygamum* Waldst. & Kit.)
       Sometimes persistent as a rare introduction.
       *West: 85, old railway track, Shepherds, near Goon-
       havern, L.J.M.
       East: 94, roadside bank, Portholland, L.J.M.

                        ACAENA MUTIS EX L.
224/1 § **A. novae-zelandiae** Kirk   Pirri-pirri-bur
       = *A. anserinifolia* (J.R. & G. Forster)
       *West: 53, by roadside, A30, Hayle Estuary, 1949,
       J.B.; 62, Carnmeal Downs, Sithney, D.S.

                             GEUM L.
216/1 **G. urbanum** L., Wood Avens, is common throughout
       the mainland, but apparently extinct in Scilly.

216/3 **G. rivale** L.   Water Avens
       Very rare, but still present in the Launceston area.
       East: 28, in three stations at Egloskerry, in one of
       which it is plentiful, 1970, L.J.M.; by R. Inny, between
       Altarnun and Laneast, 1978, L.J.M.; 38, Kensey Valley
       above Launceston (Flora), refound, 1971, G.L.K.

216/3 G. rivale x urbanum = *G. x intermedium* Ehrh.
x 1   East: 28, in small copse by R. Kensey, Egloskerry,
       1970, L.J.M.

POTENTILLA L.

Common species: 212/5 **P. anserina** L., Silverweed, 212/13 **P. erecta** (L.) Räuschel, Tormentil, 212/14 **P. anglica** Laicharding (*P. procumbens* Sibth.), Trailing Tormentil (doubtfully in Scilly), 212/15 **P. reptans** L., Creeping Clinquefoil, and 212/3 **P. sterilis** (L.) Garcke, Barren Strawberry (not in Scilly).

212/2 **P. palustris** (L.) Scop.   Marsh Cinquefoil

Very local, but in quantity in a few areas.

West: 42, Kerris Moor, J.B.; Clodgy Moor, Penzance, S.B.; 62, Poldhu Valley, LFC; 71, Crousa Downs, 1959 onwards, J.Fo.; 75, Carnkief Pond, C.J.

East: 96, Goss Moor, various recorders; 05, Starrick Moor (Suppt), 1961, J.G.T.; NE of Bugle, J.A.P.; 06, Criggan Moor, J.B.; Red Moor (Flora), still there, and in a considerable area around there, various recorders; 06, Retire Common, L.J.M.; 21, Tamar Lake, various recorders; 27, Fox Tor bog, E.W.M. and L.J.M.; 28, Treneglos, R.W.D. and L.J.M.; 39, Tamar Valley NE of Boyton, J.A.P.

[212/6 **P. argentea** L., Hoary Cinquefoil, has been long extinct (Flora).]

212/7   § **P. recta** L.   Sulphur Cinquefoil

A rare introduction.

West: 64, waste ground near Carn Brea Station, L.J.M.; 84, one plant near railway bridge, Calenick, 1967, M.W.

*East: 05, Par Harbour, L.T.M. (Thurston 1929a); large patch by railway, Par, C.S.; 97, Trevilling, Wadebridge, C.H.W.

212/13 **P. erecta** var. **sciaphila** (Zimm.) Druce

West: 63, Porkellis Moor, B.E.M.G., B.M.S., and L.J.M.; 75 (65), cliff-slope N of Chapel Porth, L.J.M.

212/14 **P. anglica** x **erecta** = *P. x suberecta* Zimmet.
x 13   West: 32, Treen, G.H.; 73, Devoran, G.H.
        *East: 27, Siblyback, 1980, BSBI.

212/13 **P. erecta** x **reptans** = *P. x italica* Lehm.
x 15   West: 32, Treen, G.H.
        Scilly: Lousley 1971.

212/14 **P. anglica x reptans** = *P. x mixta* Nolte ex Reichb.
x 15   West: 62, recorded for this square, without locality, post—1950.

FRAGARIA L.

215/1   **F. vesca** L., Wild Strawberry, is frequent and wide-spread, but absent from Scilly.
An albino form, with white fruits, occurs at
West: 74, abundant on old railway track, St Agnes Station, 1970, L.J.M.

215/2   § **F. moschata** Duchesne   Hautbois Strawberry
Many of the old records no doubt refer to the next species, but the following appears to be correct:
East: 18, roadside bank, Trewassa, near Davidstow, 1972, M.Wa.

215/3   § **F. x ananassa** Duchesne   Garden Strawberry
More frequent as a garden throw-out than these records indicate.
*West: 63, Nancegollan, L.J.M.; Four Lanes, L.J.M.; 73, Rame Common, L.J.M.; 74, railway bank, Goonbell, St Agnes, L.J.M.; 75, railway, Goonhavern, L.J.M.; Perran-porth, L.J.M.; 83, roadbank, Falmouth, J.S.R.
*East: 45, Southdown Quarry, Millbrook, 1966, J.A.P.

DUCHESNEA SM.

214/1   § **D. indica** (Andrews) Focke
Yellow-flowered Strawberry
(*Fragaria indica* Andr.)
An increasing garden throw-out.
West: 33, St Just, M.C.; 42, between Penzance and Newlyn, B.M.S.; 43, Penzance (Flora), in two places there, 1968, and in two other places, 1962, G.B.M.; 53, woods between St Ives and Carbis Bay, G.B.M.; 63, Piece, Carnkie, L.J.M.; 83, Falmouth (Flora), in two places there, 1958, R.H.
East: 97, Gonvena, Wadebridge, C.H.W.; 04, Trenarren, B.E.M.G.

ALCHEMILLA L.

220/3 **A. vulgaris** L. *sensu lato*   Lady's-mantle
West: 61, Mullion Cove, and Carn near Mullion, E.J.P.
(Thurston and Vigurs 1927); 83, garden weed, Mylor,
W.T. (Thurston 1930).
East: 18, one mile S of Camelford, R.O. (Thurston
and Vigurs 1925).

Davey's records for *A. vulgaris* L. include both the
following species:

220/3/ § **A. xanthochlora** Rothm.   Lady's-mantle
8   Probably introduced.
West: 53, waste ground, Lelant, B.M.S.; 63, Clowance
(Flora), still there, 1965, L.J.M.
East: 25, near Duloe, D.B.; 27, near Blackcombe
Farm, Henwood, N.J.F.; 36, Dupath (Flora), still there,
post—1950, I.N.

220/3/ **A. filicaulis** Buser   Lady's-mantle
2   subsp. **vestita** (Buser) M.E. Bradshaw
This is a native species, rare in Cornwall.
West: 53, near Relubbus, Hayle River, RNHS.
East: 35, near Hessenford, I.N.; 36, Hepwell Bridge,
I.N.; 37, Trecarrell Bridge, R. Inny, E.G.

APHANES L.

221/1 **A. arvensis** L., Parsley Piert, and   221/2 **A.
microcarpa** (Boiss. & Reuter) Rothm., Slender Parsley
Piert, are frequent and widely distributed throughout
the county. *A. microcarpa* is the more common of the
two, especially near the coast, in dry sandy habitats.
A. arvensis occurs mainly as a weed of cultivation.

PYRUS L.

233/2 **P. cordata** Desv.   Plymouth Pear
The following is the last known record in Cornwall for
this extremely rare tree. It still survives in a factory
yard at Plymouth.
East: 35, one bush between St Johns and Tregantle
(Flora), still there in 1932, E.Gr.

233/1 § **P. communis** L. Wild Pear

Always of garden origin.

West: 53, one large tree, Angarrack, Hayle, L.J.M.; 63, one small tree by old railway track near Gwinear Road, L.J.M.; 64, one tree, lane near Connor Downs, L.J.M.

MALUS MILLER

234/1a **M. sylvestris** Miller Crab Apple

(*Pyrus malus* L. var. *sylvestris* L.)

Extremely rare in Cornwall, and probably introduced, like the next species. Davey's records cannot be taken as reliable.

East: 97, St Minver (Flora), five trees, towards Quaker Burial Ground, 1957, R.W.D.; 15, in woods, Lerryn, 'a frequent shrub', F.R. (Thurston and Vigurs 1927); 35, Antony, 1872, T.A.B., (**BM**).

Scilly: Lousley 1971.

234/1b § **M. domestica** Borkh. Cultivated Apple

(*Pyrus malus* L. var. *mitis* Wallr.)

This occurs in a number of habitats as a self-sown tree, arising from thrown-out pips.

West: Frequent throughout the vice-county, usually as an isolated tree.

East: 97, Pentire Peninsula, L.J.M.; 27, Berriowbridge, near Northill, E.A.; 45, near Millbrook (Flora), in Southdown Quarry, L.J.M.

Scilly: Lousley 1971.

SORBUS L.

232/1 **S. aucuparia** L., Rowan, is a frequent tree in Cornwall, but more common in the wooded valleys of the East (absent from Scilly).

[232/2 § **S. domestica** L., Service-tree. Early references to this *in litt.* were dismissed as mistakes by Davey. No doubt they referred to the next species.]

232/7 **S. torminalis** (L.) Crantz Wild Service-tree

Very local, but more frequent in the extreme NE and SE of the county. Populations in these areas should be critically examined in case they contain unsuspected records for the next species.

West: 72, Gweek, R.H.; Calamansack Wood, Helford River, J.F.A.

East: 84, one tree in wood, by Sett Bridge, Ruan Lanihorne, T.M.; 06, Dunmere Forest, E.A.; 07, Helland Churchtown (Flora), post—1950, K.H.J.; between St Mabyn and Tresarret Bridge (Flora), 1946—80, R.W.D.; between St Mabyn and Dinhams Bridge (Flora), one tree, 1957, E.A.; 19, Dizzard Wood, and Millook Cliff, NCS; 20, in two places between Marhamchurch and Budd's Titson, R.W.D. and L.J.M.; 21, Stibb Farm, and Scadghill Farm, N of Bude, R.D.; 29, near Week St Mary (Suppt), two trees, 1977, B.B.; 46, three trees, Kingsmill, Landulph, I.N.; Botusfleming, five trees, E.G.; near Halton Quay, five trees, E.G.; Harewood, Calstock (Flora), five trees, E.G.

232/6/ **S. devoniensis** E.F. Warburg   Broad-leaved Whitebeam
3   (*Pyrus latifolia* Syme)

This could still exist in out-of-the-way places on the county border.

East: 20 and 39, three stations (Flora). There are no subsequent records.

COTONEASTER MEDICUS

227/3   § **C. horizontalis** Decne   Wall Cotoneaster

Increasing as a bird-sown garden escape.

*West: 64, old mine-workings near Reskadinnick, Camborne, 1972, R.J.M.; site of Camborne by-pass, R.J.M. and L.J.M.; Gilberts Coombe, Redruth, L.J.M.; 97, near Dennis Cove, Camel Estuary, L.J.M.

*East: 97, several plants, Brea Hill, Rock, 1979, E.W.M.; 45, wall, Saltash, E.G.

227/2   § **C. simonsii** Baker   Himalayan Cotoneaster

Frequent as a bird-sown introduction, chiefly in woods.

West: 42, near Paul, B.M.S.; 43, near Heamoor, B.M.S.; 64, Tolvaddon, R.J.M. and L.J.M.; Tehidy Woods, L.J.M.; 72, Porthallow, J.H. and L.J.M.; 73, Budock Water, J.F.A. and R.Go.; 74, Mt Hawke railway bank, L.J.M.; 75, Perranwell Woods, C.J.; 83, Swanpool, Falmouth, L.J.M.

*East: 96, Castle-an-Dinas, L.J.M.; 05, St Austell, 1964, B.Sh.; 15, Lerryn wood, CNT.

227/4 § **C. microphyllus** Wallich ex Lindley
Small-leaved Cotoneaster

Becoming increasingly frequent as a bird-sown garden escape, sometimes forming extensive patches on old mine-waste.

*West: 43, Ding Dong, B.M.S.; near New Mill, B.M.S.; 53, near Phillack, B.M.S.; Lelant Downs, J.B.; 62, Carnmeal Downs, Sithney, B.E.M.G. and J.A.P.; 63, Treskillard, L.J.M.; 64, near Carn Brea Station, L.J.M.; old railway near Portreath, L.J.M.; 74, frequent near St Day, L.J.M.; 85, railway near Newlyn East Halt, L.J.M.

*East: 96, Castle-an-Dinas, 1964, L.J.M.; 07, Port Isaac Station, L.B. and L.J.M.; 25, E Looe cliffs, J.A.P.; 27, mines N of Minions, J.A.P.; 35, below Tregantle Fort, S.M.: 37, Kit Hill, I.N.

MESPILUS L.

230/1 § **M. germanica** L. Medlar
(*Pyrus germanica* Hook. fil.)

An introduced tree, local in Davey's day, now very rare.

West: 42, one tree between Newlyn and Buryas Bridge, B.M.S.; 43, in hedge at Gobbens, near Penzance, B.M.S.; 62, one tree in Withy Bed, Porthleven, until 1960, H.B.S.; Nancemerrin, Culdrose, CNT.

East: 07, between St Mabyn and Tresarret Bridge (Flora), still there, 1979, R.W.D.; 29, hedge between N Tamerton and Whitstone, H.H.H. (Thurston 1930).

CRATAEGUS L.

229/2 **C. monogyna** Jacq., Hawthorn, is a common and widespread tree in all parts of the county. Cornish material appears to be referable to the subsp. *nordica* Franco.

PRUNUS L.

226/1 **P. spinosa** L., Blackthorn, is a common and widespread shrub or small tree in all sorts of situations.

226/2 § **P. domestica** L. Wild Plum
Now very rare.

East: 38, railway W of Launceston, G.L.K.; 45, Clift Creek, Antony, S.M.

subsp. **domestica**
East: 97, near Bodieve, Wadebridge, R.W.D.

subsp. **insititia** (L.) C.K. Schneider   Bullace
West: 62, Nancemerrin, Culdrose, D.M.S.; 71, near Ruan Major, and near Gwendreath, P.T.
East: 45, Saltash (Flora), Latchbrook, Saltash, 1976, E.G.; 46, near Calstock, N.J.F.
Scilly: recorded with doubt, Lousley 1971.

226/4   **P. avium** L.   Wild Cherry
Scattered throughout the county, but absent from West Penwith and from Scilly.
West: 64, Nance Wood, Portreath, J.S.R.; 72, near Helford Passage, J.S.R.; Calamansack Wood and Merthen Wood, J.F.A.; 83, Pendennis, Falmouth, L.J.M.; 84, Truro, J.A.P.; 86, St Clement Wood, L.J.M.
East: 83, Trewince Quay, Roseland, L.J.M.; Pendower Valley, L.J.M.; 97, St Minver (Flora), between St Minver and Polzeath, E.A.; Rokke Moor, Endellion, B.E.M.G. and L.J.M.; 05, Luxulyan Valley, L.J.M.; 19, Minster Valley (Suppt), 1968, J.F.A.; 26, two places near Liskeard, D.B.; 28, near Treneglos, L.J.M.; 29, Keywood, Whitstone, J.A.P.; 36, near Cadsonbury, D.B.; near St Mellion (Flora), still there, D.B.; 37, S of Greystone Bridge, J.A.P.; Luckett Reserve, R.Go.; 38, St Thomas, Launceston, N.J.F.; railway W of Launceston, G.L.K.; 45, Thanckes Wood, Torpoint, S.M.; 46, Cotehele, J.F.A.

226/5   § **P. cerasus** L.   Dwarf Cherry
Listed as common in the Flora, it certainly is not so now, but is still found frequently in Mid-Cornwall.
West: 53 (54), near Gwithian, J.S.R.; 62, Porthleven, H.B.S.; Trenethick, near Helston, L.J.M.; 63, Horsedowns, and near Drym, Leedstown, J.S.R.; between Baripper and Roseworthy, L.J.M.; 64, Sparnon Gate, Redruth, L.J.M.; Old Merrose Farm, Tolvaddon, Camborne, L.J.M.; Pool, J.S.R.; Reskadinnick, Camborne, R.J.M.; 73, Pulla Cross, Gwennap, L.J.M.; between Ponsanooth and Perran-ar-worthal, J.A.P.; 74, Goonbell, St Agnes, L.J.M.; Twelveheads, Bissoe, L.J.M.; 75, Trevellas, St Agnes, J.A.P.; 84, near St

Erme in several places, R.W.D.; 85, Benny Mill, near Newlyn East, L.J.M.; Summercourt, J.A.P.

East: 95, Trenowth Wood, Grampound, CNT; 97, in several places between Amble and St Kew, R.W.D.; 05, between Bugle and Roche, L.J.M.; 20, around Marhamchurch, J.A.P.; 26, lanes N of Menheniot, J.A.P.

226/7 § **P. laurocerasus** L. Cherry Laurel
Probably only where originally planted in the larger estates.

*West: 86, Carnanton Woods, St Mawgan, CNT.

*East: 05, Pelyn Wood, Lanlivery, CNT; 26, near Liskeard, N.J.F.; 46, Cotehele, 1968, J.F.A.

LEGUMINOSAE

CYTISUS L.

188/1a **C. scoparius** (L.) Link subsp. **scoparius** Broom
Common throughout the county in suitable habitats.

188/1b subsp. **maritimus** (Rouy) Heywood Prostrate Broom
Only on the Lizard; wind-dwarfed forms found elsewhere are not the true subspecies.

West: 61, Velland Head, and around Kynance, in several stations (Flora), still there; various recorders; Lizard Point (Flora), still there, 71, around Lizard Lighthouse, and Polpeor Cove, various recorders.

GENISTA L.

185/1 **G. tinctoria** L., prostrate form Dyer's Greenweed
The type does not occur in Cornwall. The following records refer to a prostrate form with glabrous pods that grows on cliffs from near Lands End to Crackington Haven in the North.

West: 32, Brew Moor, Sennen, B.M.S.; 33, Cape Cornwall, M.C.; Trewellard, M.C.; 43, Bosigran, between Morvah and Zennor, G.L.; 61, Mullion Cove, L.J.M.; 64, Portreath, and Porthtowan (Flora), still there, B.M.S.; 75, Penhale, Perranporth (Flora), 1978, L.J.M.; Cligga Head, C.J.; 87, NE of Park Head, T.O.D.; near Dinas Head, L.J.M.; Trevose Head (Suppt), refound, post—1950, T.H.A.; Guddna Common, near Padstow, L.G.

East: 97, Pentire Peninsula, R.W.D.; (98), Doyden, Port Quin, K.H.; 08, N of Bounds Cliff, near Port Gaverne, J.A.P.; 19, St Gennys, E.G.

subsp. **littoralis** (Corb.) Rothm.

This is the prostrate form with hairy pods, occurring commonly on the Lizard.

West: 61, 62, and 71, quite common in many stations; 75, cliff at Perranporth, A.Bi.

185/3 **G. pilosa** L.   Hairy Greenweed

Still relatively plentiful in two distinct areas of West Cornwall.

West: 61, in several stations from Mullion south to Caerthillian; 64, near Ralph's Cupboard, W of Portreath, L.J.M.; Portreath to Porthtowan (Flora), frequent, 1976, L.J.M.; Chapel Porth (Flora), plentiful, 1976, L.J.M.; 75, St Agnes (Flora), several stations between Chapel Porth and St Agnes, 1976, L.J.M.; heath between Cross Coombe and Cligga Head, 1975, L.J.M.; Perranporth (Flora), Droskyn Point, 1965, L.J.M.; Cornish hedge along road from St Agnes to Perranporth, 1968, L.J.M.; 72, one locality on the E side of the Lizard, comm. J.H.

185/2 **G. anglica** L.   Petty Whin

Except for the Lizard heathlands, where it is frequent, this plant is a rare species of old heaths in the East.

West: 61, 71, and 72, too common for listing of stations; 75, Goonhavern Moor (Flora), 1966, J.A.P.

East: 06, three plants, Red Moor, CNT; Tretoil Moor, Lanivet (Flora), 1968, J.A.P.; 21, near West Youlstone, C.C.; Woolley Barrows, L.J.M.; 28, Laneast Downs, W.H.F. (Thurston and Vigurs 1923), still there, 1970, G.L.K.; 29, near Greena Moor (Flora), 1977, C.C.; 36, heath near Bicton Wood, N of Newbridge, E.G.

ULEX L.

187/1 **U. europeaus** L., Gorse, and   187/2 **U. gallii** Planchon, Western Gorse, are common and widespread throughout the county.

[187/3 **U. minor** Roth, Dwarf Gorse, was recorded for Scilly in the Flora, but this was subsequently rejected by J.E. Lousley as most unlikely to occur.]

LUPINUS L.

183/2 § **L. arboreus** Sims   Tree Lupin

In recent years this has suddenly increased as an introduction.

*West: 52, Praa Sands, B.B.; 53, Marazion Marsh (B.E.C. 1936); railway banks near Crowlas, 1965, J.B.; 71, Lizard Town, R.L.G.L.; 73, railway, Penryn, L.J.M.; 84, railway banks near Truro, L.J.M.

*East: 95, and 05, extensively planted by the China Clay Works in these squares, and now seeding everywhere; 96, Goss Moor, A.B.; 35, Downderry, S.M.; 45, Maker Heights, S.M.; Southdown Quarry, Millbrook, L.J.M.

Scilly: Lousley 1971; A, Gugh, 1973, comm. D.E.A.

GALEGA L.

197/1 § **G. officinalis** L.   Goat's-rue

*East: 97 (98), Port Quin, 1957, A.W.; 45, Saltash Industrial Estate, E.G.

VICIA L.

Common species: 206/4 **V. cracca** L., Tufted Vetch, 206/1 **V. hirsuta** (L.) S.F. Gray, Hairy Tare, 206/2 **V. tetrasperma** (L.) Schreber, Smooth Tare, 206/11 **V. sepium** L., Bush Vetch (doubtfully in Scilly), 206/15 **V. sativa** L., subsp. **nigra** (L.) Ehrh. (*V. angustifolia* L.), Narrow-leaved Vetch, and 206/14 § subsp. **sativa**, Common Vetch.

206/9 **V. orobus** DC.   Wood Bitter-Vetch

This seems to have disappeared from the localities listed in the Flora and Suppt. The following are the latest two records:

East: 19, hedgebanks near Marshgate, 1916, W.Wi., Herb. Wise, (LAUS); Tresparrett Downs (Flora), 1956, M.P. Denne.

206/10 **V. sylvatica** L.   Wood Vetch

Very rare, but possibly gradually spreading south along the extreme north-east coast. Not refound in any of the old stations.

East: 95, McClarens Dry, Treviscoe, St Dennis, B.B. and L.G. (confirmation of this record is required); 21,

Henna Cliff, Morwenstow, 1968, J.A.P.; Marsland Mouth, and Marsland Cliff, L.J.M.

206/15 **V. sativa** subsp. **nigra**
var. **lutescens** Corbiere

West: 86, Porth, Newquay, C.C.V. (Thurston and Vigurs 1927). This yellow-flowered form of the Common Vetch should not be confused with the next species.

206/12 **V. lutea** L.   Yellow Vetch

Very rare, but rather persistent.

West: 71, Landewednack (Flora), still present, and at intervals to Kennack Sands, 1950 onwards, various recorders; 97, near Tregirls, Padstow, 1963, J.Ha. East: 35, Downderry (Flora), still there, 1957, BRC.

206/17 **V. bithynica** (L.) L.   Bithynian Vetch

Very rare, usually casual, but persistent on the Lizard.

West: 32, Gwenver, Sennen, in old bulb-field, M.C.; 64, edge of garden, Tolvaddon, Camborne, K.E.H.; 71, Housel Bay (Flora), still there, 1950 onwards, various recorders; 83, one plant, Gyllyngvase, Falmouth, 1923 (Thurston and Vigurs 1924).

LATHYRUS L.

207/11 **L. montanus** Bernh., Bitter Vetch (absent from Scilly), and   207/4 **L. pratensis** L., Meadow Vetchling, are frequent and widely distributed in Cornwall.

207/10 **L. japonicus** Willd.   Sea Pea
subsp. **maritimus** (L.) P.W. Ball

Marked as extinct by Davey (Flora), but found subsequently. The record for Scilly is an important westward extension of range for this decreasing plant. West: 43 or 53, between Penzance and Marazion, 1948, BRC; 72, St Keverne (B.E.C. 1936).

*East: 05, locality unknown, BRC.
*Scilly: M, 1972, G.B.M.

207/5 § **L. tuberosus** L.   Tuberous Pea

Firmly established in a few places.

*West: 53, Angarrack Bridge, Hayle, 1968, P.Wi.; Upton Towans, B.J. and E.J.

East: 83, near the Lighthouse, St Anthony, L.J.M.; 09, Forrabury, Boscastle, E.A.

207/6 **L. sylvestris** L. Narrow-leaved Everlasting-pea
Considerably increased since the Flora, and a feature of the SE cliffs.

West: 53, Hayle, B.S.; Angarrack Bridge, various recorders; 73, near College viaduct, Penryn, W.T. (Thurston 1928).

East: 83, W of Portscatho (Flora) 1976, L.J.M.; 97, W of Port Isaac (Flora), 1949, R.W.D.; 05, Polkerris, near Par (Suppt), 1962, B.Sh.; 15, Lansallos, near Polruan, L.J.M.; Lantivet Bay, H.W.P. (Thurston 1935), 1978, R.W.D. and L.J.M.; 25, Polperro (Flora). 1964, L.J.M.; cliffs W of Looe (Flora), 1966, I.N.; Portnadler Bay, S.M.; Bodigga Cliff, E of Looe, K.H.; 35, Seaton cliffs, (Flora), 1967, S.M.; Downderry, S.M.; St Germans Hut, S.M.; Portwrinkle, S.M.; 45, between Wearde Quay and Coombe, and by railway, Wearde, I.N.; (44), between Rame Head and Penlee Point, S.M.

Scilly: rejected, Lousley 1971.

207/8 § **L. latifolius** L. Broad-leaved Everlasting-pea
An increasing garden escape.

West: 53, Angarrack Bridge, J.B.; Upton Towans, G.A. and L.J.M.; 62, near Loe Bar, J.S.R.; 63, railway, Gwinear Road, L.J.M.; 72, Helford Passage, 1930, C.H.F.; 74, old mines Gwennap, L.J.M.; 83, Penpol, Feock (Flora), 1961, L.J.M.; cliffs, Falmouth, J.S.R.

East: 83, St Mawes, L.J.M.; Trewince Quay, Gerrans, L.J.M.; Porthluney Beach, L.J.M.; 97, roadside embankment, Wadebridge, various recorders; 05, Par (Flora), 1962, L.J.M.; 35, Downderry, S.M.; Whitsand Bay, R.M.; 38, railway W of Launceston, G.L.K.; 45, Tregonhawke cliff, S.M.

Scilly: hardly naturalised, Lousley 1971.

207/2 **L. nissolia** L. Grass Vetchling
Always a very local plant in Cornwall, but sometimes found in abundance where it does occur.

West: 53, waste ground, Lelant, W.R.H.; 74, between Baldhu and Goodern, J.A.P.; 84, Newham, Truro, K.P.

East: 05, Crinnis (Suppt), still there, 1950 onwards, various recorders; 20, Widemouth Bay, near Bude.

207/1 § **L. aphaca** L. Yellow Vetchling
Rare, and now only as a garden casual.
West: 83, garden, Penpol House, Devoran, L.J.M.
East: 94, weed in Demonstration Garden, Probus,
L.J.M.; Manor Tannery, Grampound, L.J.M.; 05, Par,
1923, Herb. F.H. Perrycoste, **(TRU)**; 25, grounds of
Trelawne, near Looe, D. and W.M.

ONONIS L.

189/1 **O. repens** L., Common Restharrow, is frequent and
widespread, especially on coastal sands.

var. **horrida** Lange
West: 63, old tip, Treskillard, Redruth, L.J.M.

189/2 **O. spinosa** L. Spiny Restharrow
Probably only casual in Cornwall. The two records in
the Flora are not supported by specimens, and may
refer to the last species.
East: 05, Par, 1947, P.Ta., **K.**

MELILOTUS MILLER

191/1 § **M. altissima** Thuill. Tall Melilot
Locally frequent, but not common.
West: 43, near Poltair Hospital, Heamoor, Penzance,
G.B.M.; 62, Porthleven, H.B.S.; 64, Dolcoath, Camborne,
L.J.M.; 73, Penryn, L.J.M.; 74, old tip, Bissoe, L.J.M.;
83, Falmouth Docks (Flora), 1970, J.A.P.
East: 05, Charlestown (Suppt), 1966, L.J.M.;
Tregorrick, St Austell, W.T. (Thurston 1928); 25,
Looe (Flora), still there, post—1950, D.B.; 35, St
Germans, J.A.P.; between Antony House and Polbathic
(Flora), 1963, S.M.; 45, St Johns, and Millbrook, S.M.;
Southdown (Flora), 1965, L.J.M.

191/3 § **M. alba** Medic. White Melilot
Now very local.
West: 42, Lariggan, Penzance, B.M.S.; 43, railway,
Long Rock, G.B.M.
East: 84, between Truro and Malpas (Flora), 1963,
L.J.M.; 97, Rock (Flora), 1979, R.W.D.; 05, Tregorrick,
St Austell, W.T. (Thurston 1928); 35, Wacker, Antony,
S.M.; 45, H.M.S. Raleigh, Torpoint, E.G.; 46, Calstock
(Flora), still there, I.N.; Cotehele Quay, I.N.

191/2 § **M. officinalis** (L.) Pallas   Ribbed Melilot
Still very local.

West: 53, Upton Towans, G.L.; 63, old tip, Treskillard, Redruth, L.J.M.; Four Lanes, L.J.M.

East: 83, on shingle, Turnaware, Fal Estuary, B.E.M.G.; 95, old quarry, Trerice, St Dennis, L.G.; railway track, Goss Moor, L.J.M.; 04, Mevagissey, W.T. (Thurston 1935); 05, Tregrehan Mills, near Garker, B.E.M.G. and L.J.M.; Par (Flora), still there, B.M.S.; 20, Bude, E.T. (Thurston and Vigurs 1926); 45, Torpoint, 1966—71, S.M.; Jeffords Quay, Saltash, I.N.; 46, Halton Quay, N.J.F.; Calstock, 1923, E.T. (Thurston and Vigurs 1924), refound, post—1950, I.N.; Cotehele Quay, till 1963, I.N.
Scilly: Lousley 1971.

191/4 § **M. indica** (L.) All.   Small Melilot
Very rare, and usually only casual.

West: 43, Penzance, S.B.; 83, weed in garden, Penpol House, Devoran, L.J.M.

East: 94, Manor Tannery, Grampound, L.J.M.; 05, Charlestown, W.T. (Thurston 1929a); St Austell, W.T. (Thurston 1928); Par, 1928, Herb. Perrycoste, (TRU); 15, waste ground, Lostwithiel, L.J.M.; 20, old station, Bude, L.J.M.

MEDICAGO L.

190/3 **M. lupulina** L., Black Medick, and   190/6 **M. arabica** (L.) Hudson, Spotted Medick, are common plants in suitable habitats.

190/2 § **M. sativa** L., subsp. **sativa**   Lucerne
Usually only a relic of cultivation.

West: 43, Eastern Green, Penzance (Flora), 1967, G.A.; 53, Copperhouse, Hayle (Flora), 1950, J.B.; 64, Mirrose Well, near Portreath, L.J.M.; near Falmouth Reservoir, L.J.M.; 86, Newquay (Flora), 1972, L.G.; 87, Constantine Bay (Flora), 1966, L.J.M.; Harlyn Bay, W.B. (Thurston 1935); Trevone, J.A.P.

East: 83, St Anthony Head, B.E.M.G.; 36, by A38, SE of Liskeard, E.G.; 45, Torpoint, 1966, now gone, S.M.
Scilly: Lousley 1971.

190/1   § subsp. **falcata** (L.) Archangeli   Sickle Medick
Very rare, but persistent. Cornish material is referable to the var. *tenuifoliolata* Vuych.

West: 43, near Gulval Church (Flora), still there, B.M.S.; between Gulval and Badgers Cross, E.A.R. (Thurston and Vigurs 1925); Eastern Green, Penzance (Flora), 1947, J.B.; 53 Hayle (Flora), between Copperhouse and Phillack, 1950, J.B.; Phillack Towans, E.A.R. (Thurston and Vigurs 1925).

East: 20, Bude (Suppt), 1945, D.E.V., 1971, L.J.M.

190/1   § **M. x varia** Martyn
x 2   (*M. sylvestris* Fr.)
     *West: 43, wall, Gulval, E.A.R. (Thurston 1935), still there, 1971, B.M.S.; 53, roadside bank between Marazion and Long Rock, L.J.M.; Carnsew, Hayle, P.J.R.

190/5   **M. polymorpha** L. (incl. *M. lappacea* Desr.)
                                                Toothed Medick
(*M. denticulata* Willd.)

Extremely local, but often plentiful where it does occur.

West: 42, Newlyn (Flora), common between Newlyn and Penzance, B.M.S.; 43, Ludgvan, as *M. lappacea*, C.W.N. (Thurston 1935); 53, plentiful near Municipal Gardens, Hayle, CRNHS; 75, Melingey Farm, Holywell Bay, D.D.; 83, Falmouth (Flora), edge of field, Marlborough Avenue, Falmouth, L.J.M.; 84, by railway, Newham, Truro, W.H.F. (Thurston and Vigurs 1927).

East: 45, Antony Passage, Tamar Estuary, I.N.

Scilly: Lousley 1971.

TRIFOLIUM L.

Common species: 192/18 T. **repens** L., White Clover, 192/17 § **T. hybridum** L., Alsike Clover, 192/21 **T. campestre** Schreber, Hop Trefoil, 192/23 **T. dubium** Sibth., Lesser Trefoil, 192/24 **T. micranthum** Viv., Slender Trefoil, 192/2 **T. pratense** L., Red Clover, and 192/4 **T. medium** L., Zigzag Clover (doubtfully in Scilly).

192/1   **T. ornithopodioides** L.   Fenugreek
(*Trigonella ornithopodioides* DC.)

Frequent along the South coast of West Cornwall, rare elsewhere.

West: 33, Carn Gloose, and Castle Quarry, St Just, M.C.; Cape Cornwall, J.A.P.; 43, Boskednan, N of Madron, B.M.S.; 52, St Michaels Mount, J.A.P.; Hoe Point, J.A.P.; Praa Sands, R.H.; near Rinsey, J.Fo.; Trewavas Head, R.H.; 53, Long Rock, J.A.P.; 61, Lizard Downs (Flora), 1971, LFC; Goonhilly Reserve, D.E.C. *et al*; Predannack Wollas, L.C.F., J.H. and M.M.; Pentreath, J.A.P.; Mullion (Suppt), 1966, J.A.P.; grounds of Polurrian Hotel, A.L.S. (Thurston and Vigurs 1927); N of Penhale, J.A.P.; 71, Lizard Green, K.E.H.; Ruan Cross, B.M.S.; Cadgwith (Flora), 1959—77, J.Fo.; 72, casual, Bosahan, G.C.D. and C.V. (Thurston 1935); Treath, near Helford, 1926, C.H.F.; Scotch Quay, Helford River, L.J.M.; 83, Pendennis Point, R.H.; Pennance Point, J.A.P.; 87, Harlyn Bay, W.B. (Thurston 1935).

East: 04, Trenarren, S of St Austell, J.G.D. and C.D. and B.E.M.G.; 45, Tregonhawke Cliff, S.M.; 45 (44), Rame Head, S.M.

Scilly: Lousley 1971.

192/14 **T. strictum** L.   Upright Clover
Confined to the Lizard.

West: 61, still present in seven stations, 1979, comm. J.H.; 71, in two stations, comm. J.H.

Scilly: rejected, Lousley 1971.

192/18 **T. repens** var. **townsendii** Beeby
Scilly: widespread on the Isles, Lousley 1971.

T. occidentale D.E. Coombe   Western Clover
First described as new to science by Dr Coombe in 1961, this distinct clover is an important addition to the Flora. It is an early-flowering species, characteristic of short-turf cliff-top situations on the Lizard and in West Penwith.

*West: 32, 33, 42, 43, 52, 53, 61, 62, 71, frequent and often abundant from Kennack right round the coast to 53 (54) Godrevy Towans on the N coast; 86 (76), an

outlier at Towan Head, Newquay, D.E.C.
*Scilly: Lousley 1971.

192/17 § **T. hybridum** L., subsp. elegans (Savi) Ascherson & Graebner

Recorded throughout Cornwall by Davey (Flora), but there are no subsequent records.

192/15 **T. glomeratum** L.   Clustered Clover

Extremely rare, except in Scilly, where it is frequent. Also sometimes occurring as a tan-bark alien.

*West: 62, native colony at Chypons, Cury, 1979, J.H.; 83, one plant as tan-bark alien, Penpol House, Devoran, 1973, L.J.M.

East: 94, tan-bark alien, Demonstration Garden, Probus, L.J.M.; 35, St Germans Hut (Flora), refound there, 1978, E.G.; a few plants at Portwrinkle, 1978, E.G.

Scilly: Lousley 1971; MN, bulbfields near Higher Town, 1975, F.W.S.

192/16 **T. suffocatum** L.   Suffocated Clover

Now very rare and mainly casual on the mainland, but no doubt native in Scilly.

West: 71, Carn Kennack, 1950, D.E.C.; 72, tan-bark alien, garden at Helford Passage, L.J.M.; 83, tan-bark alien, Penpol House, Devoran, L.J.M.

Scilly: common, Lousley 1971.

192/19 **T. fragiferum** L.   Strawberry Clover

Local and rare, in damp areas along the coast.

West: 53, Hayle (Flora), 1970, B.M.S.; Phillack Towans, R.J.M.; St Erth (Flora), W of there, 1967, J.A.P.; 61, Polurrian Cove, R.O. (Thurston and Vigurs 1925); 75, Ellenglaze (Flora), 1964, L.J.M.; Treago, near Crantock, B.B.

East: 84, Tresillian, C.N. (Thurston 1930); 97, Amble Marshes (Flora), still there, R.W.D.; 05, Par (Flora), 1928, F.H.P., Herb. F.H. Perrycoste, (TRU); 07, Eglos-hayle, Wadebridge (Flora), Sladesbridge, 1977, C.C.

Scilly: rare, Lousley 1971.

192/10 **T. striatum** L. Knotted Clover

West: Frequent and widespread, mainly along the coast.

East: 83, St Anthony Head (Flora), 1979, K.H.; sandbar, St Just, L.J.M.; Turnaware Beach, Fal Estuary, B.E.M.G.; between Portscatho and Greeb Point, L.J.M.; 97, Pentire Peninsula, R.W.D.; 05, Par (Flora), Par Green, 1966, J.A.P.; 19, St Gennys, 1923, W.B. (Thurston and Vigurs 1924); 20, Bude, J.A.P.; 21, Duckpool, J.A.P.; 35, Trevollard Green, I.N.; 45, Saltash (Flora), still there, post—1950, I.N.; between Coombe and Wearde Quay, I.N.; (44), Rame Head, J.A.P.

Scilly: Lousley 1971.

192/9 **T. arvense** L. Hare's-foot Clover

Rather local, but scattered throughout the county.

West: 32, St Just, M.C.; 42, Lamorna (Flora), 1971, B.M.S.; 52, Trewavas Head, J.A.P.; Prussia Cove, G.B.M.; 61, Kynance Cove, L.T.M. (Thurston 1930); Mullion (Flora), 1966, J.A.P.; 63, railway near Gwinear Road, L.J.M.; 71, Lizard (Flora), 1978, J.S.R.; Landewednack, B.M.S.; Kennack, J.B.; between Ruan Minor and Coverack, G.B.M.; 72, Godrevy Cove, St Keverne, J.H. and L.J.M.

East: 83, St Anthony (Flora), 1968, L.J.M.; 93, Portloe (Suppt), Camels Cove, 1976, L.J.M.; 97, Pentire Peninsula, R.W.D.; Rokke Moor, St Endellion, B.E.M.G. and L.J.M.; 04, Pentewan (Flora), 1954, J.B.; near Trenarren, W.T. (Thurston 1929a); 05, Par, B.M.S.; 08, Tintagel (Suppt), W.H.F. (Thurston 1929a); 20, old railway, Bude, L.J.M.; 25, Looe (Flora), 1969, L.J.M.; E of Millendreath, J.A.P.; 35, Downderry (Flora), still there, S.M.; Tregantle Cliff, L.J.M.; Freathy, S.M.; 45 (44), Rame Head (Flora), still there, post—1950, L.J.M. and J.M.W.

Scilly: Lousley 1971.

192/12 **T. bocconei** Savi Twin-flowered Clover

A rare clover, confined to the Lizard and Channel Isles.

West: 61, in five main stations, 1979, comm. J.H.; 71, in six stations, 1979, comm. J.H.

192/11 **T. scabrum** L.   Rough Clover

Mainly near the sea.

West: Frequent to common in dry places along the coast.

East: 83, near St Anthony (Flora), 1979, K.H.; Pendower Beach, B.E.M.G.; 15, St Catherine's Point, Fowey, L.J.M.; 35, Seaton (Flora), 1966, J.A.P.; 45 (44), Rame Head, J.S.R.

Scilly: Lousley 1971.

192/7 **T. incarnatum**   Crimson Clover
       § subsp. **incarnatum**

Formerly widely grown as a farm crop, and frequent as a relic of cultivation. Now very rarely seen.

West: 42, Kemyel, near Mousehole, J.B.; 75, Penhale Sands, L.J.M.

East: 05, Par Moor, L.T.M. (Thurston 1929a), and Par Harbour, L.T.M. (Thurston 1935).

Scilly: Lousley 1971.

192/8 subsp. **molinerii** (Balbis ex Hornem.) Syme

                              Long-headed Clover

Rare and confined to the Lizard and Channel Isles.

West: 61, four main stations, comm. J.H.; 71, three main stations, 1979, comm. J.H.

192/5 **T. squamosum** L.   Sea Clover

This is best regarded as a casual in Cornwall. Now extremely rare.

West: 43, Eastern Green (Flora, as extinct), between here and Marazion Station, J.R.P.; 71, Lizard road about a mile from Lizard Town, 1923, E.B. (Thurston and Vigurs 1924); 75, roadside bank, Perranporth, 1923 (Thurston and Vigurs 1924).

East: 05, Par (Flora), 1920, W.Wi., Herb. W. Wise, (LAUS), 1925, F.H.P., Herb. F.H. Perrycoste, (TRU); near Crinnis Beach, W.T. (Thurston 1935); 20, near Bude Canal, W.H.F. (Thurston 1929a).

192/13 **T. subterraneum** L.   Subterranean Clover

Frequent and widespread around the coastline. The following are additions to the Flora and Suppt.

West: 32, Nanquidno, S of St Just, G.L.; 33, Carn

Gloose, near St Just, M.C.; 42, St Buryan, J.B.; 43, Carnelloe, Zennor, G.L.; 52, Rinsey Head, RNHS; 53, Marazion, B.M.S.; 61, Predannack Wollas, L.C.F., J.H., and M.M.; 62, Carminowe Creek, Loe Pool, R.H.; 71, Lizard, R.H.; Parnvoose, J.Fo.; East Cove, Kennack, D.S.D.; cliffs below Poldowrian, J.A.P.; 72, Rosemullion Head, L.J.M.; Bosloe, near Durgan, 1934, C.H.F.; 73, between Swanpool and Maenporth, R.H.; 97, Dennis Hill, Padstow, L.G.

East: 94, near Boswinger, Gorran, J.S.R.; 05, Par (Flora), 1924, H.F.D. and E.T. (Thurston and Vigurs 1926); 08, cliffs S of Trebarwith, J.A.P.; (09), near Forrabury Church, Boscastle, 1930, H.W.P. (Thurston 1935); 15, Lansallos Cliffs, I.N.; 19, St Gennys, E.G.; 25, between Sandplace and Coombe, F.H.C. and J.L.; 45, St Stephens, Saltash, I.N.; Forder Hill, Cawsand, S.M.; (44), Rame Head, J.A.P.

Scilly: common, Lousley 1971.

LOTUS L.

195/1 **L. corniculatus** L., Common Bird's-foot-trefoil, and 195/3 **L. uliginosus** Schkuhr, Greater Bird's-foot-trefoil, are common and widespread in a variety of habitats.

195/2 **L. tenuis** Waldst. & Kit. ex Willd.

Narrow-leaved Bird's-foot-trefoil

It is difficult to account for the decline in this species, but it may be overlooked to some extent.

West: 62, Cury, R.O. (Thurston and Vigurs 1925); 71, Cadgwith (Suppt), refound 1971, E.W.; 86, Newquay, 1903 (Thurston 1930), G.C.D. (Thurston 1935).

East: 05, ballast-heap, Charlestown, W.T. (Thurston and Vigurs 1926); 45, quarry, Southdown, Millbrook, 1965, L.J.M., 1978, E.G.; 46, Skinham Farm, Salt Mill, Saltash, 1971, I.N.

195/4 **L. subbiflorus** Lag.   Hairy Bird's-foot-trefoil
(*L. hispidus* Desf.)

In view of Davey's classification as 'rare', this species is surprisingly frequent in West Cornwall, but, because of its general restriction in Britain, we have thought it advisable to list all post—Supplement records.

West: 32, Lands End (Flora), 1959, J.B.; Boscregan, B.M.S.; 33, Cape Cornwall (Flora), still there, post— 1950, R.H.; Bosavern, St Just, M.C.; Kenidjack Valley, J.B.; Botallack cliffs, J.A.P.; near Pendeen, S.B.; 42, near Kemyel Reserve, G.B.M.; 52, St Michaels Mount, J.A.P.; Hoe Point, J.A.P.; S of Rinsey Head, J.B.; 53, E of Marazion (Flora) 1970, B.M.S.; (54), Clodgy Point, St Ives, P.J.R.; 62, Breage (Flora), 1961, G.B.M.; Porthleven, H.B.S.; 71, Lizard (Flora), still there, various recorders; Coverack, A.S.; Kennack (Flora), still there, post—1950, R.H.; 72, Rosemullion Head, L.J.M.; Constantine, R.H.; 83, Pennance Point (Flora), 1960 onwards, L.J.M.; 97, Stepper Point, Padstow, J.A.P.

East: 83, St Mawes, and St Anthony, R.H.; near Pendower Beach, L.G.; 94, Tubbs Mill, Caerhayes, E.W.; Portholland, L.T.M. (Thurston and Vigurs 1925); 97, Pentire (Flora), still there, 1950 onwards, R.W.D.; 04, above Trenarren Beach, W.T. (Thurston and Vigurs 1927); 15, Lantic Bay, CNT; Pencarrow Head, E.G.; 25, Polperro, 1926, Herb. F.H. Perrycoste, (TRU); 35, Seaton, E.G.; St Germans Hut (Flora), 1978, E.G.; Eglarooze Cliff, S.M.; Portwrinkle, E.G.; Tregantle Cliff, J.A.P.; 45 (44), Rame Head, and Penlee Point (Flora), 1978, E.G.

Scilly: common, Lousley 1971.

195/5 **L. angustissimus** L.   Slender Bird's-foot-trefoil

A very rare plant, but occasionally plentiful locally in a good year.

West: 32, Lands End, E.G.I.; 53 (54), Godrevy Point, BRC; 62, Porthleven, H.B.S.; 64, Porthtowan, BRC; 71, near Lizard Lighthouse (Flora), still there, 1950 onwards, various recorders.

East: 95, old quarry, Trerice, St Dennis, L.G.; 97, Pentire (Flora), 1950 onwards, R.W.D.; 07, old railway cutting, Sladesbridge, L.J.M.; 15, Lantic Bay, CNT; 25, Polperro (Flora), still there, post—1950, R.L.G.L.; Looe (Flora), Portnadler, 1965, J.L.; 35, near Downderry, I.N.; Eglarooze Cliff, S.M.; St Germans Hut (Flora), 1978, E.G.; Portwrinkle, E.G.; Tregantle Cliff, J.A.P.; Sharrow Point, E.G.; 45 (44), Rame Head, and Penlee Point (Flora), plentiful in 1978, E.G.

Scilly: rejected, Lousley 1971.

ANTHYLLIS L.

193/1 **A. vulneraria** L.   Kidney Vetch
A common coastal plant of cliffs and sand-dunes in a variety of colour forms, of which the lemon-yellow form is especially common on cliffs. Now apparently extinct in Scilly.

subsp. **vulneraria**

var. **coccinea** L.
This red-flowered form is frequent along the N coast of Cornwall.

var. **langei** Jalas
West: 62, Porthleven, H.B.S.; Gunwalloe, L.J.M. East: 94, Portholland, L.J.M.; Tintagel Castle, B.E.M.G.

subsp. **corbierei** (Salmon & Travis) Cullen
*West: 53, Hazel Towans, 1933, BRC; 86, Bedruthan Steps, 1958, J.H.C.

subsp. **carpatica** (Pant.) Nyman var. **pseudovulneraria** Sagorski
*East: 05, Par Sands, 1972, B.E.M.G.

ORNITHOPUS L.

202/1 **O. perpusillus** L., Bird's-foot, is a common and widespread plant of cliffs and sandy places, as well as on old mine-waste.

202/2 **O. pinnatus** (Miller) Druce   Orange Bird's-foot
Frequent on the Isles of Scilly, but doubtfully on the mainland, unless the specimen in Herb. Willis can be located and its authenticity confirmed.
*West: 43, Mulfra, N of Penzance, 1881, Herb. Willis. Not refound.
*East: 97, near Bodieve, comm. Mr P. Sheppey. This record should not be accepted without confirmation. Scilly: frequent, Lousley 1971.

CORONILLA L.

203/1 § **C. varia** L.   Crown Vetch
Rather a rare introduction.
West: 43, New Street, Penzance, M.B.; 53, Copper-

house, Hayle (Suppt), still there, 1949, J.B.; 61, road
to Kynance Cove, post—1950, various recorders.
East: 97, Rock, E.A.

OXALIDACEAE
OXALIS L.

170/2 § **O. corniculata** L., Sleeping Beauty (absent
from Scilly), and 170/1 **O. acetosella** L., Wood-sorrel
(doubtfully in Scilly), are frequent and widespread on
the mainland of Cornwall.

170/2 § **O. corniculata** var. **repens** (Thunb.) Zucc.
(Suppt as *O. repens*)
West: 42, Lidden, Penzance, S.B.; 43, nursery, Gulval,
B.M.S. and L.J.M.; 75, Zelah Nurseries, L.J.M.

The   purple-leaved   var.   *atropurpurea* Planchon   is
naturalised at:
West: 43, Gulval, L.J.M.; 72, St Keverne, J.H. and
L.J.M.
East: 15, Fowey, L.J.M.

§ **O. exilis** A. Cunn.
*West: 64, garden, Reskadinnick, Camborne, 1969,
R.J.M.; 72, Glendurgan Gardens, B.E.M.G.
Scilly: Lousley 1971; M, 1975, D.E.A.; garden, Gugh,
1975, D.E.A.; T, hotel garden, 1975, D.E.A.

170/5 § **O. megalorrhiza** Jacq.   Fleshy Oxalis
Scilly: Lousley 1971.

170/4 § **O. fontana** Bunge   Upright Oxalis
(Flora, incorrectly, as *O. stricta*)
West: 33, St Just, M.C.; 42, Penzance (Flora), 1967,
G.B.M.;   62,   Porthleven,   H.B.S.;   63,   Penponds,
Camborne, L.J.M.
Scilly: Lousley 1971.

170/6 § **O. articulata** Savigny   Pink Oxalis
(Suppt as *O. floribunda* Lehm.)
An increasing garden escape throughout the county.
West: 33, Kenidjack Valley, St Just, M.C.; 42, Lariggan,
Penzance, G.B.M.; 43, near Madron, B.M.S.; 52, Praa
Sands, J.A.P.; 53, Phillack, B.M.S.; 64, Portreath,

L.J.M.; 72, Constantine, 1961, L.J.M.; 74, Trevissick, Mt Hawke, L.J.M.; 83, Swanpool, L.J.M.; 97, Hawkers Cove, J.A.P.

*East: 83, near Rosteague, Gerrans, B.E.M.G.; 94, Portholland, 1962, L.J.M.; 97, Pentireglaze, J.A.P.; 05, Par, L.J.M.; 20, Bude, J.A.P.; 35, Portwrinkle, S.M.; 45, Torpoint, S.M.

Scilly: common, Lousley 1971.

170/8 § **O. latifolia** Kunth   Mexican Oxalis

A troublesome weed in nurseries and gardens.

West: 42, and 43, Penzance (Suppt), still there in market-gardens, 1958 (*Watsonia*, 4: 65); 62, Porthleven, H.B.S.; 72, St Anthony-in-Meneage, R.H.; 75, Zelah Nurseries, L.J.M.; 85, Council tip, Newlyn East, L.J.M.

Scilly: Lousley 1971.

170/10 § **O. pes-caprae** L.   Bermuda Buttercup

Scilly: common, Lousley 1971.

170/11 § **O. incarnata** L.   Pale Oxalis

An increasing weed in gardens and waste places.

*West: 33, Cot Valley, St Just, M.C.; 42, common in Penzance, G.B.M.; 43, in two places at Gulval, B.M.S.; 53, between Crowlas and Ludgvan, R.G.; 83, Falmouth, 1965, L.J.M.

*East: 15, Menabilly Woods, 1957, R.M.P.; Fowey, L.J.M.

GERANIACEAE

GERANIUM L.

Common species: 168/13 **G. molle** L., Dove's-foot Crane's-bill, 168/10 **G. columbinum** L., Long-stalked Crane's-bill (absent from Scilly), 168/11 **G. dissectum** L., Cut-leaved Crane's-bill, and 168/16 **G. robertianum** L., subsp. **robertianum,** Herb. Robert (Scilly: M, refound, 1973, L.A.H.)

168/7 **G. sanguineum** L.   Bloody Crane's-bill

Rare and confined, as a native, to the Lizard and a short stretch of the N coast.

West: 61, Kynance (Flora), still plentiful, 1950 onwards, various recorders; Gew Graze, various recorders;

63, naturalised on old railway track, Nancegollan, L.J.M.; 64, Porthtowan (Flora), still plentiful there, 1950 onwards, L.J.M.; between Porthtowan and Chapel Porth, L.J.M.; 71, Downas Valley, various recorders; Black Head, Coverack (Flora), 1950 onwards; 75, Perranporth (Flora), Droskyn Point, 1964, G.B.M. East: 95, garden throw-out near Lanjeth, St Austell, L.J.M.

168/1 G. pratense L. Meadow Crane's-bill

Not native in Cornwall, but gradually increasing as an introduction.

West: 32, ruined garden, Treen, G.B.M.; Lands End, K.P.; 33, near St Just, M.C.; 43, Zennor, L.B.; 53, Carbis Bay, A.T. (Thurston 1935); Lelant, S.M.; (54), St Ives, L.B.; 62, Bochym, W.T. (Thurston 1935); 63, Piece, Carnkie, J.G.T.; Clowance, W.T. (Thurston 1935), 1965, F.G.F.; 64, near Carn Brea, G.B.M.; two places near Redruth, L.J.M.; Bel Lake, Camborne, J.G.T.; 71 or 72, between St Keverne and Traboe Cross, L.J.M.; 74, Sparnon Close, Redruth, K.P.; 83, Mylor Churchyard (Suppt), still there, post—1950, R.H.; 84, Kea Churchyard, W.H.F. (Thurston and Vigurs 1926); 87, Porthcothan, J.A.P.

East: 84, between Truro and Malpas, W.Bo. (Thurston 1935); Tresillian, J.A.P.; 05, Par Sands, N.J.F.; St Austell, B.Sh.; 08, Tintagel, E.A.; 19, St Gennys, E.G.; 20, near Poughill, Bude, J.A.P.; 25, West Looe (Flora), 1971, G.B.M.; 26, Factory, near Menheniot, S.M.; 46, Landulph, J.A.P.

168/3 § G. endressii Gay French Crane's-bill

An increasing garden throw-out.

West: 43, Bosullow, near Morvah, B.M.S.; 71, road to Church Cove, Lizard, K.E.H.; 72, Helford, R.H.; 74, Council tip, Bissoe, L.J.M.; near St Agnes (Flora and Suppt, as *G. nodosum*), still there (at Goonbell Halt) post—1950, L.J.M.

*East: 06, near Criggan, and Roche, 1954, J.B.; 37, below Kit Hill, I.N.

var. **thurstoniana** Turrill

West: 74, Goonbell Halt, with type (Thurston 1929a).

168/4 § **G. versicolor** L. Pencilled Crane's-bill
West: Common and widespread by roadsides.

East: Much less common. 97, Egloshayle, R.W.D.; 07, Keybridge, R.W.D.; 15, between Lostwithiel and Lerryn (Flora), still there, post—1950, R.W.D.; 35, Lower Tregantle (Flora), 1967, S.M.; 45, Thanckes Wood, Torpoint, S.M.; 46, Botusfleming (Flora), still there, 1950 onwards, I.N.

168/3 § **G. endressii x versicolor**
x 4 A recently recognised garden escape.

*West: 42, Lamorna area, comm. G.B.M.; 53, near St Erth, 1965, R.N.H.S.; 72, Helford Village, RNHS.

[168/5 § **G. nodosum** L., Knotted Crane's-bill, was listed in the Flora in error for *G. endressii*, and must be removed from the Cornish List. As Davey notes, the record for **G. sylvaticum** is an obvious mistake.]

168/6 § **G. phaeum** L. Dusky Crane's-bill
This old introduction is now even rarer than it was. West: 43, Boskednan, between Zennor and Penzance (Suppt), still there, post—1950, B.M.S.; Ding Dong Mine, B.M.S.

East: 05, Luxulyan Cemetery, L.G.

168/9 § **G. pyrenaicum** Burm. fil. Hedgerow Crane's-bill
This species has spread widely since the Flora.

West: 42, Penzance, G.B.M.; 53, Marazion (Flora), still there, post—1950, B.M.S.; Phillack Towans (Flora), 1966, L.A.B.; (54), St Ives, L.B.; 71, near Coverack, B.B.; 74, Council tip, Bissoe, L.J.M.; 85, Cubert turning, Newquay road, L.G.; Council tip, Newlyn East, L.J.M.; Gwylls, near Newquay (Thurston 1935); 86, Newquay (Flora), 1972, L.G.

East: 35, 45, and 46, frequent in the Lower Tamar area; 36, Paynters Cross, near Hatt, I.N.; 38, Launceston, G.L.K.

Scilly: rejected, Lousley 1971.

168/12 **G. rotundifolium** L. Round-leaved Crane's-bill
This species seems to be on the increase in W Cornwall. It is a frequent plant in the Tamar Estuary.

West: 42, Penzance (Flora), 1968, G.B.M.; St Buryan,

G.L.; 43, near the Heliport, Penzance, G.B.M.; near Gulval, B.M.S.; 52, near Perranuthnoe, K.P.; 53, Marazion, B.M.S.; Ludgvan, B.M.S.; (54), bowling-green, St Ives, and between St Ives and Clodgy Point, L.B.; 63, Piece, Carnkie, L.J.M.; 64, Pool, J.S.R.; near Portreath, J.A.P.; Bridge, Illogan (Flora), 1967, L.J.M.; Hell's Mouth, L.J.M.; 75, Mount, Perranzabuloe (Suppt), 1975, L.J.M.

East: 95, St Dennis Junction, L.J.M.; 04, Mevagissey, W.T. (Thurston 1935); 05, Par (Flora), 1977, L.J.M.; 25, Looe (Suppt), still there, J.A.P.; 26, railway, Liskeard, C.P.F. (Thurston and Vigurs 1927); 45, frequent around Torpoint and Saltash.

168/14 **G. pusillum** L.   Small-flowered Crane's-bill

Extremely local, and often recorded in error for small forms of *G. molle.*

West: 52, Perranuthnoe, L.J.M.; Keneggy, G.L.; 53, by railway, Lelant, G.L.; Gwithian, R.H.; 62, Porthleven, H.B.S.; 72, St Anthony-in-Meneage, R.H.; 75, Treworthen, Perranzabuloe (Flora), nearby on Penhale Sands, E.S.E. and L.J.M.

East: 83, arable field, Rosevine, Roseland, B.E.M.G.; 35, Seaton (Flora), still there, post—1950, J.A.P.

Scilly: Lousley 1971.

168/15 **G. lucidum** L.   Shining Crane's-bill

Considerably increased in the last fifty years, especially in the West.

West: 43, Gulval, B.M.S.; Nancledra, B.M.S.; Towednack School, G.B.M.; 53, Carbis Bay, G.B.M.; roadside near Trink Hill, L.J.M.; 75, mine spoil near St Agnes, J.A.P.; weed in Zelah Nurseries, L.J.M.; 85, old railway track between Newlyn East and Benny Mill, L.J.M.

East: 94, between Gorran and Caerhayes, T.J.P. (Thurston and Vigurs 1926); 97, Stoptide, Rock, E.A.; 07, railway NE of Helland bridge, K.H.J.; 25, near Looe, S.M.; 26, Moorswater, Liskeard, M.Bl.; 27, near Treburland, J.A.P.; 28, Polyphant, and Lewannick, L.J.M.; 38, Launceston (Flora), 1978, L.J.M.; 35, 36, 45, and 46, quite frequent in the Lower Tamar area.

*Scilly: M, garden, The Garrison, 1973, L.A.H.

168/   **G. robertianum** subsp. **maritimum** (Bab.) H.G. Baker
16c   *West: 61, Kynance Cove, 1926, C.E.S.; 71, Coverack, 1910, H.E.F.; 72, northern shore of Helford River, R.W.D.; 97, Padstow, W.B.
       *East: 05, Par, 1920, E.T.

168/   **G. purpureum** Vill., subsp. **purpureum**   Little-Robin
17a   'Probably more common around Newquay and by the estuary of the R. Camel than elsewhere in England', 1955 (*Watsonia*, 3: 163). There has been a considerable increase since 1975.
       West: 43, Eastern Green, Penzance, B.M.S.; 53, near the Bowl Rock, Trencrom, B.B.; (54), St Ives, BRC; 75, near St Agnes, J.A.P.; 86 (76), Porth Joke, J.A.P.; Crantock (Flora), 1977, C.W.; 97, Padstow (Flora), still frequent around the town, 1979, various recorders; St Issey (Flora), still there, and increasing, post—1950, R.W.D.
       East: 93, Camels Cove, Veryan Bay (B.E.C. 1946), nearby at Trewartha, B.E.M.G.; 97, Wadebridge (Flora), W of Bodieve, J.A.P.; Trebetherick, increasing rapidly, R.W.D.; Polzeath (Flora), still there, increasing, and now in a second locality, 1950 onwards, R.W.D.; 05, Par (Flora), Polmear, Par, L.T.M. (Thurston 1930).
       Scilly: possibly extinct, Lousley 1971.

168/   subsp. **forsteri** (Wilmott) H.G. Bak.
17b   West: 74, old railway track, St Agnes Station, 1967, L.J.M.

ERODIUM L'HÉR.

169/1 **E. maritimum** (L.) L'Hér., Sea Stork's-bill and 169/3b **E. cicutarium** (L.) L'Hér. subsp. **dunense** Andreas, Common Stork's-bill, are both frequent and widely distributed in coastal areas.

169/   **E. cicutarium** subsp. **cicutarium**
3a   Remarkably rare or under-recorded in the county.
       East: 83, St Mawes, and Pendower Beach, B.E.M.G.; 96, Winnards Perch, St Breock, L.J.M.
       Scilly: a frequent bulb-field weed, Lousley 1971.

169/4   subsp. **bipinnatum** Tourlet   Sticky Stork's-bill
West: 86 (76), Porth Joke, 1962, J.H.C.   This has not been confirmed.
Scilly: Lousley 1971; M, Bar Point, 1972, L.A.H.

169/2   **E. moschatum** (L.) L'Hér.   Musk Stork's-bill
Rather rare, but still in most of its old localities.

West: 32, Gwenver Cliff, Sennen, M.C.; Porthgwarra, E.G.; 33, St Just (Flora), in four places, M.C.; 42, Penzance (Flora), still there, post—1950, B.M.S.; 53, Marazion (Suppt), still there, post—1950, B.M.S.; Hayle Towans (Suppt), still at Phillack, B.M.S.; Gwithian, J.L.; (54), St Ives (Flora), 1969, L.B.; 61, Kynance, R.L.G.L.; 71, Lizard (Flora), 1959—77, J.Fo.; near Kennack Sands, J.G.T.; Coverack (Flora), still there, post—1950, R.H.; 72, Porthallow, R.H.; 87, Treburrick, Porthcothan, H.F.D. (Thurston 1928); Harlyn Bay (Flora), still there, post—1950, A.B.

East: 94, tan-bark alien, Manor Tannery, Grampound, L.J.M.; 97, Com Head, and Pentire Head, R.W.D.; St Enodoc (Flora), Shilla Valley, 1951, and Pentireglaze, 1962, R.W.D.; 05, Par (Flora), 1957, B.Sh.; 25, Polperro (Flora), still there 1934 (Thurston 1935); Looe (Flora), 1966, J.L.; 35, Downderry, and St Germans Beach (Flora), still in both places, 1966, I.N.; Tregantle Downs, S.M.
Scilly: common, Lousley 1971.

LINACEAE
LINUM L.
166/1 **L. bienne** Miller (*L. angustifolium* Huds.), Pale Flax, and 166/4 **L. catharticum** L., Fairy Flax, are found throughout the county, and are too frequent on the mainland for listing of stations.

166/2 § **L. usitatissimum** L.   Flax
Casual only. Now very rare.
West: 53, waste ground, Hayle, L.J.M.; 61, Lizard (Flora), 1971, E.A.; 85, Council tip, Newlyn East, L.J.M.
East: 05, Charlestown, W.T. (Thurston 1935).

RADIOLA HILL

167/1 **R. linoides** Roth   Allseed

Still locally common, and often in quantity, especially in the West. Very rare in the Lower Tamar area.

West: 32, Skewjack Moor, W.R.H.; Porthgwarra, S.M.; Tredinney Common, M.C.; between Zennor and Lands End (Flora), near Morvah, R.L.G.L.; 33, clayworks E of St Just, J.A.P.; 42, N of Sancreed, J.A.P.; Chy-an-hal Moor (Flora), still there, B.M.S.; 43, Georgia, near Nancledra, P.J.R.; 52, St Michaels Mount, J.A.P.; 53, Marazion (Flora), Long Rock, 1971, B.M.S.; Nanpusker Valley, near Hayle, A.B.; 61, Kynance (Flora), still there, B.M.S.; 63, Carnmenellis (Flora), Polmarth Moor, 1978, L.J.M.; Crowan Reservoir, and Black Rock, J.B.; 64, Red River Valley, near Ashill, R.J.M. and L.J.M.; moor between Redruth and Bridge, L.J.M.; 71, Goonhilly (Flora), still there, 1950 onwards, R.H.; near Ruan Pool, the Lizard, J.Fo.; Coverack (Flora), 1977, J.Fo.; Kennack, R.H.; 72, Constantine, R.H.; Rosemullion Head, J.A.P.; 73, Rame Common (Flora), 1966, L.J.M.; 74, Silverwell Moor, B.M.S.; 87, near Park Head, T.H.A.

East: 95, Goss Moor (Flora), 1967, A.B.; 96, Retire Common, R.W.D.; 06, Dunmere Forest, Bodmin, E.A.; Red Moor, E.A. and L.J.M.; Criggan Moor, L.J.M.; 16, Boconnoc Park, C.P.F. (Thurston and Vigurs 1927); 17, Candra and Treswallock Moors, St Breward, E.A.; 18, Bowithick, J.A.P.

Scilly: common, Lousley 1971.

EUPHORBIACEAE

MERCURIALIS L.

318/1 **M. perennis** L., Dog's Mercury is frequent throughout Cornwall, but much less so in the extreme West, and absent from Scilly.

318/2 § **M. annua** L.   Annual Mercury

Casual and impermanent, except perhaps around Falmouth.

West: 62, Council tip, Porthleven, H.B.S.; 83, Falmouth, R.H.; Swanpool, L.J.M.; Flushing, near Falmouth, W.T. (Thurston 1935), 1966, L.J.M.; 85, Council tip, Newlyn East.

East: 83, St Mawes, 1930, W.T. (Thurston 1935); 97, St Minver, garden weed, R.W.D.

Scilly: Lousley 1971.

EUPHORBIA L.

319/9 **E. helioscopia** L., Sun Spurge, and 319/10 **E. peplus** L., Petty Spurge, are common species throughout Cornwall.

319/1 **E. peplis** L. Purple Spurge

Always extremely rare, this species has not been seen for thirty years in Cornwall, but there are still suitable places where it could reappear.

West: 43 or 53, between Penzance and Marazion (Flora), five plants, 1934—35, E.A.R. (*Western Morning News*, 3.1.1960).

East: 25, Talland, Polperro, 1903, F.H.P., Herb. F.H. Perrycoste, (TRU); 35, Downderry, 1949, A.W.G., Herb. Lousley, (RNG).

Scilly: last seen 1936, Lousley 1971.

319/5 **E. hyberna** L. Irish Spurge

Still in fair quantity in its original station.

West: 64, Nance Wood, Portreath (Flora), many plants, 1976, L.J.M.

319/2 § **E. lathyrus** L. Caper Spurge

Casual usually, but persistent in a few places.

West: 53, Phillack Towans, B.M.S.; Lethlean Towans, L.J.M.; 61 or 62, between Chypons and Mullion, J.G.; 74, Bissoe (Flora), 1970, B.E.M.G.; 83, Falmouth (Flora), two plants at Swanpool, 1962, L.J.M.; Feock, R.H.; 85, Council tip, Newlyn East, L.J.M.; 97, Little Petherick (Flora), one plant, B.B.

East: 28, Trewint, near Altarnun, B.Sh.; 35, near Poldrissick, Landrake, I.N.; 45, allotment, Millbrook, T.W.

319/11 **E. exigua** L. Dwarf Spurge

Considerably reduced since the Flora, and mainly in arable fields on the coast.

West: 53, Gwinear Road, L.J.M.; 62, Gunwalloe, CNT and LFC; 64, Porthtowan, L.J.M.; 72, Gweek, R.H.; 84, Truro (Flora), Newham, near Truro, 1974, L.J.M.

East: 97, Lundy Bay, R.W.D.; Trebetherick, R.W.D.; 05, Carlyon Bay, R.H.; 08 (09), near Boscastle, J.A.P.; 35, Tregantle Cliff, Freathy, J.A.P.; 45, Millbrook, J.A.P.; 'common in Torpoint area', S.M.

319/12 **E. portlandica** L. Portland Spurge

Still widely distributed in coastal areas, especially along the North coast.

West:33, Pendeen Watch, J.B.; 52, Praa Sands, H.B.S.; 53, Carbis Bay (Flora), 1970, B.M.S.; from Lelant (Flora), to Godrevy Towans, post—1950, various recorders; 61, garden weed, near Mullion School, E.J.P. (Thurston 1935); 62, Loe Bar (Flora), still there, post—1950, H.B.S.; 64, Portreath (Flora), 1966, L.J.M.; Porthtowan (Flora), and Chapel Porth, 1965, J.B.; 75, Penhale Sands (Flora), 1960, L.J.M.; Holywell Bay, A.B.; 86 (76), Pentire, Newquay (Flora), 1966, J.A.P.; 87, Constantine Bay (Flora), 1965, W.G.

East: 83, Pendower Cove, J.B.; 97, Rock (Flora), 1940 onwards, R.W.D.; Lundy Bay, J.A.P.; 20, Bude (Flora), 1966, J.A.P.; Duckpool, Stanbury Mouth, and Marsland Mouth, N of Bude, L.J.M.; 35, Sharrow, and Tregantle, S.M.; 45, Whitsand Bay (Flora), 1979, K.H.

Scilly: Lousley 1971.

319/13 **E. paralias** L. Sea Spurge

Still frequent in sand-dune areas.

West: 32, Sennen Cove, J.R.P.; Gwenver Beach, near Sennen, M.C.; 53, Hayle (Flora), 1964, B.Sh.; Phillack, and Gwithian Towans (Flora), 1967, J.B.; Upton Towans, and Godrevy, G.L.; 64, Portreath Harbour, L.J.M.; Porthtowan, B.M.S.; 75, Penhale Sands (Flora), still there, various recorders; Holywell Bay (Flora), still there, R.L.G.L.; 86 (76), Cubert, K.H.; Fistral Beach, Newquay, R.L.G.L.; 87, Constantine Bay (Flora), 1965, W.G.

East: 97, Rock (Flora), 1940 onwards, R.W.D.; 15, Lantic Bay, J.C.D.

Scilly: Lousley 1971.

319/17 **E. amygdaloides** L. Wood Spurge
Very local, but persistent in many of the old localities
West: 61, Kynance (Flora), 1955, J.B.; 63, W of
Camborne (Flora), 1963, L.J.M.; 71, Poltesco (Suppt)
still there, post—1950, R.H.; Kennack Sands, and Black
Head, J.A.P.; 73, Penryn, near the reservoir, R.H.
between Perranwharf and Devoran (Flora), 1950
onwards, L.J.M.; 83, Feock, R.H.; 84, Bishops Woods,
Idless (Suppt), 1960 onwards, J.B.
East: 83, near Percuil, St Mawes (Flora), 1950 onwards
L.J.M.; 93, Nare Head, J.B.; Portloe, M.E.B.; 94,
Tregoney (Flora), 1960, L.J.M.; 19, The Strangles,
St Gennys, J.A.P.; 35, Seaton Valley, L.J.M.; 36, about
Notter Bridge (Flora), still there, I.N.; 37, Greenscombe
Wood, Luckett, CNT; Carthamartha Wood, L.J.M.; S of
Greystone Bridge, J.A.P.; 45, locally common around
Torpoint, S.M.; 47, Gunnislake, I.N.
Scilly: Lousley 1971; T, Merchants Point, 1975, D.E.A.;
between New Grimsby and Frenchman's Point, 1975,
D.E.A.

POLYGALACEAE

POLYGALA L.

114/1 **P. vulgaris** L. (incl. *P. oxyptera* Reichb.), Common
Milkwort, and 114/2 **P. serpyllifolia** J.A.C. Hose (*P. serpyllacea* Weihe), Heath Milkwort, are frequent in
Cornwall in suitable habitats.

ACERACEAE

ACER L.

173/1 § **A. pseudoplatanus** L., Sycamore, is a common and
widespread tree in the county, being often planted as a
windbreak in exposed areas, and seeding itself readily in
the native vegetation.

173/3 **A. campestre** L. Field Maple
Very rare, and present mostly as planted hedges, but
possibly native in a few stations in the N and SE.
West: 72, Trelowarren, J.S.R.; 73, one bush, Budock,
W.D.W. (Thurston and Vigurs 1926).
East: 85, Ladock, A.S.; 05, near Tregrehan, St Austell,
W.T. (Thurston 1929a); 35 St Erney, L.J.M.; 36, lane by

Patheda Wood, Tideford Cross, I.N.; 38, Launceston (Flora), 1970, G.L.K.; 45, near Saltash (Flora), Cowdray Hill, one tree, I.N.; Coombe Valley, Saltash, several trees, E.G.; 46, near Haye Farm, I.N.; Cargreen, I.N.; Landulph Cross, I.N.

HIPPOCASTANACEAE
AESCULUS L.

175/1 § **A. hippocastanum** L., Horse-chestnut, is frequent as a planted tree that occasionally seeds itself in woodland. Absent from Scilly.

BALSAMINACEAE
IMPATIENS L.

171/4 § **I. glandulifera** Royle   Indian Balsam
This handsome plant has rapidly increased since it was first recorded in the county at the turn of the century, and is now a feature of the larger rivers of E Cornwall. It is still widely grown as a garden plant, and occurs frequently as an escape. Absent from Scilly.

AQUIFOLIACEAE
ILEX L.

176/1 **I. aquifolium** L., Holly, is common and widely distributed in the county on hedgebanks and in woods. Doubtfully native in Scilly.

CELASTRACEAE
EUONYMUS L.

177/1 **E. europaeus** L., Spindle, is widespread and frequent in the East, less so in W Cornwall, and absent from West Penwith and Scilly.

RHAMNACEAE
RHAMNUS L.

[179/1 **R. catharticus** L., Buckthorn, was rejected by Davey (Flora) as an obvious mistake, a decision with which we entirely agree.]

148

FRANGULA MILLER

180/1 **F. alnus** Miller   Alder Buckthorn
(*Rhamnus frangula* L.)

Widely distributed E of Hayle and Helston, but never common.

West: 62, Loe Pool (Flora), Penrose Woods, 1959–77, J.Fo.; 72, Gweek (Flora), still there, post–1950, R.H.; Rosevean, Mawgan, R.H.; Merthen Wood, J.F.A.; 73, Devichoys Wood, R.Go.; 74, Carrine Common, R.H.; Tregavethan, near Truro, L.J.M.; Helston Water, Bissoe, W.D.W. (Thurston 1928); 85, Newlyn East (Flora), on Newlyn East Downs, 1970, CNT.

East: 96, Goss Moor, N.J.F.; 05, Luxulyan (Flora), two bushes, 1979, E.A. and E.W.M.; 06, Foxpark, near Red Moor, J.F.A.; Halgavor Plantation, Lanhydrock, E.A.; Dunmere Forest, E.A.; W of Lanivet, E.A.; Withiel (Flora), Retire Common, 1977, L.J.M.; 07, Shell Woods, E.A.; 16, near Glynn Bridge, L.J.M.; 28, Red Down, Egloskerry, L.J.M.; 37, between Golberdon and Caradon Town, I.N.; Luckett, and between there and Latchley, I.N.; wood near Trecoombe, Stoke Climsland, I.N.; 36, between Pillaton and St Mellion, I.N.; Clapper Bridge (Flora), 1966, I.N.; 46, Halton Quay, E.G.; Danescombe Valley, Calstock, I.N.; near Cleave, St Dominick, I.N.; 47, Albaston, I.N.; by the Tamar near Gunnislake, I.N.

VITACEAE
PARTHENOCISSUS PLANCHON

182/2 § **Parthenocissus** sp.   Virginia Creeper

Now naturalised in a number of localities, mostly on old ruins. The following have not been critically examined, but some, if not all, may belong to the next species.

West: 64, Tregajorran, near Carn Brea, L.J.M.; 74, several clumps along road to Chacewater Station, 1965, L.J.M.; 75, Trevaunance Coombe, St Agnes, L.J.M.

East: 38, old railway, Launceston, L.J.M.; Torpoint, 1971, S.M.

§ **P. inserta** (A. Kerner) Fritsch

West: 53, near Carnsew Spit, Hayle, L.J.M.; 74, roadside, near Silverwell Moor, 1965, L.J.M.

TILIACEAE
TILIA L.

162/2 § **T. x vulgaris** Hayne   Lime
x 1   Frequent and widespread in the more wooded parts of the county, but always recorded as planted, though it does produce some viable seed, and may occur as a self-sown tree.

MALVACEAE
MALVA L.

163/2 **M. sylvestris** L., Common Mallow, is frequent and widespread throughout Cornwall.

163/1 **M. moschata** L.   Musk Mallow
Locally frequent, except in the extreme West.
West: 62, Porthleven, H.B.S.; 61 or 62, between the Lizard and Helston (Flora), still there, post—1950, J.G.T.; 63, Godolphin, H.B.S.; 64, Portreath, S.B.; 72, Rosemullion Head, L.J.M.; Durgan, Herb. Tech. Coll.; 74, United Mines, Gwennap, L.J.M.; 75, Penhale Sands, C.J.; 87, near Porthcothan, J.A.P.; 97, Padstow (Flora), between Tregirls and Stepper Point, 1972, L.G.; quarry near Sea Mills, 1966, J.A.P.; Little Petherick (Flora), 1976, B.B.
East: 83, St Anthony, Herb. Tech. Coll.; 94, Tregidgeo, near Kestle, and near Polmassick, St Ewe, D.B.; 95, St Dennis Junction, B.B.; 05, mine-waste E of St Blazey, J.A.P.; 15, Lansallos, J.A.P.; Lantic Bay, R.W.D. and L.J.M.; 25, Polperro (Flora), between there and Talland, M.M.P. (Thurston 1930); 26, Liskeard (Flora), railway near Liskeard, 1966, J.L.; 28, railway, Egloskerry, L.J.M.; 35, Antony (Flora), 1966, S.M.; Seaton, S.M.; Polbathic (Flora), still there, post—1950, S.M.; Trerulefoot, S.M.; 36, Landrake (Flora), still there, S.M.; Tilland, near Tideford Cross, S.M.; Hatt, S.M.; near Trematon, D.B.; 38, Launceston (Flora), 1971, N.J.F.; 39, R Tamar, NE of Boyton, J.A.P.; 45, Millbrook (Flora), 1966, S.M.; 46, Landulph (Flora), 1966, J.A.P.; St Dominick (Flora), 1971, N.J.F.
Scilly: rare, Lousley 1971.

The white-flowered form is found at

West: 74, United Mines, Gwennap, L.J.M.

East: 94, near Grampound, K.H.J.; 17, Bolventor, L.J.M.

163/5 § **M. pusilla** Sm. Small Mallow

Nearly always associated with old mills, now extremely rare.

West: 62, by derelict mill between Gweek and Helston, R.H. (*Proc. B.S.B.I.*, **3**: 398); 75, Goonhavern 1926, Herb. F.H. Perrycoste, (TRU); Perranporth Gliding School, B.M.S.

Scilly: Lousley 1971.

163/4 **M. neglecta** Wallr. Dwarf Mallow

(*M. rotundifolia* auct.)

Now very rare in Cornwall.

West: 32, Treen, J.B.; 33, St Just (Flora), Boswallas Moor, 1972, M.C.; near St Just, 1966, J.A.P.

East: 45, St Stephens, Saltash (Flora), till 1960, I.N.; Torpoint, habitat destroyed in 1971, S.M.

Scilly: common, Lousley 1971.

LAVATERA L.

164/1 **L. arborea** L., Tree-mallow, is widespread and frequent around the entire coastline.

164/2 **L. cretica** L. Cretan Mallow

Locally frequent in Scilly, but extremely rare and sporadic on the mainland.

West: 72, Gillan Creek, Helford River, 1978, R.M.B.

East: 84, waste ground by Boscawen Park, Truro, E.S.T. (Thurston and Vigurs 1924).

Scilly: frequent, Lousley 1971.

ALTHAEA L.

[165/1 **A. officinalis** L., Marsh-mallow. Davey (Flora) dismisses three early records as mistakes, and as there are no voucher specimens, and no subsequent records, we must remove this plant from the Cornish list.]

THYMELAEACEAE

DAPHNE L.

251/2 **D. laureola** L. Spurge-laurel

Very rare, most of the records being bird-introductions.

West: 61, Penhale, Lizard, E.J.P. (Thurston 1928); 64, three plants in roadside thicket, Bridge, near Portreath, L.J.M.; 86 (76), Crantock, B.M.S.; 97, three plants near Trevone, E.A.; a few bushes, old railway, Wadebridge, CNT.

East: 06, Grogley Halt, C.J.; 15, wood at Pont, Fowey, F.R. (Thurston 1930); 20, Helebridge, near Bude, R.O. (Thurston and Vigurs 1925).

Scilly: one plant, Lousley 1971.

ELAEAGNACEAE

HIPPOPHAE L.

252/1 § **H. rhamnoides** L. Sea-buckthorn

Originally introduced, now gradually increasing.

West: 53, Phillack Towans, 1923, T.J.P. (Thurston and Vigurs 1924), still there, various recorders; Upton Towans, J.B.; near St Erth Station (Flora), 1949, J.B.; 86 (76), Newquay (Flora), still there, 1972, L.G.

East: 97, Daymer Bay, Camel Estuary, E.A.; 04, Gribben Head (Suppt), 1951—54, J.B., 1977, B.B.

GUTTIFERAE

HYPERICUM L.

Common species: 115/4 § **H. calycinum** L., Rose-of Sharon (absent from Scilly), 115/1 **H. androsaemum** L., Tutsan (absent from Scilly), 115/11 **H. pulchrum** L., Slender St John's-wort, 115/14 **H. elodes** L., Marsh St John's-wort (very rare in Scilly), 115/9 **H. humifusum** L., Trailing St John's-wort, 115/8 **H. tetrapterum** Fries, Square-stalked St John's-wort (absent from Scilly), and 115/5 **H. perforatum** L., Perforate St John's-wort (absent from Scilly).

115/3 § **H. hircinum** L. Stinking Tutsan

A garden outcast, persistent in places.

West: 73, between Rame and Porkellis, R.W.D.; Council tip, Falmouth, B.E.M.G.; 83, Falmouth, and Swanpool (Flora), still in both places, L.J.M.

East: 05 or 15, roadside near Menabilly, L.T.M. (Thurston 1935, as *H. elatum*).

Scilly: Lousley 1971.

115/13 **H. montanum** L.   Pale St John's-wort

Always extremely rare in Cornwall, this species is still extant in one of its old localities, and has been recently found in a new station.

West: 53, railway between Lelant and Carbis Bay (Flora), refound in 1948, J.B., two plants, 1978, L.J.M.

East: 45, a few plants by the main railway line at Wearde, Saltash, 1979, E.G.   This is across the creek from the old site at Antony.

115/10 **H. linarifolium** Vahl   Flax-leaved St John's-wort

Now restricted to a few localities in Britain; the following new record is therefore of special importance. In our opinion, all previous records for the county were mistakes for forms of *H. humifusum*, which is variable.

*East: 07, very abundant on rocky slopes of railway cutting near Sladesbridge, 1978, B.E.M.G.

115/7 **H. undulatum** Schousboe ex Willd. Wavy St John's-wort

Still frequent and widespread in marshes throughout the county, but in view of its limited distribution in Britain as a whole, we are listing all post—Supplement localities.

West: 32, moors near the Lands End (Flora), Skewjack Moor, 1966, R.W.D. and L.J.M.; 42, near Boscawen, Lamorna, J.S.R.; Kemyel, near Mousehole, 1948, J.B.; Clodgy Moor, Sheffield, near Paul, CNT; Kerris, G.L.; Chy-an-hal Moor, G.L.; 53, Marazion Marsh (Flora), 1979, L.J.M.; 63, Bolenowe Valley, near Troon, L.J.M.; 64, Red River Valley, R.J.M. and L.J.M.; 71, Crousa Downs, J.A.P.; 72, Gweek, R.H.; Penryn, R.H.; 73, Mabe (Flora), 1979, L.J.M.; Falmouth (Flora), Tregenver, and Swanvale, 1961, L.J.M.; 74, Gwennap (Flora), Trevince Moor, 1966, L.J.M.; Allet Bog, G.A. and J.B.; 75, Ventongimps Moor (Flora), 1964, G.A. and J.B.; Goonhavern, J.A.P.

East: 83, St Anthony, L.J.M.; 84, Fentongollan, B.E.M.G.; 94, Paramoor Wood, Sticker, L.J.M.; 95, between Ladock and Brighton, L.J.M.; 96, Goss Moor,

J.S.R.; St Breock Downs, J.A.P.; 06, Withiel (Flora), Retire Common, 1977, L.J.M.; 20, New Road Plantation, N of Bude, L.J.M.; 21, Wrasford Moor, J.A.P.; Tamar Lake, O.G.; 28, near Red Down, Egloskerry, J.A.P.; 29, S of Greenamoor Bridge, J.A.P.; 36, between St Mellion and Pillaton (Flora), marshy spot below Pillaton, I.N.; Smeaton Wood, near Pillaton, 1979, E.G.; 46, between Hatt and Kingsmill (Flora), between Stockadon Farm and Kingsmill, I.N.

115/6b **H. maculatum** Crantz   Imperforate St John's-wort
subsp. **obtusiusculum** (Tourlet) Hayek

Rare, or under-recorded. Not refound in any of the stations in the Flora or Suppt.

West: 53, Hayle, B.M.S.

East: 84, near Pencalenick Creek, L.J.M.; 05, in three places near Tywardreath, W.T. (Thurston 1928); 21, roadside, Coombe, near Bude, L.J.M.; Tamar Lake, J.G.D. and C.D.; 26, in three places near Liskeard, D.B.; 29, Greenamoor Bridge, L.J.M.; 35, Seaton, 1924, F.H.P., Herb. F.H. Perrycoste, (TRU); 36, lane to Patheda Wood, Tideford Cross, I.N.; 39, R Tamar near N Tamerton, T.S.S. (Thurston 1935), still there, 1967, L.J.M.

VIOLACEAE

VIOLA L.

Common species: 113/4 **V. riviniana** Reichenb., Common Dog-violet (in a great number of forms, including subsp. **minor** (Murb. ex E.S. Gregory) Valentine), 113/9b **V. palustris** L., subsp. **juressi** (Link ex K. Wein) Coutinho (incorrectly in Suppt as *V. epipsila* Ledeb.), Marsh Violet (absent from Scilly), and 113/13 **V. arvensis** Murray, Field Pansy.

113/1 **V. odorata** L.   Sweet Violet

The mauve forms that are widespread throughout Cornwall are usually cultivars. The native mauve plant is very rare and not distinguished from these in the following records:

West: 33, St Just, M.C.; 42, near Mousehole, J.S.R.; 43, Gulval (Flora), 1971, B.M.S.; 53, Gwinear, J.S.R.; 61, between Poltesco and Carleon, H.B.S.; Polurrian

Cove, K.P.; 62, Bonython Plantations, Mullion, J.A.P.; 63, near Gwinear, J.S.R.; Crowan, J.S.R.; 64, Portreath, J.S.R.; 72, near Mawnan, J.S.R.; 75, Trevellas, R.W.D.; 83, near Devoran, J.S.R.

East: 97, St Minver (Flora), in many places near Polzeath, 1950—79, R.W.D.; 05, Tregrehan Mill, near St Austell, W.T. (Thurston 1929); 16, Braddock Church, J.A.P.; 25, Morval, near Looe, J.A.P.; 28, Coombshead, Lewannick, J.A.P.

Scilly: Lousley 1971.

var. **dumetorum** (Jord.) Rouy & Fouc.   White Violet
(forma *alba* Lange)

This variety is undoubtedly native.

West: 64, Nancemellin, near Gwithian, L.J.M.; 84, Cowlands, near Truro, J.A.P.; near Nancevallon Wood, Truro, W.H.F. (Thurston 1935).

East: 08 (09), Forrabury, Boscastle, L.J.M.; 26, S of Liskeard, D.B.

Scilly: Lousley 1971.

var. **sulfurea** (Car.) Rouy & Fouc.

West: 43, near Castle-an-Dinas, Gulval, E.A.R. (Thurston 1935).

113/2a **V. hirta** L., subsp. **hirta**   Hairy Violet

Not the common plant it is in Eastern counties, but usually on fixed dunes.

West: 53, Carbis Bay (Flora), between there and Lelant, 1966, L.J.M.; (54), Godrevy Towans, L.J.M.; 61, Kynance (Flora), still there, post—1950, J.A.P.; 64, Porthtowan (Flora), 1963, L.J.M.; 75, Penhale Sands (Flora), 1961 onwards, L.J.M.; Cubert Common, L.J.M.; 86 (76), Crantock (Flora), 1979, K.H.; 87, Constantine Bay, L.J.M.

East: 97, St Enodoc (Flora), Rock Dunes, 1979, R.W.D.; 07, railway W of St Mabyn, J.A.P.; St Kew (Flora), 1971, L.J.M.; Castle Killibury, near Wadebridge (Suppt), still there, post—1950, J.A.P.; 20, Widemouth Bay, J.A.P.; 25, near Duloe, D.B.; 26, in three places near Liskeard, D.B.; near St Ive, D.B.; in two places near Cadsonbury, D.B.; N of Trematon, and Paynters Cross, D.B.

113/2b subsp. **calcarea** (Bab) E.F. Warburg
Rare, and only on fixed dunes.
West: 53 (54), Godrevy Towans, R.J.M. and L.J.M.;
64, Porthtowan (Flora), still there, 1950 onwards,
L.J.M.; 75, Penhale Sands (Flora), 1961 onwards,
L.J.M.
East: 97, St Enodoc (Flora), 1979, R.W.D.

113/5 **V. reichenbachiana** Jordan ex Boreau   Early Dog-violet
Extremely rare and local. All mainland records except
the following probably relate to forms of *V. riviniana.*
East: 46, Cotehele (Flora), refound, 1967, I.N.; two
clumps, Morden Mill, near Cotehele, 1973, I.N.
Scilly: Lousley 1971; the Scilly populations need
further study, and may well prove to be dark-spurred
forms of *V. riviniana,* such as occur on the mainland.

113/5 **V. reichenbachiana x riviniana**
x 4   *East: 46, Cotehele, with both parents, 1967, I.N. The
sole station.

113/6 **V. canina** L., subsp. **canina**   Heath Dog-violet
Rare, but much over-recorded in Cornwall, the majority
of the records being referable to *V. lactea x riviniana.*
The following are the only reliable records:
West: 53, Carbis Bay, B.M.S.; 72, Rosemullion Head,
L.J.M.; 75, Penhale Sands, L.J.M.; 87, Constantine
Bay, W.G.
Scilly: Lousley 1971.

113/7 **V. lactea** Sm.   Pale Dog-violet
Still frequent and widespread on heathland throughout
the county, and especially characteristic of maritime
heaths.
West: 32, Lands End (Flora), between there and
Sennen, 1977, W.R.H.; Nanjulian cliffs, M.C.; 33,
Botallack, M.C.; 52, Rinsey Head, RNHS; 53, Marazion
Marsh, J.B.; 61, N of Kynance, J.A.P.; near Ruan Pool,
J.Fo.; Goonhilly Reserve, S.T. *et al;* N of Penhale, the
Lizard, J.A.P.; 63, between Crowan and Black Rock,
J.B.; 64, Portreath (Flora), 1972, L.J.M.; Porthtowan
(Flora), 1976, L.J.M.; 71, E of Kennack, J.Fo.; Goon-
hilly Downs, E.A.; 72, Gweek, R.H.; 73, Stithians

(Flora), 1962, L.J.M.; 74, Gwennap (Flora), still there, post—1950, L.J.M.; Mt Hawke, L.J.M.; Carrine Common, L.J.M.; railway between Perranwell and Truro, L.J.M.; 75, St Agnes cliffs, L.J.M.; 85, Newlyn Downs, E.T. (Thurston and Vigurs 1925).

East: 95, between Sticker and Coombe, L.J.M.; Goss Moor, E.T. (Thurston and Vigurs 1925); 06, Innis Downs, L.J.M.; Red Moor, L.J.M.; Retire Common, L.J.M.; 16, between Cardinham and Panters Bridge (Flora), Cardinham, 1963, E.A.; 19, between Otterham and Collamoor Head, J.A.P.; 26, St Cleer (Flora), 1966, J.L.; 29, Greena Moor (Flora), post—1950, R.W.D.; 36, Cadsonbury (Flora), 1965, J.A.P.; Kit Hill, 1923, E.T. (Thurston and Vigurs 1924), 1970, L.J.M.; Hingston Down (Flora), 1950 onwards, R.W.D.

Scilly: rejected, Lousley 1971.

113/7 **V. lactea x riviniana**
x 4 This small neat plant, with Cambridge-blue flowers and yellow spurs, occurs throughout Cornwall, and is often wrongly recorded as *V. canina*. It is amazingly constant in morphological characters, and is often subfertile. Records of *V. lactea* var. *pumiliformis* Rouy & Fouc., *V. canina x lactea*, and *V. canina x riviniana* probably all belong here.

West: 32, Nanquidno, W.R.H.; Porthgwarra, W.R.H.; 43, Georgia, near Nancledra, P.J.R.; near Wicca Pool, Zennor, L.J.M.; 52, Rinsey Head, R.G.; 63, mine-waste near Troon, L.J.M.; 64, Gilberts Coombe, Redruth, L.J.M.; Connor Downs, L.J.M.; Hells Mouth, L.J.M.; Greenbank Cove, N Cliffs, L.J.M.; Porthtowan, L.J.M.; 71, Brays Cot, Lizard, R.P. and J.M.M.; Lizard, G.C.D. (Thurston 1935); 85, Newlyn Downs, E.T. (Thurston and Vigurs 1925).

East: 19, Tresparrett Down, 1923, T.N.S.P. (Thurston and Vigurs 1924); 28, Laneast Downs, L.J.M.; 37, Kit Hill, 1923, E.T. (Thurston and Vigurs 1924).

[113/ **V. lutea** Hudson, Mountain Pansy, was correctly rejected
11 for Cornwall, in our opinion.]

113/ **V. tricolor** L., subsp. **tricolor**   Wild Pansy
12a Very local and rare.

West: 32 or 33, Kelynack, B.M.S.; 43, Gulval, B.M.S.;

74, Council tip, Bissoe, B.E.M.G.

East: 93, Portloe, M.E.B.; 26, S of Liskeard, D.B.; 36, N of Trematon, D.B.

Scilly: Lousley 1971; M, between Newford House and the pond, 1973, L.A.H.

113/ 12b subsp. **curtisii** (E. Forster)Syme   Seaside Pansy

Extremely rare.

West: 32, Sennen, F.J.H. (Thurston 1928); 71, between the Lizard lighthouse and the coast (Flora), refound 1954, R.W.D., the only extant station.

113/13 x 12a **V. arvensis x tricolor**

East: 38, Launceston, B.Sh. 1960.

113/14 **V. kitaibeliana** Schultes   Dwarf Pansy

(*V. arvensis* var. *nana* DC.)

Only in the Isles of Scilly.

Scilly: local and rare, Lousley 1971.

[CISTACEAE   118/3 **Helianthemum canum** (L.) Baumb., Hoary Rock-rose, was rightly rejected by Davey (Flora). No member of this genus occurs here.]

TAMARICACEAE

TAMARIX L.

120/2   § T. **gallica** L. (incl. *T. anglica* Webb)   Tamarisk

Frequent and widespread as a planted windbreak in coastal areas, rarely self-sown.

ELATINACEAE

ELATINE L.

122/1   E. **hexandra** (Lapierre) DC.   Six-stamened Waterwort

In a few scattered stations throughout the county.

West: 62, Loe Pool (Flora), still plentiful there, 1968, T.M. and L.J.M.; Coronation Lake, Helston, L.J.M.; 73, pond, Budock Bog, near Falmouth, L.J.M.

East: 17, abundant in Dozmary Pool, 1953, R.W.D.; 21, Tamar Lake, D.H.

Scilly: Lousley 1971.

LYTHRACEAE
LYTHRUM L.

249/1 **L. salicaria** L., Purple Loosestrife, and 250/1 **L. portula** (L.) D.A. Webb (*Peplis portula* L.), Water Purslane, are both frequent and widespread in Cornwall.

250/1 **L. portula** var. **longidentata** Gay
West: 63, Newton Moor, Troon, L.J.M.; Porkellis Moor, L.J.M.; 73, Stithians Reservoir, L.J.M.; 85, Penhallow Moor, L.J.M.
East: 95, Goss Moor, CNT.
Scilly: T, Middle Down, 1975, D.E.A.

ONAGRACEAE
FUCHSIA L.

257/1 § **F. magellanica** Lam.   Fuchsia
(*F. riccartoni* auct.)

This popular hedging shrub is gradually increasing as a garden throw-out.
West: 33, Kenidjack Valley, and Cot Valley, St Just, M.C.; 42, cliffs at Lamorna Cove, R.L.G.L.; cliffs near Mousehole, J.S.R.; 43, Zennor (Flora), 1946, onwards, J.B.; near Gulval, B.M.S.; 52, NW of Rinsey Head, R.G.; 63, Porkellis Moor, L.J.M.
East: 05, near Charlestown, J.A.P.; Porthpean, B.Sh.; 25, near Looe, J.A.P.; 45, in two places at Torpoint, S.M.; (44), near Rame Church, S.M.
Scilly: Lousley 1971; M, J.A.P.

cv. 'Molinae'
East: 04, near Trenarren, B.E.M.G. and L.J.M.

var. **gracilis** Lindley
West: 64, Redruth Coombe, L.J.M.; 85, Newlyn East Downs, L.J.M.

CIRCAEA L.

258/1 **C. lutetiana** L., Enchanter's-nightshade, is common and widespread as a woodland plant. Also in hedges and gardens.

forma **cordifolia** Lasch
West: 62, Loe Pool, A.B.

OENOTHERA L.

256/2 § **O. erythrosepala** Borbas, Large-flowered Evening-primrose, is quite common on the mainland on waste ground, but rather local in Scilly.

256/1 § **O. biennis** L.   Common Evening-primrose
Once the more frequent species, now very rare.
West: 53, Marazion (Flora), until 1964, B.M.S.; Lelant Towans, A.T. (Thurston 1935); 74, Carrine Common, R.H.; 75, mine-waste, Chyverton, G.A.; 86, Newquay, 1931, G.C.D. (Thurston 1935); 87, Constantine Bay, W.G.
East: 97, Rock (Flora), 1966, J.A.P.; 20, Bude, L.J.M.

256/3 § **O. stricta** Ledeb. ex Link   Fragrant Evening-primrose
(*O. odorata* auct.)
Rare, but persistent on dunes.
West: 53, Upton Towans, L.J.M.; 71, Coverack, 1910, H.E.F. (Thurston 1929a); 75, Perranporth, on edge of dunes, L.J.M.; 85, Council tip, Newlyn East, L.J.M.
East: 20, Bude (B.E.C. 1940), 1960, B.Sh.

EPILOBIUM L.

Common species: 255/1 E. **angustifolium** L., Rosebay Willowherb (absent from Scilly), 254/1 E. **hirsutum** L., Great Willowherb, 254/2 E. **parviflorum** Schreber, Hoary Willowherb, 254/3 E. **montanum** L., Broad-leaved Willowherb, 254/4 E. **lanceolatum** Sebastiani and Mauri, Spear-leaved Willowherb (absent from Scilly), 254/7 E. **tetragonum** L., subsp. **tetragonum**, Square-stalked Willowherb, 254/9 E. **obscurum** Schreber, Short-fruited Willowherb, and 254/10 E. **palustre** L., Marsh Willowherb.

254/1 **E. hirsutum x parviflorum** = *E. x subhirsutum* Genn.
x 2   Recorded for East (Flora).   No subsequent records.

254/3 **E. montanum x obscurum** = *E. x aggregatum* Čelak
x 9   Recorded for East (Flora).   No subsequent records.

254/4 **E. lanceolatum x montanum** = *E. x neogradiense* Borbás
x 3   West: 83, Falmouth, 1911 (B.E.C. 1936).
East: 25, Polperro, 1924 (B.E.C. 1936).

254/4 **E. lanceolatum x obscurum** = *E. x lamotteanum* Hausskn.
x 9   Recorded for East (Flora). No subsequent records.

254/8 **E. tetragonum**
       subsp. **lamyi** (F.W. Schultz) Nyman
                                        Southern Willowherb
       West: River Fal, 1907, E.D. and H.D. (Thurston
       1935), exact station and square unknown.
       Scilly: Lousley 1971.

254/5 **E. roseum** Schreber   Pale Willowherb
       Slightly increased since the Flora, but still very local and
       rare.
       West: 62, Porthleven, H.B.S.; 64, roadside, South
       Tehidy, Camborne, L.J.M.; 72, tan-bark alien in garden,
       Helford Passage, L.J.M.; 83, Falmouth (Flora), a few
       plants, 1962, L.J.M.
       East: 94, St Ewe village, R.W.D.; 15, by bridge,
       Lerryn, near Lostwithiel, L.J.M.; 38, garden weed,
       Launceston, T.N.S.P. (Thurston 1935); 45, Saltash, I.N.;
       46, old quarry near Cotehele Quay, I.N.

254/10 **E. palustre x parviflorum** = *E. x rivulare* Wahlenb.
x 2   Recorded for East (Flora). No subsequent records.

254/6 § **E. ciliatum** Raf., subsp. **ciliatum** American Willowherb
       = *E. adenocaulon* Hausskn.
       *First recorded for Cornwall during the Mapping Scheme,
       1950 onwards, that culminated in the *Atlas of the
       British Flora*, this alien has since spread rapidly, and is
       now probably the most common willowherb of waste
       ground in the county.
       *Scilly: M, Star Castle, 1975, D.E.A.; Hugh Town,
       1975, D.E.A.; T, Old Grimsby, 1975, D.E.A.

254/6 **E. ciliatum x parviflorum**
x 2   West: 73, marsh near Mabe, 1979, L.J.M.
       East: 06, Bodmin, near the Industrial Estate, 1979,
       R.W.D. and L.J.M.

254/6 **E. ciliatum x montanum**
x 3   An increasingly found hybrid.
       West: 63, Upper Grillis, near Four Lanes, L.J.M.; 64,
       Tehidy Woods, Camborne, CNT; 73, near the viaduct,

Penryn, 1963, L.J.M.; 74, Carn Marth, Redruth, R.J.M. and L.J.M.

254/6 **E. ciliatum x lanceolatum**
x 4 East: 16, Bodmin Road Station, 1963, L.J.M.

254/6 **E. ciliatum x roseum**
x 5 West: 62, Porthleven, 1964, H.B.S.

254/6 **E. ciliatum x tetragonum** subsp. **tetragonum**
x 7 West: 73, near Carnmenellis Chapel, 1979, L.J.M.

254/6 **E. ciliatum x palustre**
x 10 West: 63, Porkellis Moor, 1968, L.J.M.

254/13 **E. brunnescens** (Cockayne) Raven and Engelhorn
New Zealand Willowherb
subsp. **brunnescens** = *E. nerterioides* A. Cunn.

This prostrate willowherb was first recorded in Cornwall during the Mapping Scheme, 1950 onwards, and has since then rapidly colonised waste ground, mine-waste, china clay tips, and old walls.

*West: 33, clayworks E of St Just, J.A.P.; 43, Gulval, B.M.S.; Ludgvan, G.W.; 53, Carbis Bay, B.M.S.; 64, Brea Village, near Camborne, L.J.M.; Rosewarne Carpark, Camborne, J.S.R.; 73, Swanvale, Falmouth, 1961, L.J.M.; 74, United Mines, Gwennap, L.J.M.; 75, Treamble, near Perranporth, J.A.P.; 83, Falmouth, R.M.P.; 86, W of harbour, Newquay, B.B.

*East: 94, Demonstration Garden, Probus, L.J.M.; 95, near Indian Queens, RNHS; St Stephen, J.A.P.; Trerice, near St Dennis, L.G.; Goss Moor, CNT; Nanpean, J.A.P.; 05, Bugle, L.J.M.; St Austell, L.J.M., 1962; Carvear Moor, B.E.M.G.; 06, Dunmere Forest, E.A.; 07, Shell Woods, Helland, E.A.; 16, Cardinham Woods, B.B.; Deerpark Wood, Herodsfoot, S.M.; 25, Trenant, Looe, E.G.; 26, near Caradon, I.N.; 36, Holwood Quarry, Pillaton, E.G.

HALORAGACEAE
GUNNERA L.

260/1 § **G. tinctoria** (Molina) Mirbel
More or less naturalised where thrown out of gardens.
*West: 32, Porthcurno, N.J.F.; 62, Porthleven, 1964,

H.B.S.; 72, The Hutches, near Rosemullion Head, L.J.M.; 84, by stream, Truro, L.J.M.

*East: 06, Lanivet, B.Sh.; 08, Trebarwith, 1959, B.Sh.

MYRIOPHYLLUM L.

[259/ M. verticillatum L., Whorled Water-milfoil, was recorded
1 in the past from both West and East, but these records were dismissed by Davey (Flora), and since there have been no further records, we must remove the species from the couhty list.]

259/4 **M. alterniflorum** DC.   Alternate Water-milfoil

Frequent and widespread in the West, but rather rare in East Cornwall.

West: 42, boating lake, Penzance, G.B.M.; 53, Marazion Marsh (Flora), 1949, J.B.; Gwithian Marsh, L.J.M.; 61, near Penhale, the Lizard (Suppt), 1966, J.A.P.; Ruan Pool, and Hayle Kimbro Pool, J.Fo.; 63, Porkellis Moor (Flora), 1964, L.J.M.; 64, Pendarves Lake, S.T.; 71, Lizard (Flora), 1971, LFC; between Goonhilly Downs and Traboe (Suppt), Croft Pascoe Pool, 1971, LFC; 72, Leech Pool, J.A.P.; Crousa Common, J.Fo.; 73, Penryn Reservoirs (Flora), still there, 1950 onwards, L.J.M.

East: 05, Walden Pond, W of St Blazey, J.A.P.; 06, Red Moor, L.J.M.; 18, R Camel near Camelford, E.A.; 21, Tamar Lake, D.H.; 27, Trebartha, and Northill, S.M.; 38, Launceston (Flora), 1966, J.A.P.

Scilly: Lousley 1971.

259/2 **M. spicatum** L.   Spiked Water-milfoil

Less frequent than the preceding species, and preferring less acid conditions.

West: 53, Winnard Mill, Hayle River, CRNHS; millpond, Hayle, J.B.; 75, Carnkief Pond (Flora), 1976, L.J.M.

East: 95, Goss Moor (Flora), 1968, J.B.; 07 or 17, De Lank River near St Breward, R.W.D.; 20, Bude Canal (Flora), 1972, L.J.M.; 21, Tamar Lake, J.G.D. and C.D.; 38, St Stephens, Launceston, post—1950, BRC.

CORNACEAE
CORNUS L.
265/1   **C. sanguinea** L.   Dogwood
Only in East Cornwall. Frequent in the Tamar Estuary.
East: 15, between Trenewan and Lansallos, originally
planted, F.H.P. (Thurston and Vigurs 1927); 35, quarries
SW of Trematon, J.A.P., Sheviock (Flora), Trethill
Wood, 1966, S.M., St. Erney, near St Germans, L.J.M.;
Landrake (Flora), Poldrissick, 1966, I.N.; 45, Saltash
(Flora), frequent around Saltash, I.N.; St Johns (Flora),
still there, I.N., two plants, Mt Edgcumbe, E.G.; 46,
Cargreen, I.N.; Botusfleming, and between there and
Moditonham, I.N., Landulph (Flora), still plentiful,
I.N.

ARALIACEAE
HEDERA L.
H. hibernica (Kirchner) Bean, Irish Ivy, the tetraploid,
appears to be the only species in Cornwall. It is very
common and widespread throughout the county in a
variety of habitats.

UMBELLIFERAE
HYDROCOTYLE L.
269/1   **H. vulgaris** L., Marsh Pennywort, is common and widely
distributed in marshy places.

SANICULA L.
270/1   **S. europaea** L., Sanicle, is a frequent plant of woodland
in Mid and East Cornwall, but becoming rare in the
West, and absent from West Penwith and Scilly.

ERYNGIUM L.
272/1   **E. maritimum** L.   Sea-holly
On sandy beaches. Frequent, and still in most of its
old localities.
West: 32, Whitsand Bay (Flora), 1967, L.J.M.; 43,
between Marazion and Penzance (Flora), Long Rock,
1964, G.L.; Eastern Green, Penzance, G.B.M.; 53,
Marazion, B.M.S.; Carnsew Spit, Hayle, L.B.; Phillack
Towans (Flora), one plant, 1977, L.J.M.; 62, Gunwalloe
(Flora), 1964, G.L.; Loe Pool (Flora), Loe Bar, 1960,

H.B.S.; 64, Portreath, L.J.M.; Porthtowan (Flora), 1968,
J.B.; 75, Holywell Bay (Flora), 1967, A.B.; 86 (76),
Cubert, K.H.; 87, Porthcothan (Flora), 1964, T.H.A.;
Constantine Bay, W.G.

East: 83, Pendower Beach (Flora), one plant, 1969,
B.E.M.G.; 94, Hemmick Beach (Flora), 1954, J.B.; 97,
Old Polzeath, 1940, now gone, R.W.D.; Daymer Bay,
R.W.D.; 05, Par (Flora), 1957, B.Sh.; 20, Bude (Flora),
still there, post—1950, D.H.; 35, Tregantle, S.M.

Scilly: Lousley 1971.

272/2 **E. campestre** L.   Field Eryngo
Now all but extinct in Cornwall.

East: 97, Polzeath, 1980, comm. B.E.M.G.; 05, Par
(Flora), still there, 1934 (Thurston 1935), and last seen,
1950, R.W.D.; 15, c six plants between Fowey and
Tregaminion Church, Polkerris, M.E.M. (Thurston 1935).

CHAEROPHYLLUM L.

273/1 **C. temulentum** L., Rough Chervil, is frequent throughout the county but absent from Scilly.

ANTHRISCUS PERS.

274/2 **A. sylvestris** (L.) Hoffm., Cow Parsley, is a common and
widely distributed plant of roadsides.

274/1 **A. caucalis** Bieb.   Bur Chervil
Rather local, and always by the coast.

West: 32, Brew Moor, Sennen, 1949, S.B.; 53, Hayle
Towans (Suppt), Phillack Towans, 1950 onwards,
B.M.S.; Gwithian, R.H.; 75, Perranporth (Flora), still
there, post—1950, B.M.S.; 86, Mawgan Porth, J.A.P.;
87, Constantine Bay, L.J.M.; Trevone, T.H.A.

East: 97, Rock (Flora), Daymer Bay, 1959, E.A.;
Pentire Peninsula, R.W.D.

Scilly: Lousley 1971.

SCANDIX L.

275/1 **S. pecten-veneris** L.   Shepherd's-needle
Once a frequent weed of cultivation, now almost
extinct.

West: 86 (76), Porth Joke, J.A.P., 1978, B.B.

Scilly: rare, Lousley 1971.

SMYRNIUM L.

280/1 § **S. olusatrum** L., Alexanders, is a common plant of roadsides in coastal areas.

CONOPODIUM KOCH

293/1 **C. majus** (Gouan) Loret, Pignut, is widespread and common in old pastures and by roadsides.

PIMPINELLA L.

294/1 **P. saxifraga** L., Burnet-saxifrage, is frequent, though rarely in quantity, on hedgebanks. Mostly in E Cornwall, rare in West Penwith and Scilly.

294/2 **P. major** (L.) Hudson   Greater Burnet-saxifrage
Extremely local in the Lower Tamar area.
East: 35, Wivelscombe (Flora), still there, 1966, I.N.; 45, between Wiggle and Millbrook (Flora), still there, post—1950, I.N.; in churchyard, St Stephens, Saltash, 1966, I.N.

AEGOPODIUM L.

295/1 § **A. podagraria** L., Ground-elder, is a common and widespread introduction in gardens, roadbanks, and waste places.

BERULA KOCH

297/1 **B. erecta** (Hudson) Coville   Lesser Water-parsnip
(*Sium erectum* Huds.)
Now very rare, but possibly overlooked in mistake for *Apium nodiflorum.*
West: 62, Poldhu Cove (Flora), in Poldhu Marsh, 1968, L.J.M.; 75, marsh near the Lost Church, Penhale Sands, 1968, L.J.M.
Scilly: Lousley 1971.

CRITHMUM L.

298/1 **C. maritimum** L., Rock Samphire, is common on cliffs along the entire coastline.

OENANTHE L.

300/5 **O. crocata** L., Hemlock Water-dropwort, is a very common plant of damp places throughout the county.

300/1 **O. fistulosa** L.   Tubular Water-dropwort
Extremely local and rare.
West: 62, Gunwalloe (Flora), still there, 1978, L.J.M.
East: 26, SE of Liskeard, D.B.
Scilly: locally plentiful, Lousley 1971.

300/2 **O. pimpinelloides** L.   Corky-fruited Water-dropwort
Very rare, but still extant in two stations.
West: 53,   Marazion   (Flora),   1971,   B.M.S.;   62,
Gunwalloe (Flora), still there, B.M.S.

300/4 **O. lachenalii** C.C. Gmelin   Parsley Water-dropwort
Frequent in the upper parts of salt-marshes.
West: 53, Carwin Moor, Hayle (Flora), still there,
B.M.S.; Loggans Moor, J.A.P.; Gwithian Marsh, L.J.M.;
62, Poldhu Marsh, L.J.M.; 84, Calenick Creek, W.B.
(Thurston 1935); 86, The Gannel, Newquay (Flora),
1979, K.H.
East: 84, Lamorran, D.R.; 97, Amble (Flora), still
there, R.W.D.; 07, one plant, Egloshayle Marsh, L.T.M.
(Thurston and Vigurs 1925), Sladesbridge, C.C.; 25, E
Looe Valley (Flora), 1966, J.A.P.; 35, Tiddy Estuary,
St Germans, J.A.P.; Erth Island, K.H.; Wivelscombe
(Flora), still there, I.N.; near Poldrissick, Landrake,
I.N.; 45, St Johns (Flora), still there, post—1950, I.N.;
46, Salt Mill, Saltash, I.N.; Salters, Landulph, C.P.H.
(Thurston 1935); Cotehele Quay, I.N.
Scilly: very rare, Lousley 1971.

AETHUSA L.

301/1 **A. cynapium** L., Fool's Parsley, is less common than it
used to be, but there are too many records to justify
listing of localities. Very rare in Scilly.

FOENICULUM MILLER

302/1 **F. vulgare** Miller, Fennel, is frequent and widely distributed in coastal areas.

PHYSOSPERMUM CUSSON

281/1 **P. cornubiense** (L.) DC.   Bladderseed
(*Danaa cornubiensis* Burnat)

Still plentiful in a number of localities from Bodmin to
the Tamar.

East: 06, near Boscerne, between Bodmin and Wadebridge, K.H.J.; Dunmere Forest (Flora), 1963, E.A.; 07,
Pencarrow Wood (Flora), 1961, E.A.; 07 and 17, De
Lank River, 1961, E.A.; 16, Fletchers Bridge, K.H.J.;
wood near Glynn Bridge, L.J.M.; Cardinham (Flora),
wood near Cardinham, K.H.J.; near Respryn Bridge,
comm. E.A.; 16 or 26, St Pinnock (Suppt), still there
(B.E.C. 1924); 36, Amy Down, on road to Tideford,
K.H.J.; Clapper Bridge (Flora), 1966, I.N., *c* 1000
plants, 1979, E.G.; Cadsonbury, J.A.P.; Pillaton, I.N.;
New Down near Clapper Bridge, 'thousands of plants',
E.G.; Crendle Down, St Mellion (Suppt), 1966, I.N.,
1979, E.G.; Hammett Down, Quethiock (Flora), 150
plants, 1979, E.G.; valley between Smeaton Farm and
Sillaton, '*c* 300 plants', E.G.; Pencrebar Wood,
Callington, 1923, H.H.H. (Thurston and Vigurs 1924);
Dupath, Callington (Flora), 1966, I.N.; lane above
Cleave, St Dominick, I.N.; 37, Ashlake Wood, near
Caradon Town, one plant, E.G.; from Clapper Bridge to
Leigh Farm, E.G.; near Harrowbarrow (Flora), Silver
Valley, 'thousands of plants', 1979, E.G.; valley E of
Silver Valley '*c* 600 plants', 1979, E.G.; valley N of
Haye, Callington, 'thousands of plants', E.G.; Luckett,
I.N.; between Luckett and Broadgate, B.E.M.G. and
J.A.P.; 46, Calstock (Flora), still there, post—1950, I.N.;
Harewood (Flora), 1966, I.N., 1979, E.G.; Albeston,
Calstock, K.H.J.; Halton Quay (Flora), 1974, E.G.; 47,
NE end of Hingston Down, E.G.; near Latchley, J.M.W.

CONIUM L.

282/1 **C. maculatum** L., Hemlock, is frequent and widespread
in Cornwall.

BUPLEURUM L.

283/2 **B. rotundifolium** L.   Thorow-wax

A rare casual. The old records may be correct — Davey's
specimen from Malpas Road, Truro, Herb. Davey,
(TRU), is correctly named — but recent records almost

certainly refer to the next species, and those received have been placed there.

West: 53, near filling-station, Loggans Moor, Hayle, G.B.M.; 61, Mullion Village, E.J.P. (Thurston 1935); 62, by new lake, Helston, R.O. (Thurston and Vigurs 1925); 86, Newquay, G.C.D. (Thurston 1935).

East: 84, Malpas Road, Truro (Flora), 1923, A.Gr. (Thurston and Vigurs 1924).

B. lancifolium Hornem.   Narrow Thorow-wax

An increasing bird-seed casual, mainly in gardens.

*West: 42 or 43, Morrab Road, Penzance, comm. G.B.M.; 64, garden, Portreath, K.E.H.; 74, garden, Baldhu School, comm. N.D.W.; 75, garden Polberro, St Agnes, E.We.; church precincts, Perranporth, 1967, A.Bi.

East: 45, waste ground, Torpoint, S.M.; garden, Saltash, I.N.

Scilly: Lousley 1971.

APIUM L.

285/2   A. nodiflorum (L.) Lag., Fool's Water-cress, is abundant throughout the county in ditches, and by streams.

285/1   **A. graveolens** L.   Wild Celery

Frequent in brackish habitats near the sea.

West: 53, Porthminster Beach, St Ives, L.J.M.; Marazion (Flora), 1977, L.J.M.; St Erth, S.B.; near Hayle (Flora), Copperhouse, 1972, CRNHS; 62, Gunwalloe (Flora), 1964, B.M.S.; 71, Lizard (Flora), between Lizard and Cadgwith, J.Fo.; 72, St Anthony-in-Meneage, R.H.; Gweek, R.H.; 86, The Gannel, Newquay, R.L.G.L.; 87, Constantine Bay, W.G.

East: 83, Gerrans (Flora), Froe Creek, 1968, L.J.M.; St Anthony (Flora) 1979, K.H.; Towan Beach, L.J.M.; Porthbean beach, near Portscatho, B.E.M.G.; 84, Ruan Lanihorne, B.E.M.G.; Pencalenick (Flora), 1969, CNT; 97, Amble Marshes (Flora), still there, post—1950, R.W.D.; 04, along Pentewan road, W.T. (Thurston 1935); 20, Widemouth Bay, L.J.M.; Bude (Flora), by canal there, post—1950, L.J.M.; 45, Wilcove (Flora), 1967, S.M.; 46, Halton Quay, I.N.

Scilly: rejected, Lousley 1971.

285/4 **A. inundatum** (L.) Reichenb. fil.   Lesser Marshwort
Rather local, but often in quantity where it does occur.
West: 32, Sennen (Flora), between Sennen and Lands
End, 1966, J.A.P.; Porthgwarra (Suppt), 1978, R.G.; 42,
Paul, B.M.S.; 61, Ruan Pool, J.A.P.; Hayle Kimbro
Pool, E.J.P. (Thurston 1936), 1959–77, J.Fo.; 71,
Goonhilly Downs (Flora), Croft Pascoe Pool, 1962,
L.J.M.; Crousa Downs, J.A.P.; 72, Leech Pool, J.A.P.;
73, Mabe (Flora), in the reservoir, 1979, L.J.M.;
Stithians Reservoir, L.J.M.
East: 95, Goss Moor (Flora), 1954, J.B.; 05, Carbis
Moor, Penwithick, B.E.M.G. and L.J.M.; 06, Red Moor
(Flora), 1963, E.A. and L.J.M.
Scilly: Lousley 1971.

PETROSELINUM HILL

286/1 **P. crispum** (Miller) A.W. Hill   Garden Parsley
(*Carum petroselinum* Benth. & Hook. fil)
Undoubtedly a garden introduction in places, but we
agree with Davey in regarding this species as native in
Cornwall, at least in the Camel Estuary.
West: 32, Nanquidno, B.M.S.; Gwendra, Sennen,
E.S.E. and L.J.M.; 52, St Michaels Mount, J.A.P.; 61,
Mullion (Flora), post—1950, B.M.S.; 71, Cadgwith
(Flora), still there, R.L.G.L.; 86 (76), Crantock (Flora),
1966, J.A.P.; 87, Constantine Bay, L.J.M.; between
Padstow and Harlyn Bay (Flora), Trevone, 1966, J.A.P.;
Park Head, K.H.; 97, Dennis Cove, Padstow, L.J.M.;
lanes N of St Issey, J.A.P.
East: 97, around Pentire Farm, Pentire Peninsula,
R.W.D.; 25, Polperro (Flora), still there, various
recorders; 38, Launceston, G.L.K.
Scilly: Lousley 1971; S, South Hill, 1973, J.Be.

286/2 **P. segetum** (L.) Koch   Corn Parsley
(*Carum segetum* Benth. & Hook. fil.)
Much reduced since the Flora, and now very local.
West: 61, Mullion (Flora), N of Penhale, Mullion,
B.E.M.G. and J.A.P.; 61 or 62, Poldhu, R.H.; 72,
Maenporth, near Mawnan, R.H.
East: 97, Wadebridge (Flora), roadside bank, 1978,
L.J.M. and E.W.; lane at Rock, W.W.M. (Thurston

1935); Pentire Peninsula, R.W.D.; 35, Seaton Valley, L.J.M.

SISON L.

287/1 S. amomum L. Stone Parsley

Local and rare, but very persistent in a few places. West: 53, near Phillack, E.A.R. (Thurston 1930), 1949, S.B.; 84, Truro (Flora), still in two places around Truro, 1979, L.J.M.; 85, near Council tip, Newlyn East, B.E.M.G.

East: 83, Gwendra, Pendower Beach, B.E.M.G.; 84, Lamorran, B.E.M.G.; between Truro and Malpas, W.B. (Thurston 1936); 05, Tregaminion (Flora), near Polkerris, H.W.P. (Thurston 1935), 1954, J.B.; Par (Flora), 1962, L.J.M.; St Blazey, B.M.S.; 20, Bude (Flora), 1971, L.J.M.; 35, one plant, Seaton, E.G.; 46, Landulph (Flora), still there post—1950, I.N.; Cargreen, and Botusfleming, I.N.

FALCARIA FABR.

290/1 § F. vulgaris Bernh. Longleaf

A very rare introduction.

*West: 87, near Trevose Farm, near Trevose Head, two plants, R.W.D.

CARUM L.

291/2 C. carvi L. Caraway

Always sporadic in the county, now apparently gone, the following records being the last:

West: 62, tip, Helston, R.O. (Thurston 1928); 83, Falmouth Docks, R.O. (Thurston 1928).

East: 84, near Boscawen Park, Truro, W.B. (Thurston 1935); 05, Tregorrick, near St Austell, W.T. (Thurston 1935).

291/1 C. verticillatum (L.) Koch Whorled Caraway

Very local, and only in the NE of the county, where it is frequent along the upper reaches of the Tamar.

East: 20, S of Moreton Pound, C.C.; in three places near Launcells Cross, C.C.; near Buttsbear Cross, C.C.; near Bevills Hill, C.C.; 27, East Moor, near Fox Tor, G.L.K. and I.N.; 28, marshy field near Holy Well, St

Clether, I.N.; 29, in seven places near East Balsdon, C.C.; 39, Tamerton (Suppt), in five stations N of N. Tamerton, 1977, C.C.

ANGELICA L.

307/1 **A. sylvestris** L., Wild Angelica, is a common and widespread plant of damp places.

PASTINACA L.

310/1 **P. sativa** L.   Wild Parsnip

Local and rare in Cornwall.

West: 32, Brew Moor, Sennen, B.M.S.; 53, by the Power Station, Hayle, L.J.M.; 71, Church Cove, the Lizard, G.L.

East: 95, on railway ballast, Goss Moor, L.J.M.; 05, Par (Flora), still plentiful, post—1950, B.M.S.; 36, E side of Liskeard, E.G.; 45, Saltash, I.N.; (44), near Rame Church, L.J.M.

Scilly: Lousley 1971.

HERACLEUM L.

311/1 **H. sphondylium** L., Hogweed, is a common and widely distributed plant, present in a number of different habitats.

311/2 § **H. mantegazzianum** Sommier and Levier

Giant Hogweed

A recent introduction from gardens, now spreading.

*West: 33, Cot Valley, St Just, 1974, M.C.; 53, near Angarrack, J.S.E.; 72, Porthousetock, only where planted, J.H.

*East: 26, Liskeard, D.B.; 36, N of Trematon, D.B.; 38, near Launceston, R.C.L.H.; 46, two plants by Tamar below Slimeford, Calstock, 1979, E.G.

TORILIS ADANSON

277/1 **T. japonica** (Houtt.) DC., Upright Hedge-parsley, is a frequent plant of waysides and waste places (doubtfully in Scilly).

277/3 **T. nodosa** (L.) Gaertner   Knotted Hedge-parsley
(*Caucalis nodosa* Scop.)

Now much reduced and very local.

West: 32, Brew Moor, Sennen, B.M.S.; 33, Boscean, near St Just, M.C.; 42, Paul, and Chy-an-hal Moor, B.M.S.; 53, Gwithian, R.H.; 61, between Lizard village and Kynance Cove, H.B.S.; 62, Gunwalloe, R.H.; 71, near Kynance Turn, B.M.S.; 87, Dinas Head, near Padstow, L.J.M.; Stepper Point, Padstow, T.H.A.
East: 97, Pentire (Suppt), 1940, R.W.D.
Scilly: frequent, Lousley 1971.

CAUCALIS L.

278/1 **C. platycarpos** L.   Small Bur-parsley
(*C. daucoides* L.)

This very rare casual is probably extinct in Cornwall. There are no more recent records than the following:

West: 53, Copperhouse, Hayle, R.O. (Thurston and Vigurs 1925).

East: 84, near Boscawen Park, Truro, E.B. (Thurston and Vigurs 1925).

DAUCUS L.

314/1a **D. carota** L., subsp. **carota**, Wild Carrot and 1b subsp. **gummifer** Hooker fil., Sea Carrot (doubtfully in Scilly) are frequent and widespread in suitable habitats.

The following umbellifers were dismissed by Davey (Flora) as mistakes and we have no hesitation in removing them from the Cornish list:

[288/1 **Cicuta virosa** L., Cowbane, 296/1 **Sium latifolium** L., Greater Water-parsnip, 300/3 **Oenanthe silaifolia** Bieb., Narrow-leaved Water-dropwort, 300/6 **Oenanthe aquatica** (L.) Poiret, Fine-leaved Water-dropwort, and 304/1 **Meum athamanticum** Jacq., Spignel.]

PYROLACEAE

MONOTROPA L.

362/1 **M. hypopitys** L.   Yellow Bird's-nest
An obvious introduction here.
*West: 74, Baldhu Plantation (Thurston and Vigurs 1926).

ERICACEAE

ERICA L.

357/1 E. tetralix L., Cross-leaved Heath (absent from Scilly), and **357/4 E. cinerea** L., Bell Heather, are common heathland plants throughout the county.

357/3 E. ciliaris L. Dorset Heath

Remarkably frequent within an area bounded by Redruth, St Agnes, Perranporth, Mitchell, and Truro, with a few scattered outliers. Still in its old stations. West: 42, Chy-an-hal Moor, originally planted by E.A. Rees in 1934, still there, post—1950, J.B.; 53, similarly planted on Marazion Marsh in 1934, E.A.R., not reported since; 71, near Erisey, the Lizard, R.H.; 72, Drytree, Goonhilly, R.H.; E of Gweek, R.H.; 73, Carclew Woods (Flora), still there in 1934 (Thurston 1935); 74, Carrine Common (Flora), still plentiful, various recorders; Chacewater (Flora), still there, J.H.S. (Thurston and Vigurs 1927); Penstraze Moor, P.Ga.; in two places near Tywarnhayle, P.Ga.; Mt Hawke (Flora), S of Mt Hawke, 1961, L.J.M.; Chapel Coombe, Mingoose, L.J.M.; Silverwell Moor (Suppt), still plentiful, various recorders; in two places near Silverwell, P.Ga.; Penwartha House (Suppt), 1954, P.Ga.; Trevaskis, near Tregavethan, P.Ga.; Allet Common (Flora), 1967, G.A.; Tresawsen, P.Ga.; 75, Mithian (Flora), 1965, L.J.M.; Chyverton (Flora), Wentworth Mines, post—1950, B.E.M.G.; Ventongimps Moor, still plentiful, various recorders; Carnkief, 1951, BRC, 1976, L.J.M.; Goonhavern, R.W.D.; 85, Newlyn East Downs (Flora), still plentiful, various recorders; Penhallow Moor, 1954, BRC; 1968, R.G.

*East: 85, SE of Carland Cross, 1956, BRC, 1976, in plenty, B.B.; 05, moorland NE of Bugle, J.A.P.

357/3 E. ciliaris x tetralix = E. x watsonii Benth.
x 1 A frequent hybrid wherever both parents occur.

West: 42, Chy-an-hal Moor, A.C.L. and R.B.; 71, and 72, on both Lizard sites for *E. ciliaris*, P.Tu; 74, Silverwell Moor (Suppt), still there, various recorders; Chacewater, J.H.S. (Thurston and Vigurs 1927); Carrine Common (Flora), still there, 1976, L.J.M.; 75, Goonhavern, R.W.D.; Carnkief, L.J.M.; Ventongimps Moor,

G.A. and L.J.M.; Wentworth Mine, Chyverton, P.Tu. *et al;* 85, Newlyn Downs (Flora), 1979, P.Tu.

*East: 85, SE of Carland Cross, P.Tu. *et al.*

357/1   **E. tetralix x vagans** = *E. x williamsii* Druce
x 8   A very rare hybrid heath, usually as a single plant. West: 61, near Kynance Farn, J.A.P.; Kynance Downs, A.C.L. and R.B.; 71, Goonhilly Reserve, D.E.C.; 72, between Bochym and Goonhilly Downs, one mile from the station in Suppt (Thurston and Vigurs 1925).

357/6   § **E. lusitanica** Rudolphi   Spanish Heath
        Naturalised in quantity along the main railway line between Lostwithiel and St Germans.

   *West: 73, originally planted at Perranwell Station, and now spreading onto nearby banks, L.J.M.; 85, two bushes on railway bank between Goonhavern and Shepherds, 1968, L.J.M.

   East: 16, near Restormel, Lostwithiel, D.Mc.; N of E Taphouse, D.Mc.; Doublebois Station (Suppt), 1958, D.Mc.; 26, in three spots near Looemills, Liskeard, D.Mc.; SE of Liskeard, D.Mc.; near Coldrenick, D.Mc.; 35, Trerulefoot, I.N.; W of St Germans, D.Mc.

357/8   **E. vagans** L.   Cornish Heath
        The characteristic heath of the Lizard Peninsula from Trelowarren and Gweek to Lizard Point and St Keverne, with one outlier at Connor Downs.

   West: 32, Porthgwarra, BRC (this record needs to be confirmed); 53, Connor Downs (Flora), still plentiful in the lane from Connor crossroads to Angarrack, various recorders; railway cutting E of Angarrack, J.S.R.; 61, 62, 71, and 72, common on the Lizard heathland. Scilly: only as a garden throw-out, Lousley 1971.

357/7   § **E. erigena** R. Ross   Irish Heath
        A very rare introduction.

   *East: 26, two plants by roadside two miles SE of Menheniot, 1958, D.Mc.
        Scilly: Lousley 1971.

CALLUNA SALISB.

356/1 **C. vulgaris** (L.) Hull, Heather, is common and wide-spread throughout the county. It is one of the first colonists of mine spoil-heaps.

RHODODENDRON L.

345/1 § **R. ponticum** L.   Rhododendron

Frequent and widespread, seeding itself readily, and becoming a nuisance in forestry plantations.

VACCINIUM L.

358/2 **V. myrtillus** L., Bilberry, is frequent and widely distributed over much of the county, but absent from the extreme West, and from Scilly.

358/4 **V. oxycoccus** L.   Cranberry

In view of its great scarcity in the whole of the South-West, this addition to the county flora is particularly welcome.

*East: 27, peat-bog below Fox Tor, Bodmin Moor, 1979, CNT, comm. B.B.

PRIMULACEAE

PRIMULA L.

367/5 **P. vulgaris** Hudson, Primrose, is common and wide-spread in a variety of habitats, but is doubtfully native in Scilly.

[367/4 **P. elatior** (L.) Hill, Oxlip, was wrongly recorded in the past in mistake for the hybrid between *P. vulgaris* and *P. veris.*]

367/3 **P. veris** L.   Cowslip

Often said to be rare in Cornwall, as indeed it is in inland areas, but abundant in many parts of the North coast, especially on fixed dunes. Absent from Scilly.

367/3 **P. veris x vulgaris** = *P. x tommasinii* Gren. & Godron
x 5   False Oxlip

(*P. x variabilis* Goup.)

Although the two species often occur close together on cliffs, the hybrid between them is very rare.

West: 86 (76), Crantock Wood (Flora), refound, 1979, L.G.

East: 97 (98), Port Quin, C.H.W.; 38, Hexworthy, near Lawhitton, R.B.R. (Thurston 1935).

CYCLAMEN L.

369/1 § **C. hederifolium** Aiton   Cyclamen

A rare garden escape, often naturalised in churchyards.

West: 43, Ludgvan, hundreds around the church, F.G.F.; 62, Breage churchyard, R.B.G.; 72, Mawnan Smith, R.B.G.; plentiful around Mawnan Church, K.E.H.

*East: 97, Gonvena, Wadebridge, C.H.W.; 08, Trewetha, near Port Isaac, L.B.

LYSIMACHIA L.

370/1 **L. nemorum** L., Yellow Pimpernel, is a frequent woodland plant in most of the county. Its absence from much of West Penwith and from Scilly reflects the lack of woodland in these places.

370/3 **L. vulgaris** L.   Yellow Loosestrife

Throughout the county, but rather local.

West: 42, Paul, B.M.S.; 62, Gunwalloe Valley (Flora), 1968, CNT; Poldhu Valley (Suppt), 1968, L.J.M.; 75, Trebisken Moor (Flora), 1967, C.W.; Bolingey, J.A.P.; Holywell Beach, L.J.M.

East: 84, Ruan Lanihorne, D.R.; 94, Tregoney, C.W.; 96, Goss Moor, various recorders; 08 (09), Boscastle, W.H.F. (Thurston 1929), 1979, L.J.M.; 15, Lostwithiel Moor, R.Pe. (Thurston 1935); between Lostwithiel and Lerryn, F.R. (Thurston 1935); 20, Bude (Suppt), 1971, L.J.M.; 27, Trebartha Hall, E.A.; 28, Egloskerry Marsh, L.J.M.; 38, Launceston (Flora), in two places, 1970, G.L.K.

Scilly: Lousley 1971.

370/2 § **L. nummularia** L.   Creeping-Jenny

A rare introduction, but completely naturalised in a few places.

West: 63, near lodge-gates, Pendarves, Camborne, L.J.M.; 73, hedgebank, Maen Valley, Budock, L.J.M.; 75, near Perranzabuloe Church, W.H.F. (Thurston and Vigurs 1927); 83, Swanpool (Flora), still there, post– 1950, L.J.M.; 85, Pencorse, Summercourt, B.B. and L.G.

East: 05, lawn, Duporth, W.T. (Thurston and Vigurs 1926); 08, Trebarwith, 1920, R.W.D.; 21, Tamar Lake, J.G.D. and C.D.; 25, Watergate, W Looe Valley, L.J.M.; 29, SE of Canworthy Water, J.A.P.; 38, old railway E of Launceston, L.J.M.
Scilly: Lousley 1971.

370/5   § **L. punctata** L.   Dotted Loosestrife
An increasing garden throw-out, often confused with the preceding species, *L. vulgaris*.

*West: 43, hedge near Nancledra, 1956, S.B. (as *L. vulgaris*), Herb. Bannister, (TRU); 63, N of Penponds, Camborne, R.M.; on mine-spoil, Wheal Basset, Carnkie, L.J.M.; 64, roadside, Dolcoath, Camborne, L.J.M.; 74, Southgate, Redruth, L.J.M.; United Mines, Gwennap, L.J.M.; Threemilestone, K.P.

*East: 19, Marshgate, R.W.D. and L.J.M.

GLAUX L.

373/1   **G. maritima** L., Sea-milkwort, is frequent and widespread in salt-marshes, but also on damp cliffs and raised beaches.

ANAGALLIS L.

372/4   **A. minima** (L.) E.H.L. Krause   Chaffweed
(*Centunculus minimus* L.)
Probably not so common as it once was, but certainly overlooked to some extent.

West: 42, Chy-an-hal (Flora), 1948, J.B.; 63, Porkellis Moor, R.H.; 71, Kennack Cliff, J.Fo.; Coverack to Black Head, J.Fo.; Black Head, 1933, C.H.F.; 72, Drytree, and near Burnoon Farm, Goonhilly, R.H.; 74, Silverwell Moor, B.M.S.; 75, near Carnkief Pond, E.T. and F.R. (Thurston and Vigurs 1927).

East: 95, Goss Moor, L.J.M.; 96, Rosenannon Bog, C.H.W.; 97, Pentire Peninsula, R.W.D.; 05, Duporth, W.T. (Thurston and Vigurs 1927); 06, Criggan Moor, near St Austell, L.J.M.; 07, Hellandbridge, K.H.J. Scilly: Lousley 1971; T, Middle Down, D.E.A.

372/1   **A. tenella** (L.) L.   Bog Pimpernel
Frequent and widespread throughout the county in a variety of damp habitats.

372/2 **A. arvensis** L., Scarlet Pimpernel, is common in waste places and cultivated fields, but also in fixed dunes and on cliffs. A number of colour forms exist.

var. **carnea** Schrank, with salmon-pink flowers, is common along the coast.

forma **azurea** Hyl., with bright blue flowers:
West: 53, garden, Marazion, E.Th.; Marazion Marsh, L.J.M.; 64, Rosewarne Horticultural Station, Camborne, S.B.; 83, garden, Point, Devoran, L.J.M.
East: 93, car-park, Carne, Veryan, B.E.M.G.
Scilly: Lousley 1971.

372/3 **A. foemina** Miller   Blue Pimpernel
In all probability, the majority of early records for this species refer to the preceding blue form of *A. arvensis*. The following seem to be the only reliable records:
West: 71, garden, Lizard village, J.M.Y.; 87, Harlyn Bay, 1923, L.M.

SAMOLUS L.

374/1 **S. valerandi** L.   Brookweed
Frequent and widespread along the coasts, especially in damp flushes at the base of cliffs.
West: Too common for listing of localities.
East: 97, Daymer Bay, J.A.P.; Pentire Peninsula, R.W.D.; 08, Trebarwith Strand, R.W.D. and L.J.M.; 45, near Rame (Flora), Rame Head, 1963, J.M.W. and L.J.M.; E end of Whitsand Bay, E.G.; 46, Halton Quay, I.N.
Scilly: Lousley 1971; T, S end of Great Pool, D.E.A.

PLUMBAGINACEAE
ARMERIA WILLD.
366/1a **A. maritima** (Miller) Willd., Thrift, is common and widespread distributed along the entire coastline, in a number of different maritime habitats.

LIMONIUM MILLER
[365/1 **L. vulgare** Miller, Common Sea-lavender, was earlier recorded for several localities in mistake for the next species, but these were rejected by Davey (Flora),

although he accepted an unlocalised record based on a herbarium specimen. In view of the possiblity of a further error here, we have thought it best to exclude this species from the Cornish list.]

365/
5/1
L. binervosum (G.E.Sm.) Salmon   Rock Sea-lavender
Rather rare, but at scattered localities along most of the coast.

West: 32, Portgwarra (Flora), 1976, E.G.; cove W of Logan Rock, G.H.; 53, near the level-crossing, Hayle, 1949, S.B.; 62, cliff by Gunwalloe Church (Flora), still there, post—1950, D.E.C.; 64, Chapel Porth (Flora), still there, 1976, L.J.M.; 75, Holywell Bay, L.J.M.; 86 (76), West Pentire (Flora), 1979, L.J.M.; 87, Porthcothan (Flora), 1958, E.A.; St Merryn (Flora), Booby Bay, 1962, E.A.; Trevose Head, L.J.M.; Crugmeer, Guddna Common, L.G.; between Padstow and Trevone, E.A.

East: 83, cliff E of St Mawes, L.J.M.; 97, between Polzeath and the Camel Estuary (Flora), Cockett Haven, New Polzeath, R.W.D.; between Pentire Haven and Pentire Point, and the Rumps, R.W.D.; 08, Trebarwith Strand, J.E.L. (Thurston and Vigurs 1926); 20, Bude (Flora), 1967, R.Be.; 35, Tregantle (Flora), 1966, S.M.; Long Sands, Antony, S.M.

OLEACEAE

FRAXINUS L.

376/1 **F. excelsior** L., Ash, is common and widespread. Like the Sycamore, it is able to withstand severe winds, and has been extensively planted around upland farms.
*Scilly: M, W of old lighthouse, one tree, 1972, J.P.B.; T, W of Abbey, 1972, J.P.B.

SYRINGA L.

377/1 § **S. vulgaris** L.   Lilac
A rare garden throw-out.

*West: 74, hedgebank, Bissoe Valley, 1966, L.J.M.
*East: 07, St Kew Highway, 1971, C.H.W.; 35, two bushes, Wacker Mill, Antony, S.M.; 38, near Polson Bridge, Launceston, L.J.M.; 45, Vanderbands, St Johns, S.M.; Millbrook, L.J.M.

LIGUSTRUM L.

378/1 L. vulgare L., Wild Privet, and 378/2 § **L. ovalifolium** Hassk., Garden Privet, are frequent throughout the county.

GENTIANACEAE

CICENDIA ADANSON

380/1 **C. filiformis** (L.) Delarbe   Yellow Centaury
(*Microcala filiformis* Hoffmanns. & Link)

A characteristic plant of wet heathland in West and Mid Cornwall, absent east of Bodmin, and from Scilly. Rarely present in quantity, and constantly threatened by land drainage.

West: 32, Skewjack Moor, near Sennen, R.W.D. and L.J.M.; 42, Kemyel, near Lamorna, J.B.; N of Sancreed, J.A.P.; Trungle Moor (Flora), 1968, J.A.P.; W of Sheffield, J.A.P.; 53, Marazion (Flora), 1970, B.M.S.; 61, Kynance (Flora), still there, post—1950, B.M.S.; Lizard (Flora), post—1950, E.A.; Penhale, Lizard, H.F.D. (Thurston 1928); 64, Red River Valley (Flora), 1971, R.J.M. and L.J.M.; 74, Silverwell Moor (Suppt), still there, B.M.S.; 75, Ventongimps Moor, B.E.M.G. and L.J.M.

East: 95, Goss Moor (Flora), 1965, E.A.; 96, NW corner of Retire Common, abundant, 1951, R.W.D.; 06, E side of Retire Common, two plants, L.J.M.

BLACKSTONIA HUDSON

383/1 **B. perfoliata** (L.) Hudson   Yellow-wort
Very local, and mainly on fixed dunes.

West: 75, St Agnes, J.S.R.; Gear Sands, Penhale Sands, various recorders; 83, Penpol, Feock (Flora), still there, L.J.M.; 87, Porthcothan, B.B.; Constantine Bay (Suppt), still there, but rare, various recorders; 97, Stepper Point (Flora), 1966, J.A.P.; old railway line between Padstow and Wadebridge, S.M.

East: 83, St Anthony Head, L.J.M.; 95, McClaren's Dry, Trerice, near St Dennis, L.G.; 97, Rock (Flora), 1966, J.L.; St Enodoc, E.A.; Trebetherick Dunes, S.M.; New Polzeath, R.W.D.; Lundy Bay, 1930, W.P.A. (Thurston 1936); 20, Bude (Flora), 1972, L.J.M.

CENTAURIUM HILL

382/7 **C. scilloides** (L. fil.) Samp.   Perennial Centaury
Extremely rare and impermanent.
*West: 32, near St Levan, 1952, E.G.C. (*Proc. B.S.B.I.*, 1: 174, 1954); Porthgwarra Cove, 1957, S.B., Herb. Bannister, (TRU), 1962, R.H. In all probability these two stations were the same.
*East: 20, Sandymouth, Bude, D.H., now gone.

382/4 **C. erythraea** Rafn (*C. umbellatum* Gilib.), Common Centaury, is very frequent and widespread in a number of different habitats.

var. **capitatum** (Willd.) Melderis
(*C. capitatum* Rendle and Britten)
There are no recent localised records, though in Perring and Walters 1962 the plant is marked post–1930 for squares 75 and 19. A specimen from Penhale, the Lizard, in Herb. Davey, (TRU) is correct.
West: 32, near Logan Rock, 1931, G.C.D. (Thurston 1935).
Scilly: one record, Lousley 1971.

var. **subcapitatum** (Corb.) Ubsdell
Frequent in submaritime habitats right round the coast.

[382/3 **C. latifolium** (Sm.) Druce, Broad-leaved Centaury, and 382/6 **C. littorale** (D. Turner) Gilmour (*C. vulgare* Rafn), Seaside Centaury, were both recorded for Cornwall in the past. It is most unlikely that either ever occurred, and we accordingly reject them.]

382/1 **C. pulchellum** (Swartz) Druce   Lesser Centaury
In submaritime habitats, mainly in E Cornwall. Absent from West Penwith and Scilly.
West: 53, Marazion Marsh, 1948, J.B.; Hayle, G.C.D. (Thurston 1935), Phillack Towans, R.J.M.; Upton Towans, B.E.M.G. and J.A.P.; (54), Gwithian, R.H.; edge of marsh, Gwealavellan, near Godrevy, R.J.M., and L.J.M.; 62, Gunwalloe Towans, L.J.M.; 71, Poltesco, J.B.; 72, Gweek, R.H.; 73, near Devoran Bridge, L.J.M.; Pulla Cross, Gwennap, R.B.G.; 75, Rose, near Perranporth, B.M.S.; Perranporth (Flora), Penhale Sands, 1968, G.A. and L.J.M.; Cligga Head, CNT; 83, Feock,

R.H.; 86, Newquay (Flora), the Gannel, 1950 onwards, R.L.G.L.; 87, Booby Bay, R.W.D.; 97, quarry near Sea Mills, Camel Estuary, J.A.P.

East: 83, between Portscatho and Greeb Point, L.J.M.; 84, Tresillian, C.N. (Thurston 1935); Ruan Lanihorne, B.E.M.G.; 96, quarry, Tregamere, NE of St Columb Major, J.A.P.; 97, Pentire Peninsula, R.W.D.; 20, Bude, 1924, W.Wi.; 21, slopes Duckpool, L.J.M.; 45, Southdown Quarry, Millbrook, S.M.; (44), Penlee Point (Flora), 1965, L.J.M.

[GENTIANA L.   384/1 G. pneumonanthe L., Marsh Gentian, was dismissed by Davey (Flora), as an undoubted error, and, as no further evidence has come to light, we must agree with this.]

GENTIANELLA MOENCH

385/1   **G. campestris** (L.) Börner   Field Gentian
(*G. baltica* Murb.)

This is a plant that has declined dramatically since the Flora. Now very rare, and mainly on the Lizard.

West: 61, Lizard Downs (Flora), near old Windmill, M.C.H.; Mullion Cliff, and Kynance, J.H.; 71, Black Head, near Coverack, R.H.; Goonhilly Downs (Flora), near Croft Pascoe Pool, W of Gwenter, and W of Trelan, comm. J.H.; 72, near Rosuic, Traboe Cross, comm. J.H.
East: 19, Crackington Haven, J.E.L. (Thurston and Vigurs 1926).

385/3/ **G. amarella** (L.) Borner   Autumn Gentian
1   Always rare in Cornwall, this species has decreased further in recent years.

West: no recent records.
East: 97, Rock Dunes, 1967—79, R.W.D.; 17, SW side of Dozmary Pool, C.P.F. (Thurston and Vigurs 1925).

385/4b **G. anglica** (Pugsley) E.F. Warburg
subsp. **cornubiensis** Pritchard   Cornish Gentian
(Flora, as *Gentiana lingulata* C.A. Agardh, var. *praecox* Townsend)

First described by Dr N. Pritchard in 1959 (*Watsonia*, 4: 184), this subspecies of the Early Gentian appears to be confined to Cornwall, where it is exceedingly local and uncertain of appearance.

*West: 64, between Porthtowan and Chapel Porth (Flora, as *G. lingulata*), 1966—79, L.J.M.; 75, Penhale Sands (Flora), in three distinct colonies, 1961—79, L.J.M.

385/3/ **G. amarella x anglica** subsp. cornubiensis
1 x *West: 75, Penhale Sands, a huge hybrid swarm, 1966,
385/4b L.J.M.

MENYANTHACEAE
MENYANTHES L.
386/1 **M. trifoliata** L.   Bogbean
Lost in some localities through drainage, but still widespread, and often in quantity.

West: 42, Clodgy Moor, Sheffield, Penzance, CNT; Chy-an-hal Moor (Flora), 1948, J.B.; Kerris, B.M.S.; 53, Marazion Marsh, J.R.P.; Loggans Moor, B.M.S.; (54), Red River Valley, L.J.M.; 62, Poldhu (Flora), 1968, LFC; Gunwalloe (Flora), 1962, L.J.M.; 73, Stithians (Flora), reservoir, 1968, J.B.; 74, Trevince Moor, Gwennap (Flora), 1963, L.J.M.; 75, Penhale Sands (Flora), 1965, NCS; Ventongimps (Flora), 1964, J.B.
East: 84, near Polwhele Farm, N of Truro, K.H.J.; 96, Goss Moor (Flora), 1954, J.B.; 96, Retire Common, R.W.D.; 05, Starrick Moor, near St Austell (Suppt), 1954, J.B.; Luxulyan (Flora), 1961, B.Sh.; 06, Retire Common, L.J.M.; near Lowertown, Lanlivery, L.J.M.; Red Moor (Flora), Helmentor, 1954, J.B.; 17, Temple Bridge, L.J.M.; Brown Willy (Flora), still there, post—1950, L.J.M.; Dozmary Pool (Flora), Penkestle Moor, 1967, C.W.; 17 or 27, Upper Fowey Valley, S.M.; 21, Tamar Lake, J.G.D. and C.D.; 27, Lower Langdon Farm, Fowey Valley, E.A.; Witheybrook, NE of Siblyback, S.M.; 28, Treneglos, near Wilsey Down, R.W.D. and L.J.M.; Laneast Downs, G.L.K.

NYMPHOIDES SEGUIER
387/1 § **N. peltata** (S.G. Gmelin) O. Kuntze Fringed Water-lily
Only where originally planted.
*West: 53, plentiful in pool, Winnard Mill, Hayle River, CRNHS; 72, old reservoir, Gweek, 1961, R.B.G.

APOCYNACEAE

VINCA L.

379/1 § **V. minor** L., Lesser Periwinkle (absent from Scilly), and 379/2 § **V. major** L., Greater Periwinkle, are common and widespread garden introductions.

379/2 **V. major** var. **oxyloba** Stearn   Least Periwinkle
= subsp. *hirsuta* (Boiss.) Stearn
*West: 42, naturalised in woods, Lamorna Valley, L.J.M.; 53, lane by creek, Lelant, 1960 onwards, L.J.M.

RUBIACEAE

SHERARDIA L.

481/1 **S. arvensis** L., Field Madder, is frequent and widely distributed, especially in coastal areas.

GALIUM L.

Common species: 485/8a **G. palustre** L., Common Marsh-bedstraw, 485/4 **G. verum** L., Lady's Bedstraw, 485/3a **G. mollugo** L., Hedge Bedstraw (rare in Scilly), 485/5 **G. saxatile** L., Heath Bedstraw, and 485/12 **G. aparine** L., Cleavers.

485/1 **G. odoratum** (L.) Scop.   Woodruff
(*Asperula odorata* L.)

Rare, except in the wooded valleys of East Cornwall, a garden escape in much of the West.

West: 33, Cot Valley, St Just, M.C.; 43, Madron (Flora), 1970, B.M.S.; 61, Wheal Unity, near Mullion, E.J.P. (Thurston and Vigurs 1927); 63, garden escape, Bolenowe, Troon, L.J.M.; 72, Manaccan, R.H.; 73, wood at Perran-ar-worthal, L.J.M.; 84, Truro (Flora), 1965, J.A.P.; 85, near Legonna, Quintrell Downs, B.B.
East: 94, St Ewe, E.T. (Thurston and Vigurs 1925); 05, Charlestown, W.T. (Thurston 1935); Hustyn Mill (Flora), Hustyn Wood, 1966, J.A.P.; Polbrock Wood, Grogley, L.J.M.; 07, St Breward, E.A.; 08 (09), Boscastle C.H.W.; 19, Dizzard Wood, J.A.P.; Millook Cliff, J.F.A.; wood in Millook Valley, L.J.M.; 21, Coombe Valley, R.O. (Thurston and Vigurs 1925); 25, Looe, plentiful, J.L.; 26, Liskeard (Flora), plentiful, J.L.; 37, Greystone Wood (Flora), 1966, J.A.P.; 46, above Cotehele, I.N.

485/10 G. uliginosum L.   Fen Bedstraw

Local and rare, except in the Upper Tamar area.

West: 61, Kynance Valley, R.O. (Thurston and Vigurs 1925), still there, 1968, CNT; Ponsonjoppa, J.H.; 62, near Bochym, R.O. (Thurston and Vigurs 1925); 71, N of Erisey, J.H.; 72, Main Dale, J.H. and L.J.M.

East: 84, Ruan Lanihorne, D.R.; 08, St Teath, C.C.; 19, near Otterham, in several places, C.C.; moors at Newham, and Cocksport, C.C.; near Tresparrett Posts, C.C.; 21, Shorston Moor, near Woolley Barrows, C.C.; in two places at Alderbeer, near Wrasford Moor, C.C.; Tamar Lake, J.G.D. and C.D.; 28, marsh at Treneglos, R.W.D. and L.J.M.; marsh by railway, Egloskerry, L.J.M.; 38, near Launceston (Flora), Newchurches, 1977, C.C.; 39, in three places by the Tamar, near N Tamerton, C.C.

485/8b G. elongatum C. Presl

(*G. palustre* var. *elongatum*)

Much overlooked, and usually not separated from *G. palustre*.

West: 53, Marazion Marsh, L.J.M.; Gwithian Marsh, L.J.M.; (54), Gwealavellan Marsh, near Godrevy, R.J.M.; 62, Poldhu Valley, L.J.M.; Gunwalloe Valley, M.C.H. *et al;* 75, Penhale Sands, G.A., R.Go., and L.J.M.; 86, near Trevemper Bridge, L.J.M.

East: 84, Lamorran, L.J.M.

*Scilly: Lousley 1971, with doubt. First certain record: M, Lower Moors, 1975, D.E.A.

485/3a G. mollugo x verum = *G. x pomeranicum* Retz.

x 4   Not infrequent where both parents occur together.

West: 62, Gunwalloe, B.M.S.; 71, between Penhale and Erisey, the Lizard, R.O. (Thurston and Vigurs 1925); Kennack Sands (Flora), still there, 1978, L.J.M.; 72, near Traboe Cross, Goonhilly Downs, L.J.M.

East: 83 or 93, Pendower Beach, B.E.M.G.; 94, Porthluney Beach, L.J.M.; 97 (98), Doyden, Port Quin, K.H.; 45, Maker Heights, near Kingsand, L.J.M.; (44), Penlee Point, L.J.M.

485/3b **G. album** Miller   Upright Hedge Bedstraw
(*G. erectum* Huds.)

Rejected by Davey (Flora), but very recently found.
*West: Near R Hayle below Townshend, 1980, L.J.M.

485/6   **G. pumilum** Murray   Slender Bedstraw
(*G. asperum* Schreb.)

*West: 61, Lizard, 1901, S.J.C., UCNW, det. K.M.G.
East: 20, Efford Down, Bude (Flora), specimen collected 1882, W.M.R., BM.
Not found since in either locality.

485/11 § **G. tricornutum** Dandy   Corn Cleavers
(*G. tricorne* Stokes)

Probably never more than casual, now extremely rare.

West: 53, Copperhouse, Hayle, R.O. (Thurston and Vigurs 1925).
East: 20, in two localities near Bude, A.D.C., comm. E.A.

CRUCIATA MILLER

484/1   **C. laevipes** Opiz   Crosswort
(*Galium cruciata* Scop.)

Extremely rare and local and possibly introduced in all its localities. Gone from (98), Portquin (Flora).

East: 83, churchyard and roadbank, St Just-in-Roseland, 1967, C.W.; 95, old china-clay area, Treviscoe, by mineral railway line, B.B.; 15, Lost-withiel (Suppt), near Railway, E.T. (Thurston and Vigurs 1925); 16, five miles from Liskeard, near Bodmin road, E.T. (Thurston and Vigurs 1925); 20, Bude Canal, comm. R.D.

RUBIA L.

486/1   **R. peregrina** L., Wild Madder, is frequent and widespread, especially along the coast, but it is rare in inland parts of E Cornwall.

CONVOLVULACEAE
CUSCUTA L.
407/3 **C. epithymum** (L.) L., Dodder, is a frequent parasite, more common in coastal areas, but rare in Scilly. An interesting variant, with bright yellow stems, occurs on fixed dunes at

West: 53, Upton Towans, L.J.M.; 87, Constantine Bay, L.J.M.

DICHONDRA J.R. and G. FORSTER
404/1 § **D. micrantha** Urban   Kidney Weed
= *D. repens* auct.

*West: 53, Phillack Towans, 1955, M.M.W. *et al.* (*Proc. B.S.B.I.*, 2: 21), very little surviving in 1979, B.M.S.

CALYSTEGIA R.BR.
406/1 **C. sepium** (L.) R.Br., subsp. **sepium,** Hedge Bindweed, and 406/3 § **C. silvatica** (Kit.) Griseb. (Suppt as *C. inflata* auct.), Large Bindweed, are both common and widespread plants of waste places and hedges.

406/4 **C. soldanella** (L.) R.Br.   Sea Bindweed
Widespread and usually common on dunes around the coast.

West: 32, Sennen (Flora), 1966, J.A.P.; 43, between Marazion and Penzance (Flora), 1963, J.R.P.; 53, Marazion (Flora), 1967, J.B.; Lelant (Suppt), post—1950, L.J.M.; Upton Towans, L.J.M.; (54), Gwithian (Flora), 1948, J.B.; 62, Gunwalloe (Flora), post—1950, J.B.; Loe Bar (Flora), 1962, H.B.S.; 64, Portreath (Flora), 1967, L.J.M.; Porthtowan (Flora), 1968, J.B.; 71, Kennack Sands (Flora), 1978, J.S.R.; 72, Godrevy Cove, near St Keverne, J.H. and L.J.M.; 75, Perranporth (Flora), Penhale Sands, 1965, NCS; Holywell Bay (Flora), 1967, A.B.; 86, Newquay (Flora), (76), Pentire, post—1950, L.J.M.; 87, Porthcothan, T.H.A.; Constantine Bay (Flora), 1965, W.G.

East: 83, Pendower Beach (Suppt), 1969, B.E.M.G.; 97, St Enodoc (Flora), Daymer Bay, 1940—78, R.W.D.; 05, Crinnis (Suppt), 1965, R.D.P.; 20, Bude (Flora), 1972, L.J.M.; 35, Long Sands, Tregantle, S.M.; Seaton

(Flora), 1967, S.M.; between Luggars Cove and Wrinkle (Flora), Portwrinkle, 1967, S.M.
Scilly: common, Lousley 1971.

C. sepium subsp. **roseata** Brummitt

This recently recognised taxon, with deep magenta-pink flowers, is probably native in West Cornwall and Scilly.

*West: 42, between Raginnis and Penzer Point, near Mousehole, L.J.M.; 53, near Lelant Church, 1964, L.J.M.; waste ground, Hayle, L.J.M.; Upton Towans, L.J.M.; Marazion, S.M.; between Hayle Causeway and St Erth, L.J.M.; between Angarrack and Gwinear, L.J.M.; near St Erth Praze, J.A.P.; 63, near Stennack, R.J.M.
Scilly: Lousley 1971.

The name 'var. *coloratus* Lange' was applied to pink forms in earlier floras, and would probably best be regarded as pink-flowered subsp. *sepium*, which has been found at

West: 32, Gwenver Beach, Sennen, M.C.; 83, Mylor Bridge, L.J.M.

East: 05, Par Lane, L.T.M., as *Volvulus dahuricus* (Thurston 1928).

406/2 **C. pulchra** Brummitt & Heywood   Hairy Bindweed

An increasing introduction, much confused with other pink-flowered bindweeds.

*West: 63, waste ground near Four Lanes, L.J.M.; N of Penponds, Camborne, R.M.; 73, near Falmouth Hospital, 1962, L.J.M.; Union Corner, Falmouth, L.J.M.; St Gluvias, L.J.M.; 85, Gwills, near Newquay, L.J.M.
East: 05, Par Harbour, L.T.M. (B.E.C. 1926); 08, near Lanivet Inn, L.J.M.; 26, waste ground, Liskeard, J.L.

CONVOLVULUS L.

405/1 **C. arvensis** L., Field Bindweed, is common throughout the county.

BORAGINACEAE

LITHOSPERMUM L.

401/2 **L. officinale** L.   Common Gromwell

Rather local, and mainly in coastal areas.

West: 53, St Erth (Flora), still there, B.M.S.; Hayle (Flora), 1948, S.B.; Phillack Towans, B.M.S.; Gwithian — Gwinear road, F.G.F.; (54), between Gwithian and Lower Nanterrow Farm, L.J.M.; 64, near Kehelland, J.S.R.; Portreath, J.S.R.; between Ashill and Hell's Mouth, L.J.M.; 75, Goonhavern (Flora), 1976, L.J.M.; Perranporth (Flora), Penhale Sands, R.L.G.L.; 86, Watergate Bay, L.J.M.; (76), Cubert, K.H.; Porth Joke, L.J.M.; 87, near Porthcothan, B.B.; 97, quarry near Sea Mills, Camel Estuary, J.A.P.

East: 94, Port Holland (Flora), still there, L.J.M.; 97, St Enodoc (Flora), Rock, 1969, E.A.; 05, Bodelva, St Blazey Gate, L.T.M. (Thurston and Vigurs 1925); Charlestown, W.T. (Thurston and Vigurs 1927); 46, hedge near Landulph Cross, I.N.

BUGLOSSOIDES MOENCH

401/3 **B. arvensis** (L.) I.M. Johnston   Field Gromwell
(*Lithospermum arvense* L.)

Always rare in Cornwall, now the merest casual.

West: 73 or 74, two plants as garden weeds, Lanner, W.D.W. (Thurston and Vigurs 1926).

East: 16, Warleggan, 1955, C.Je.

ECHIUM L.

403/1 **E. vulgare** L.   Viper's-bugloss

Mainly on sandy areas near the coast. Very local, but occasionally in quantity.

West: 32 or 33, Nanjulyan, St Just, B.M.S.; 53, Phillack Towans, B.M.S.; (54), Gwithians Towans (Flora), post—1950, R.H.; Godrevy Towans, L.J.M.; 61, Lower Predannack Farm, Mullion, E.J.P. (Thurston 1936); 75, Perranwell (Flora), plentiful at Cocks, 1970, C.W.; Treworthen (Flora), Penhale Sands, post—1950, R.H.; 86, old airfield, St Eval, J.A.P.; Watergate Bay, L.J.M.; (76), Kelsey Head, near Newquay, CNT; 87, Constantine Bay (Flora), post—1950, T.H.A.

East: 93, Portloe, M.E.B.; 97, Rock Sandhills, R.W.D.; 15, between Polperro and Lansallos (Flora), cliffs below Lansallos, 1967, J.A.P.; 25, Windwhistle, near Millendreath, Looe, S.M.; 35, Seaton (Flora), 1967, S.M. Scilly: casual and rare, Lousley 1971; B, 1975, J.S.

403/2 **E. plantagineum** L.   Purple Viper's-bugloss
Regarded by Davey (Flora) as a colonist, but now
generally accepted as a native of Cornwall. Only in the
extreme West of the county, casual elsewhere.
West: 32, Trevorian Common, near Sennen, BRC;
Nanquidno, E.A.R. (Thurston 1930), 1963, G.L.;
Boscregan Farm, E.A.R. (Thurston 1930), 1973, M.C.;
Hendra Farm, E.A.R. (Thurston 1930), 1979, B.M.S.;
Gazick and Gurland Farms, E.A.R. (Thurston 1930);
32 or 33, Kelynack, S.B.; 33, Letcha, E.A.R. (Thurston
1930), 1976, J.M.M.; Bosavern, B.M.S.; Nanjulian,
E.A.R. (Thurston 1930); 43, Grumbla, near Sancreed,
R.W.D. and L.J.M.; 62, Helston Station, W.T. (Thurston
1930); 87, Trevose Head, around remains of building,
T.H.A.
East: 25, Polperro, 1935, BRC.
Scilly: very rare, Lousley 1971.

SYMPHYTUM L.

The earlier records for the next two species are confused.
Both are frequent and widespread. We have listed below
only those records that belong unequivocally to one
species or the other.

392/1 **S. officinale** L.   Common Comfrey
Usually by rivers.
West: 84, Calenick Creek, near Truro, L.J.M.; 86,
Watergate Bay, L.J.M.
East: 35, Antony, S.M.; 37, above Horsebridge, J.A.P.;
S of Greystone Bridge, J.A.P.; Inny Foot, by the Tamar,
L.J.M.; 45, Carbeile, Torpoint, S.M.
*Scilly: regarded as doubtful by Lousley 1971, but
recorded since: M, Garrison Walk, 1968, J.P.B.; below
Star Castle, D.E.A.

392/2 § **S. asperum** Lepechin x **officinale**   Russian Comfrey
x 1   = *S. x uplandicum* Nyman (Suppt as *S. peregrinum*
Ledeb.)
An increasing introduction, frequent in damp, waste
places.
West: 62, between Helston and the Lizard (Suppt),
near Cross Lanes, post—1962, J.A.P.; 71, Kennack, J.B.;
75, Perranzabuloe (Suppt), Perranwell, 1966, L.J.M.;
83, Flushing, Falmouth, L.J.M.

East: 83, between Veryan and Portscatho (Suppt), at Portscatho, 1969, B.E.M.G.; 08, Bossiney, and near Tintagel, J.A.P.; (09), Boscastle (Suppt), post—1962, J.A.P.; 16, Doublebois, H.P.; 20, Helebridge, near Bude, J.A.P.; 26, W of Liskeard, J.A.P.

Scilly: Lousley 1971.

392/6 **S. tuberosum** L. Tuberous Comfrey

Extremely rare and local. Possibly an ancient introduction.

West: 73, riverside by viaduct, Ponsanooth (Flora), refound, 1966, J.A.P.

*East: 36, Clapper Bridge, reported independently by E.G. and I.N.; 46, near Cotehele, 1971, I.N.

392/7 § **S. ibiricum** Steven Creeping Comfrey

A garden outcast.

*East: 94, Tregony, 1959, L.D.; 08, by Stream, Bossiney, 1971, C.H.W.

392/3 § **S. orientale** L. White Comfrey

A rare garden outcast, but possibly on the increase.

West: 97, Padstow (Suppt), still there, post—1950, R.W.D.

East: 83, Treluggan, and Treworthal, near Philleigh, B.E.M.G.; 84, Ruan Lanihorne (Suppt), refound post— 1950, J.A.P.

ANCHUSA L.

396/2 § **A. ochroleuca** Bieb. Yellow Alkanet
(Suppt as *A. procera* Bess.)

Formerly frequent on part of Upton Towans, now much reduced.

West: 53, Upton Towans (Suppt), still there, 1950— 76, various recorders.

396/1 § **A. officinalis** L. Alkanet

Always a very rare introduction, but still present.

West: 53, Upton Towans (Suppt), still there, various recorders, in small amount; 75, Perranporth sandhills, C.N. (Thurston 1935).

East: 05, Par Harbour, L.T.M. (Thurston 1928).

396/3 § **A. azurea** Miller Garden Anchusa
(Suppt as *A. italica* Retz.)
A denizen on Upton Towans, a rare garden escape elsewhere.
West: 53, Upton Towans (Suppt), still there, 1950–79, various recorders.
Scilly: garden escape, Lousley 1971.

396/2 **A. ochroleuca x officinalis**
x 1 *West: 53, Upton Towans, 1950–79, various recorders.

397/1 **A. arvensis** (L.) Bieb. Bugloss
(*Lycopsis arvensis* L.)
Very local, but persistent in most of the known stations.
West: 32, Porthgwarra, S.M.; 53, Hayle Towans (Suppt), Phillack Towans, 1970, B.M.S.; Upton Towans, L.J.M.; 63, mine-waste near Troon, L.J.M.; 75, Penhale Sands (Flora), 1964, L.J.M.; Holywell Bay, L.J.M.; 86 (76), Newquay (Flora), Pentire, 1961, L.J.M.; 87, Constantine Bay (Flora), 1965, W.G.; Harlyn Bay (Flora), 1968, J.A.P.
East: 93, near Veryan (Suppt), Carne, 1974, B.E.M.G.; 97, Rock (Suppt), Daymer Bay, 1979, R.W.D.; cornfields from Pentireglaze to Lundy Bay, 1950–79, R.W.D.; 35, arable near Downderry, R.W.D. and L.J.M.; St Germans Hut, S.M.
Scilly: common, Lousley 1971.

PENTAGLOTTIS TAUSCH

395/1 § **P. sempervirens** (L.) Tausch (*Anchusa sempervirens* L.), Green Alkanet, is a frequent and widespread introduction, except in Scilly, where a single station still survives.

BORAGO L.

393/1 § **B. officinalis** L. Borage
Frequent as an introduction in waste places in the West, but unaccountably rare in most of the East.
West: Too frequent and widespread for listing of localities.
East: Recorded, without locality, for squares 25, 35, and 45, during the Mapping Scheme; 97 (98), Port Quin, D.P.W.
Scilly: rare, Lousley 1971.

393/2 § **B. laxiflora** Willd. Slender Borage
*West: 72, St Anthony-in-Meneage, 1957, R.W.D.;
Porth Navas, D.T.

[402/1 **Mertensia maritima** (L.) Gray, Oysterplant, is a most
unlikely plant ever to have occurred in Cornwall, and
we follow Davey (Flora) in rejecting it for the county.]

MYOSOTIS L.

Common species: 400/8 **M. arvensis** (L.) Hill, Field
Forget-me-not, 400/10 **M. ramosissima** Rochel (*M.
collina* Hoffm.), Early Forget-me-not, 400/9 **M. discolor**
Pers. (*M. versicolor* Sm.), Changing Forget-me-not,
400/2 **M. secunda** A. Murray (*M. repens* D.Don), Creeping Forget-me-not, and 400/4 **M. laxa** Lehm., subsp.
caespitosa (C.F. Schultz) Hyl. (*M. caespitosa* Schultz),
Tufted Forget-me-not (rejected for Scilly, Lousley
1971).

400/1 **M. scorpioides** L. Water Forget-me-not
(*M. palustris* Hill)

Rather local and rare, avoiding very acid waters. Often
reported in error for large-flowered forms of *M. secunda*.
West: 62, Poldhu Marsh, R.W.D. and L.J.M.; 75,
Treago stream, Crantock, J.A.P.; 83, Falmouth (Flora),
Swanpool, post—1950, L.J.M.
East: 97, Amble Marshes, Camel Estuary, R.W.D.; 08,
R Camel above Egloshayle, J.A.P.; 15, by R Fowey, S
of Lostwithiel, L.J.M.; 20, Mere Marsh, Bude, L.J.M.;
25, near Sandplace, Looe, D.B.; 37, above Horsebridge,
R Tamar, J.A.P.; 38, Launceston (Flora), in two places
near Launceston, 1970, G.L.K.
Scilly: one station, Lousley 1971.

OMPHALODES MILLER

390/1 § **O. verna** Moench Blue-eyed-Mary
A rare denizen.

West: 74, hedge, Chacewater, W.E.B. (Thurston and
Vigurs 1925); 86, deserted garden, Colan, near, Newquay,
L.G.
East: 84, Pencalenick (Flora), still in the woods there,
1968, L.J.M.

CYNOGLOSSUM L.

389/1 **C. officinale** L.   Hound's-tongue
Local and rare, and mostly on sand-dunes.

West: 53, Hayle Towans, G.B.M.; Phillack Towans
(Flora), 1977, J.A.P.; (54), Gwithian Towans (Flora),
1971, B.M.S.; Godrevy Towans, B.M.S.; 75, Penhale
Sands (Flora), 1961, L.J.M.; Holywell Bay (Flora),
post—1950, R.L.G.L.; 86 (76), Porth Joke, L.J.M.;
Crantock (Flora), post—1950, R.L.G.L.

East: 97, St Enodoc (Flora), Trebetherick, 1939—79,
R.W.D.

VERBENACEAE

VERBENA L.

444/1 **V. officinalis** L., Vervain, is a frequent plant of pastures
and waste places throughout the county.

CALLITRICHACEAE

CALLITRICHE L.

262/1 **C. stagnalis** Scop., Common Water-starwort, is a common
plant of wet places.

262/3 **C. obtusangula** Le Gall   Blunt-fruited Water-starwort
Very local, and confined to slow-flowing, brackish
streams.

West: 62, Gunwalloe (Flora), 1953, R.W.D.; 87,
Constantine Bay, L.J.M.

East: 97, Amble Marshes (Flora), post—1950, R.W.D.;
20, Mere Marsh, Bude, L.J.M.

Scilly: common on St Marys, Lousley 1971.

262/2 **C. platycarpa** Kutz.   Various-leaved Water-startwort
This species has only recently been understood. It is
probably common in Cornwall.

*West: 53, St Erth, 1962, L.J.M.; pool along Hayle
River, CRNHS; Tremelling Wood, Hayle, CNT; 62,
Gunwalloe, L.J.M.; 63, Porkellis Moor, B.J., E.J., and
S.M.T.; 73, Carnmenellis Moor, L.J.M.; 84, ponds near
Coombe, S of Truro, L.J.M.; Moresk, Truro, L.J.M.; 87,
Constantine Bay, L.J.M.

East: 83, Pendower Beach, L.J.M.; 95, Goss Moor,
L.J.M.; 05, Par, 1962, L.J.M.; 06, Red Moor, L.J.M.; 07

or 17, De Lank, C.H.W.; 38, R. Kensey W of Launceston, G.L.K.; 45, Borough Road, Torpoint, S.M.
Scilly: rejected, Lousley 1971.

262/4 **C. hamulata** Kutz. ex Koch Intermediate Water-starwort
(*C. intermedia* Hoffm.)
Rather local, in moorland pools and streams.
West: 33, Bostraze Moor, St Just, J.A.P.; 53, St Erth, B.M.S.; 73, near Carnmenellis, L.J.M.; flooded quarry, Mabe, L.J.M.; Stithians Reservoir, L.J.M.
East: 05, Par Harbour, L.T.M. (Thurston and Vigurs 1927); 07, Killibury Castle, R.W.D.; 19, Newham, near Tresparrett Posts, R.W.D. and L.J.M.; 21, Tamar Lake (Flora), 1965, J.A.P.
Scilly: Lousley 1971.

262/4 **C. brutia** Petagna
(*C. intermedia* var. *pedunculata* DC.)
In similar situations to the last species.
West: 43, Gurnards Head, C.W.N. (Thurston 1930); 63, Porkellis Moor, L.J.M.; 73, Garlidna, near Rame, L.J.M.; Swanvale, Falmouth, L.J.M.
East: 06, Red Moor, E.A. and L.J.M.; 17, Dozmary Pool, R.W.D.
Scilly: Lousley 1971 (included with *C. intermedia*); T, SW margin of Great Pool, D.E.A.

LABIATAE

AJUGA L.

471/2 **A. reptans** L., Bugle, is common and widely distributed throughout the county.

471/3 § **A. genevensis** L.
(Suppt as *A. pyramidalis* L.)
Naturalised for about fifty-five years on Upton Towans, after its discovery there by E.A. Rees in 1915, now gone.
West: 53, Phillack Towans (Suppt — E.A.R., in his reminiscences, says it was Upton Towans); 1950 onwards, various recorders.   Finally disappeared *c* 1970.

TEUCRIUM L.

470/4 **T. scorodonia** L., Wood Sage, is common and widespread in suitable habitats throughout Cornwall.

470/1 **§ T. chamaedrys** L.   Wall Germander
A long-standing introduction.   Very local and rare.
West: 33, St Just (Flora), Kenidjack, 1970, B.M.S.;
53, Perranuthnoe (Flora), still there, 1950 onwards, various recorders.
*Scilly: M, 1975, J.S.

SCUTELLARIA L.

469/2 **S. minor** Hudson, Lesser Skullcap, is frequent on wet heaths (absent from Scilly).

469/1 **S. galericulata** L.   Skullcap
Local and rather rare.
West: 53, Marazion Marsh (Flora), 1965, L.J.M.; 62, Loe Pool (Flora), 1965, H.B.S.; 73, Enys Woods, Mylor, L.J.M.; marsh above Swanpool, L.J.M.; 75, Perranporth (Flora), Penhale Sands, 1965, NCS.; 83, Swanpool (Flora), 1964, J.B.
East: 97, Amble Marshes, R.W.D.; 06, Red Moor, E.A. and L.J.M.; 17, Cardinham Moor, R.Go.; 25, near Looe (Flora), freshwater lake, E Looe River, S.M.; 36, S of Newbridge, Callington, J.A.P.; 37, marsh near Caradon Town, R.W.D. and L.J.M.; marsh near Inny Foot, Tamar Valley, J.A.P.; 46, Cargreen, I.N.; R Tamar below Slimeford, E.G.
Scilly: rare, Lousley 1971.

469/1
x 2   **S. galericulata x minor** = *S. x hybrida* Strail
Recorded for both vice-counties (Flora), but there have been no subsequent records.

MARRUBIUM L.

468/1 **M. vulgare** L.   White Horehound
Now much decreased, and apparently surviving in one station only.
West: 53, Phillack Towans (Flora), Upton Towans, B.M.S.; 63, casual, Council tip near Carnkie, Redruth, L.J.M.; 72, Treviades, near Constantine, W.T. (Thurston 1929a); 83, Tregew, Mylor, W.T. (Thurston 1929a).
Scilly: rejected, Lousley 1971.

MELITTIS L.

56/1 **M. melissophyllum** L. Bastard Balm
Still present in a large number of localities, bur rarely in quantity. Absent from West Penwith and Scilly. The following records are additional to those of the Flora and Suppt, 32 of which have been refound from 1950 onwards.

West: 72, wood near Manaccan, L.A.B.; Bareppa, near Maenporth, L.J.M.; Porthallow, R.H.; 74, Tregavethan, near Truro, L.J.M.; hedge near Treworder, Truro, J.G.T.; 83, near St Anthony, B.M.S.; 84, near Idless, Truro, L.J.M.; old railway, Calenick, Truro, J.G.D. and C.D.; St Michael Penkevil, A.T. (Thurston 1935).

East: 97, Hawke Wood Reserve, E.A.; 07, Coombe Lane, Trelill, St Kew, C.W.; 16, wood near Hollycoombe, G.B.M.; 20, near Ivyleaf Farm, Stratton, F.D. (Thurston 1929a); 21, Lee Wood, Coombe Valley, F.D. (Thurston 1929a); 25, Duloe, J.L.; between Sandplace and Coombe, F.H.C. and J.L.; 26, NW of Dobwalls, K.P.; N of Menhniot Station, J.A.P.; 28, woods E of Lewannick, A.B.; 35, Poldrissick, near Landrake, I.N.; Grove, S of Trematon, J.A.P.; old railway, Wivelscombe, I.N.; Sconner, and Wacker, S.M.; 37, Luckett, recorded independently by I.N. and J.A.P.; Lower Trebullett, N.J.F.; 46, Ziggerson Hill, Botusfleming, I.N.; 47, near Latchley, I.N.

GALEOPSIS L.

465/4/ **G. tetrahit** L., Common Hemp-nettle, is common in
1 suitable habitats throughout the county, but is very rare in Scilly.

465/1 **G. angustifolia** Ehrh. ex Hoffm. Red Hemp-nettle
A very rare cornfield weed, now only as the merest casual.
East: 36, N of Trematon, post—1950, D.B.
Scilly: rejected, Lousley 1971.

465/5 **G. speciosa** Miller Large-flowered Hemp-nettle
A rare and local weed of cultivation.
West: 83, Feock Downs, 1959, A.J.S.
East: 17, Dozmary Pool, 1959, B.Sh.; 26 or 27, Draynes Valley, (Thurston 1935).

465/4/ **G. bifida** Boenn.

2   (*G. tetrahit* L., var. *bifida*)

This species needs further investigation, as most of the Cornish material is intermediate with *G. tetrahit sensu stricto*. The following records should therefore be regarded as provisional.

West: 74, near Goodern, Baldhu, J.A.P.

East: 93 or 94, Ruan Highlanes (B.E.C. 1932); 26, SE of Liskeard, D.B.

LAMIUM L.

462/4 **L. purpureum** L., Red Dead-nettle, is widespread as a weed of cultivation, and of waste places (rare in Scilly)

462/6 § **L. maculatum** L.   Spotted Dead-nettle

Mainly as a garden outcast.

West: 42, Lamorna, B.M.S.; 53 or 63, in a field at Trenerth, near Fraddam, F.G.F.; 75, roadside near Mount, Perranporth, L.J.M.

462/5 **L. album** L.   White Dead-nettle

Frequent and widespread, mainly in the East, but absent from many areas.

West: 33, Portheras, near Morvah, L.B.; 53, by stream, Hayle, L.J.M.; 62, Loe Valley (Suppt), 1974, L.J.M.; 63, Crenver, near Clowance, L.J.M.; Bolenowe, Troon, L.J.M.; between Carwynnen and Gurnick, S of Camborne, L.J.M.; Porkellis village, L.J.M.; 74, Redruth (Flora), Carnmarth, 1972, R.J.M. and L.J.M.

East: Too frequent for listing of stations, but rare in a few parts of the vice-county.

Scilly: no recent records, Lousley 1971.

462/3 **L. hybridum** Vill.   Cut-leaved Dead-nettle

Locally frequent in the West, but rare in the East. West: 32, field S of Treen, G.H.; 33, Bosavern, St Just, M.C.; 43, arable field near Zennor, L.J.M.; 53, Lelant, L.J.M.; near Phillack, J.A.P.; 61, Lizard (Flora), 1976, LFC; Poldhu, R.W.D. and L.J.M.; Mullion (Flora) quarry E of Mullion, 1970, B.E.M.G. and J.A.P.; 62, Gunwalloe (Flora), still there, post—1950, R.H.; 63, Penhale Moor, near Praze, L.J.M.; Roseworthy, near Camborne, L.J.M.; 64, near Rosewarne, Camborne,

R.J.M.; cornfield, Treswithian, Camborne, L.J.M.; 71, Lizard (Flora), 1965, RNHS; 72, Trenoweth, Manaccan, R.H.; Helford Passage, R.H.; 73, Treverva, near Mabe, L.J.M.; field near Falmouth Reservoir, L.J.M.; 83, Marlborough Avenue, Falmouth, L.J.M.

East: 83, Philleigh, B.E.M.G.; 20, cornfield near Northcutt Mouth, Bude, L.J.M.; 35, arable field near Downderry, R.W.D. and L.J.M.

Scilly: frequent, Lousley 1971.

462/1 **L. amplexicaule** L.   Henbit Dead-nettle

Local and rare in West Cornwall, very rare in the East. Mostly near the sea.

West: 52, Perranuthnoe, R.H.; Praa Sands, J.A.P.; 53, Marazion, B.M.S.; Lelant, L.J.M.; Penmare, Hayle, E.A.R. (Thurston and Vigurs 1927); Phillack Towans (Flora), post—1950, B.M.S.; Upton Towans, J.A.P.; Angarrack Bridge, B.M.S.; Gwinear, J.S.R.; 62, Porthleven, H.B.S.; 63, Merrymeeting, near Camborne, L.J.M.; old Council tip, Treskillard, L.J.M.; flower-field, Carwynnen, Camborne, R.J.M. and L.J.M.; 64, Penhallick, near Carn Brea, L.J.M.; Tehidy, J.S.R.; 75, between Holywell Bay and Porth Joke, L.J.M.; 83, Restronguet, R.H.; 85, Council tip, Newlyn East, L.J.M.

East: 83, field near Porthcurnick, Portscatho, L.J.M.; 97, St Enodoc, E.A.; 45, Torpoint (Flora), in several places around Torpoint, 1966, S.M.; garden weed, Saltash, I.N.; between St Stephens, Saltash, and Wearde, I.N.

Scilly: very rare, Lousley 1971.

LAMIASTRUM HEISTER EX FABR.

461/1 **L. galeobdolon** (L.) Ehrend. & Polatschek

                             Yellow Archangel

subsp. **montanum** (Pers.) Ehrend. & Polatschek

(*Lamium galeobdolon* Crantz)

Very local and rare, though sometimes occurring in quantity. Some of the records from the West may belong to the garden variety.

West: 43, Trewern, near Madron, B.M.S.; near Bosullow, S of Morvah, B.M.S.; Tredorwen, Nancledra, L.M.L.; 53, St Erth Woods, J.B.; 63, Pendarves Wood (Flora), refound, 1969, L.J.M.; 72, Gweek, R.H.; 73,

Penjerrick, T.J.P. (Thurston 1936), still there, 1980, CNT.

East: 25, Looe Valley (Flora), in several places around Sandplace, Duloe, and Plashford, 1966, F.H.C. and J.L.; 26, St Keyne valley, F.H.C. and J.L.; 37, Carthamartha Wood, L.J.M.; woods at Greystone Bridge (Flora), 1966, J.A.P.; 38, Tamar Valley below Launceston, J.A.P.; 46, edge of Cotehele Woods, E.G.; 47, Latchley, I.N.

var. **variegatum** hort. = *Galeobdolon argentatum* Smejkal A well-known garden plant, now becoming thoroughly naturalised in Cornwall.

*West: 53, nut-walk, Carbis Bay, L.J.M.; 64, The Coombe, Redruth, L.J.M.; road-verge, Illogan, J.S.R.; lane to top of Carn Brea, L.J.M.; 73, lane to Chyvogue, Perranwell, L.J.M.; 74, Council tip, Bissoe, L.J.M.; 83, Swanpool, K.P. (probably this); Penpol, Devoran, 1975, L.J.M.

*East: 84, Trehane, near Ladock, K.P.; 94, between Grampound and Sticker, L.J.M.; 07, Michaelstow, J.G. and C.W.; 26, well established at Draynes, B.E.M.G.; 29, by track to woods, Week St Mary, 1978, L.J.M.

[463/1 **Leonurus cardiaca** L.   Motherwort

Listed as a denizen for a number of places in the county (Flora and Suppt), but we have not been able to trace any later record than Thurston's from St Tudy, in 1915, and we therefore have no alternative but to mark it as extinct in Cornwall.]

BALLOTA L.

460/1b **B. nigra** L., subsp. **foetida** Hayek   Black Horehound A frequent and widely distributed plant of waste places and roadsides, rarely found in great quantity.

460/1a § subsp. **nigra** = subsp. *ruderalis* (Swartz) Briq. A rare casual.

*East: 05, Par, E.S.T. (B.E.C. 1933).

STACHYS L.

Common species: 458/1 **S. officinalis** (L.) Trevisan, Betony (absent from Scilly), 459/7 **S. sylvatica** L., Hedge Woundwort, 459/6 **S. palustris** L., Marsh Woundwort,   459/6 x 7 S. x ambigua Sm.   = *S. palustris x sylvatica* (absent from Scilly), and   459/3 S. arvensis (L.) L., Field Woundwort.

459/1   § S. annua (L.) L.   Annual Woundwort
Casual and usually impermanent.
West: 53, Phillack (Suppt), on the towans, 1965, B.M.S.
East: 20, waste ground, Bude, L.J.M.; 37, Linkinhorne (B.E.C. 1923).

NEPETA L.

466/1   N. cataria L.   Cat-mint
Always rare in Cornwall, this species has further decreased in recent years, and is now known only from one station.
West: 53, three plants, Phillack Towans, E.A.R. (Thurston and Vigurs 1925); 75, Penhale (Flora), still there in 1925, E.T. (Thurston and Vigurs 1926); near Treamble Quarry, Rejerrah, W.T. (Thurston and Vigurs 1926).
East: 97, Pentire, St Minver (Flora), still at Pentire Farm, 1950—79, R.W.D.

GLECHOMA L.

467/1   G. hederacea L. (*Nepeta hederacea* Trev.), Ground-ivy, is common and widely distributed throughout the county.

PRUNELLA L.

457/1   P. vulgaris L., Selfheal, is common and widespread in Cornwall.

457/2   P. laciniata (L.) L., x vulgaris = *P. x intermedia* Link
x 1   Occurring in the absence of one parent (*P. laciniata*).
        *East: 35, Poldrissick, Landrake, 1966—71, I.N.

MELISSA L.

454/1   § M. officinalis L., Balm, has become completely naturalised in the county in too many stations to justify listing. Rare in Scilly.

ACINOS MILLER

452/1 **A. arvensis** (Lam.) Dandy   Basil Thyme
(*Calamintha acinos* Clairv.)

Always very rare in Cornwall, this species seems to have now disappeared. The following record requires confirmation.

East: 36, hedge bottom in lane near Hepwell Bridge, Quethiock, 1971, I.N.

Scilly: rejected, Lousley 1971.

CALAMINTHA MILLER

451/2 **C. sylvatica** Bromf.   Common Calamint
subsp. **ascendens** (Jordan) P.W. Ball
(*C. montana* Lam.)

A frequent plant of waysides and grassy hillsides, very rare or absent from granite areas.

[451/3 **C. nepeta** (L.) Savi, Lesser Calamint, has been recorded several times for the county, but Davey (Flora) regarded these with suspicion, and, as it is an eastern plant, we are bound to do the same.]

CLINOPODIUM L.

453/1 **C. vulgare** L.   Wild Basil

Rare and local in the extreme SE of Cornwall, with a few scattered stations elsewhere.

West: 64, roadside, Porthtowan, L.J.M.

East: 96, Withiel, 1939, R.W.D.; 15, near Lerryn, H.W.P. (Thurston 1935); Readymoney Wood, Fowey, H.W.P. (Thurston 1935); 21, roadside, Wrasford Moor, L.J.M.; 25, Sandplace, near Looe (Flora), 1962, E.A.; Talland Beach, L.J.M.; 35, between Triffle and St Winnalls, near Downderry, S.M.; roadside near Tideford, L.J.M.; 38, St Stephens, Launceston, G.L.K.; 46, Landulph (Flora), 1966, J.A.P.

ORIGANUM L.

447/1 **O. vulgare** L.   Marjoram

Rare and local, mainly in the East.

West: 63, field border near Gwinear Road Station, L.J.M.; 64, Bel Lake, Camborne, J.G.T.; 72, Porth Navas, R.H.

East: 97, between Trewornan and Wadebridge, 1946,
R.W.D.; 05, Charlestown, W.T. (Thurston and Vigurs
1927); 07, St Mabyn, 1939, R.W.D., 1979, E.W.M.;
between Wadebridge and St Mabyn (Flora), 1956, E.A.;
25, between Sandplace and Looe (Flora), 1966, F.H.C.
and J.L.; 26, near Cartuther, Liskeard, L.T.M. and E.T.
(Thurston 1935); 35, hedgebanks, St Erney, L.J.M.;
Tideford (Flora), post—1950, I.N.; Trevollard (Flora),
post—1950, I.N.; near Poldrissick, Landrake, I.N.; 45,
embankment at Saltash Goods Station, I.N.
Scilly: rejected, Lousley 1971.

THYMUS L.

448/3   **T. praecox** Opiz   Wild Thyme
subsp. **arcticus** (E. Durand) Jalas
(incl. *T. serpyllum sensu* Davey)

This is the common Thyme of Cornwall, widespread
except on the more acid soils. Rare in Scilly.

448/1   **T. pulegioides** L.   Large Thyme
(*T. ovatus* Mill.)

The stations given for this species in the Flora and
Suppt should be treated with caution. Mostly they
refer to forms of the preceding species, but the following
record is apparently correct, and it is possible that
Briggs' records from the Tamar Estuary (Flora) are of
the true species.

East: 15 or 16, near Lostwithiel, 1909, W.N.E., **BM**.

LYCOPUS L.

446/1   **L. europaeus** L., Gipsywort, is frequent in damp
places throughout the county, but uncommon in Scilly.

MENTHA L.

Common species: 445/3 **M. arvensis** L., Corn Mint
(absent from Scilly), and   445/4 **M. aquatica** L., Water
Mint (rare in Scilly).

445/1   § **M. requienii** Bentham   Corsican Mint
A rare garden escape, but possibly overlooked.
  *West: 75, weed in Zelah Nurseries, 1971, L.J.M.
  *East: 07, weed in drive, Lamellan, St Tudy, E.A. and
B.E.M.G.

445/2 **M. pulegium** L. Pennyroyal

There has been a spectacular decline in the occurrence of this species in the last fifty years, in keeping with its general disappearance in Britain.

West: 43, Rosehill, Penzance, 1961, G.B.M.; 53, Hayle, 1926, E.A.R.; 61, Mullion (Flora), quarry E of Mullion, 1970, B.E.M.G. and J.AP.; quarry near Mullion Cove, 1978, R.M.B.; 72, old pasture, Mawnan Smith, R.B.G.

East: 15, Lantivet Bay, H.W.P. (Thurston 1935). Scilly: no recent records, Lousley 1971.

var. **erecta** Martyn

West: 32, Escall Moor, Sennen, 1923, E.A.R. (Thurston and Vigurs 1924); 71, Lizard (Flora), Arrowan Farm, H.F.D. (Thurston 1928).

East: 05, Charlestown, W.T. (Thurston 1929a); Trethurgy, near St Austell, W.T. (Thurston and Vigurs 1927).

445/4 **M. aquatica x arvensis** = *M. x verticillata L.*
x 3 Whorled Mint
(*M. sativa* L.)

Frequent in damp fields, but often overlooked.

West: 53, Marazion Marsh, S.M.; N of St Erth, J.A.P.; 63, between Praze and Crowan, L.J.M.; Crowan Reservoir, J.B.; 72, Maenporth, L.J.M.; 73, Falmouth Reservoir, L.J.M.; Stithians Reservoir, S.M.; Polmarth Moor, Carnmenellis, L.J.M.; 74, Wheal Ellen, near Mt Hawke, L.J.M.; near Chacewater Station, L.J.M.; 75, Perranporth (Flora), Penhale Sands, 1979, L.J.M.; 83, Swanpool, C.L., R.S.B., and A.E.D.; 86, Watergate Bay, R.W.D.

East: 05, Par Moor, L.T.M. (Thurston 1935); Luxulyan Valley, L.J.M.; 06, Red Moor, E.A. and L.J.M.; Criggan Moor, J.A.P.; 15, by R. Fowey S of Lostwithiel, L.J.M.; 28, near Red Down, Egloskerry, J.A.P.; 37, above Horsebridge, J.A.P.

445/3 **M. arvensis x spicata** = *M. x gentilis L.* Bushy Mint
x 5 Sparingly distributed in the county.

West: 53, between Marazion and Long Rock, L.J.M.; Hayle, G.C.D. (B.E.C. 1931); 63, near Polgear, Four

Lanes, K.P.; 73, Tregolls, near Stithians, R.A.G.; Carvedras Valley, near Constantine, R.B.G.; 74, Hicks Mill, near Gwennap, R.A.G.

East: 04, Pentewan (B.E.C. 1931); 15, by R. Fowey S of Lostwithiel, L.J.M.; 18, Watergate, near Camelford, L.J.M.; 36, Pillatonmill, C.P.H. (Thurston 1935).

var. **gracilis** (Sole)
West: 73, Garlidna, near Rame, L.J.M.

var. **variegata** (Sole) Sm.
West: 63, Praze-an-Beeble, W.T. (Thurston 1935); 74, Goonvrea Valley, St Agnes (Thurston 1929).

445/4 **M. aquatica** x **arvensis** x **spicata** = *M. x smithiana* R.A.
x 3 x 5 Graham
(*M. rubra* Sm.) Tall Mint
Very local and rare, but possibly overlooked.
West: 32, Sennen (Flora), still there, 1926 (B.E.C. 1938); 63, Porkellis Moor (Flora), still there, 1976, J.R.D.
East: 45, Wearde, Saltash, J.G. and C.W.; Southdown, near Millbrook, I.N.

445/4 **M. aquatica** x **spicata** = *M. piperita* L. Peppermint
x 5 Rare and local, a decreasing taxon.
West: 32, Sennen, 1926, (B.E.C. 1926); 33, Kenidjack Valley, near St Just, M.C.; 53 (54), near Godrevy Bridge, K.E.H.; 62, Loe Pool, 1942, R.W.D.; 63, old pasture, Treskillard, 1963, now gone, L.J.M.; Porkellis, J.R.D.; 73, Carvedras, near Constantine, R.B.G.; Polmarth Moor, L.J.M.; 74, Menagissey, near Mt Hawke (Suppt), 1961, L.J.M.
East: 93, Veryan (Suppt), Carne, 1973, B.E.M.G.; 97 (98), Port Quin, R.W.D.; 06, Red Moor, L.J.M.; 07, railway near Hellandbridge, K.H.J.

nm. **citrata** (Ehrh.) Boivin Eau-de-Cologne Mint
(*M. aquatica* var. *citrata*)
Extremely local.
West: 42, Trungle Moor, Paul (Flora), 1948, J.B.; 71, Tresaddern Farm, Ruan Minor (Flora), 1935, A.L.S. (B.E.C. 1935); 73, waste ground near Rame, L.J.M.

206

206

East: 35, ditch between Lower Tregantle and Millbrook road, S.M.

445/4 **M. aquatica x suaveolens** = *M. x maximilianea* F.W.
x 7 Schultz

One of Britain's rarest mints.

*West: 43, Bone Valley, N of Penzance, 1954, B.M.S. (*Watsonia*, 4: 75); 71, Tresaddern Farm, Ruan Minor, 1840, Herb. Borrer; 73, near Menherion Farm, Stithians, 1967, R.B.G.

445/7 **M. suaveolens** Ehrh.   Round-leaved Mint
(*M. rotundifolia* Huds.)

Still a frequent plant in West Cornwall, less so in the East.

West: 32, Brew Moor, Sennen, B.M.S.; Porthcurno, L.J.M.; 33, Higher Bosavern, St Just, M.C.; Lower Boscaswell, Pendeen, M.C.; Kenidjack, R.B.G.; 42, Trewidden, Penzance, B.M.S.; 43, Portheras, L.B.; Zennor, J.B.; 63, Clowance, Camborne, L.J.M.; 64, Chapel Porth, J.S.R.; near Old Merrose Farm, Tolvaddon, L.J.M.; 71, Landewednack (Flora), Church Cove, 1978, J.S.R.; 72, Gweek (Flora), 1965, L.J.M.; 73, Trewithen Moor, Stithians, L.J.M.; Devoran (Flora), post—1950, L.J.M.; 74, Cusgarne (Flora) 1965, L.J.M.; Hicks Mill (Flora), post—1950, B.M.S.; 75, Ellenglaze, Penhale Sands (Suppt), 1964, L.J.M.

East: 96, Castle-an-Dinas, near St Columb, L.J.M.; 97, Chapel Amble, R.W.D.; (98), Port Quin, R.W.D.; 25, Sowdens Bridge, near Looe (B.E.C. 1931); 29, wild garden, Week Ford, L.J.M.; 35, Seaton, L.J.M.; between Antony and Tregantle, S.M.; 45, Rame (Flora), between Rame and Tregonhawke, 1967, S.M.; near Coombe Farm, Kingsand, L.J.M.

445/5 **M. spicata x suaveolens** = *M. x villosa* Hudson
x 7 A little understood and variable mint, probably on the increase.

West: 33, St Just, M.C.; 53, St Erth, B.M.S.; 64, Tregea Hill, Portreath, L.J.M.; 73, Hicks Mill, Bissoe (B.E.C. 1935); 74, United Mines, Gwennap, L.J.M.; 86, Watergate Bay, 1913, C.C.V. (Thurston 1928); 87, Porthcothan, L.J.M.

East: 83, Pendower Beach, L.J.M.; 97 (98), Port Quin, H.E.F. (B.E.C. 1926); 25, Sowdens Bridge, near Looe, F.R. (Thurston and Vigurs 1927).

§ nm. **alopecuroides** (Hull)   Large Apple Mint
Scattered but well-established in a few places.

West: 43, near Heamoor, Penzance, R.W.D. and L.J.M.; 53, by stream, Hayle, L.J.M.; 73, College Viaduct, Penryn, W.T. (Thurston 1928); 83, between Pandora Inn and Halwyn Farm, Restronguet, R.B.G.

East: 04, Pentewan, G.C.D. (B.E.C. 1931).
Scilly: Lousley 1971.

[445/6 **M. longifolia** (L.) Hudson   Horse Mint
This taxon has been wrongly recorded in the county, and should be removed from the Cornish list. Plants recorded as this are mainly hairy variants of the next species.]

445/5   § **M. spicata** L.   Spear Mint
(incl. *M. cordifolia* auct.)

An increasing garden escape. Extremely variable, and forming local populations of distinct clones.

West: 32, Sennen Village, J.A.P.; Porthgwarra, S.M.; 33, Boscean, St Just, M.C.; Carnyorth Farm, Pendeen, M.C.; 53, Lelant, S.M.; Long Rock, L.J.M.; 61, Goonhilly Reserve, D.E.C. *et al*; Poldhu Cove, 1949, J.B.; 63, Treskillard, L.J.M.; 64, Portreath Valley (Flora), near Portreath, 1963, L.J.M.; Porthtowan, L.J.M.; 73, Trewithen Moor, Stithians, L.J.M.; near Penryn Viaduct, L.J.M.; 74, Mt Hawke (Suppt), 1961, L.J.M.; Hicks Mill, near Gwennap (Flora), still there, R.A.G. (*Proc. B.S.B.I.*, 3: 193); 75, Lambourne, Perranzabuloe (Suppt), 1948, F.R.; Perranporth (Suppt), 1964, L.J.M.

East: 08, Port Gaverne Valley, L.J.M.; Trebarwith, R.W.D. and L.J.M.; 15, wood near Fowey, H.W.P. (Thurston 1935); Polridmouth, H.W.P. (Thurston 1935); 19, Tresparrett Posts, R.W.D., and L.J.M.; 20, Bude (Flora), 1959, B.Sh.; (10), Widemouth Bay, L.J.M.; 25, between Sandplace and Looe, J.A.P.; 35, Polbathic, S.M.; Freathy valley, below farm, S.M.; 45, Antony road, Torpoint, S.M.
Scilly: Lousley 1971.

208

SALVIA L.

[455/2 S. **pratensis** L., Meadow Clary, is rejected by Davey (Flora) and Lousley 1971, as an obvious mistake.]

455/3 § S. **nemorosa** L. Balkan Sage
(*S. sylvestris* L.)
A rare introduction.
West: 53, Phillack Towans (Suppt), still there, 1950 onwards, B.M.S.; near lifeboat-house, Hayle, E.A.R. (Thurston 1928).
East: 05, Par (Flora), still there in 1923 (B.E.C. 1923).

455/4 S. **verbenaca** L. Wild Clary
(incl. *S. clandestina* L.)
Considered too common by Davey (Flora) to warrant listing of localities, but, since this species is confined to coastal habitats where human pressure is greatest, we have thought fit to list all post—1950 records. The Kennack plant, formerly thought to be a distinct species, is now recognised only as a narrow-leaved form.
West: 53, near Hayle, RNHS; Lelant Dunes, L.J.M.; near Upton Towans, J.S.R.; (54), St Ives, L.B.; near Godrevy, J.S.R.; between Gwithian and Nanterrow Farm, L.J.M.; 62, Gunwalloe, J.B.; 64, Porthtowan, various recorders; 71, Kennack Sands (Flora), 1949, H.B.S., 1978, J.S.R.; 72, Maenporth, L.J.M.; 75, Penhale Sands, L.J.M.; 86, Mawgan Porth, L.J.M.; (76), Crantock, R.L.G.L.; Vugga Bay, and Kelsey Head, A.B.; West Pentire, Newquay, J.B.; 87, Porthcothan, Constantine Bay, and Harlyn Bay, L.J.M.; Trevone, J.S.R.
East: 97, Daymer Bay, E.A.; 07, between Treworran and Dinham, recorder unknown; 20, Bude, L.J.M.; 35, Seaton, S.M.; Downderry, J.A.P.; Tregantle Downs, S.M.
Scilly: Lousley 1971.

455/1 § S. **verticillata** L. Whorled Sage
A rare but persistent introduction.
West: 53, Phillack Towans (Suppt), still there, post—1950, B.M.S.
East: 05, Par (Flora), still there in 1929, L.T.M. (Thurston 1930).

SOLANACEAE

NICANDRA ADANSON

408/1 § **N. physalodes** (L.) Gaertner   Shoo-fly Plant
Casual, and rare, but occasionally in quantity.
West: 43, Heamoor, Penzance (Flora), one plant by Penzance Railway Station, 1976, C.O.; 62, Council tip, Helston, 1978, R.J.M. and L.J.M.; 63, several plants in arable field, Coswinsawsen Farm, near Camborne, NAAS (Camborne).
*East: 45, one plant by Saltash Bridge, 1974, E.Wh.; three plants on waste ground, Saltash, E.G.
Scilly: often plentiful, Lousley 1971.

LYCIUM L.

Because of previous confusion of nomenclature, it is not clear whether both species are in the county. We have therefore included all records under the following:

409/1 § **L. barbarum** L.   Duke of Argyll's Teaplant
(incl. *L. chinense* Miller)
Widespread and persistent as an old introduction.
West: 53, Copperhouse, Hayle, J.A.P.; Marazion, J.B.; 62, Porthleven, H.B.S.; 71, Cadgwith area, J.H.; 83, Castle Beach, Falmouth, L.J.M.; Mylor (Thurston and Vigurs 1925).
East: 97, Rock Quay, R.W.D.; 05, Par, L.J.M.; 20, Bude, E.T. (Thurston and Vigurs 1926), 1966, J.A.P.; 35, Seaton, B.Sh.; Downderry, N.J.F.

ATROPA L.

410/1 **A. bella-donna** L.   Deadly Nightshade
Probably originally introduced. Not subsequently refound at Mt Edgcumbe (Flora).
East: 28, Penheale Manor, near Egloskerry, W.Wi., Herb. W. Wise, (LAUS), in shrubbery 'not truly wild', undated.

HYOSCYAMUS L.

411/1 **H. niger** L.   Henbane
Local and rather rare, in coastal areas of Cornwall, but very rare in the East. Remarkably persistent in most of its stations.

West: 42, path to beach, Porthcurno, G.B.M.; 43, Eastern Green, Penzance (Flora), 1974, comm. G.B.M.; 53, Phillack Towans (Flora), 1970, B.M.S.; Upton Towans, J.R.; Hayle Towans, G.B.M.; (54), Gwithian (Suppt), 1949, S.B.; 62, Poldhu (Flora), 1968, M.C.H., T.M., and L.J.M.; Gunwalloe (Flora), post—1950, R.H.; Loe Pool (Flora), post—1950, R.H.; 72, Porthallack, Helford River, recorder unknown; St Anthony-in-Meaneage (Flora), post—1950, R.H.; W of Mawnan Shurch, A.J.S.; 75, Holywell Valley, A.B.; Penhale Sands (Flora), 1968, G.A.; 86 (76), Porth Joke (Flora), 1967, J.A.P.; East Pentire (Flora), 1956, C.W.

East: 05, Par Sands (Suppt), L.T.M. (Thurston 1935); 19, Crackington Haven (Flora), 1979, K.H.

Scilly: Lousley 1971.

SALPICHROA MIERS

414/1 § **S. origanifolia** (Lam.) Baillon   Cock's Eggs
Well-established in one locality.

*West: 53, St Michael's Mount, K.E.B. (*Proc. B.S.B.I.*, 2 (1956): 144).

SOLANUM L.

413/3 **S. nigrum** L., Black Nightshade, and 413/1 **S. dulcamara** L., Bittersweet, are both frequent and widely distributed throughout the county.

DATURA L.

415/1 § **D. stramonium** L.   Thorn-apple
Widespread as a casual, rarely persistent.

West: 33, Trewellard, near Pendeen, M.C.; 53, garden, Hayle, letter in *The Cornishman*, 5.10.1967; 64, Council tip, Tolvaddon, L.J.M.; building site, Portreath, L.J.M.; Rosewarne, Camborne, J.R.; 72, garden, Helford, R.H.; St Anthony-in-Meneage, T.M.; 87, near Porthcothan, B.S.

East: 83, Penhallow Farm, near Philleigh, B.E.M.G.; 95, Sticker, St Austell (Thurston 1929a); 96, St Columb Major, T.O.D.; 05, Luxulyan, B.Sh.; 07, garden, St Breward, E.A.; 20, Council tip, Bude, L.J.M.; 38, one plant in orchard, St Stephen, Launceston, W.W. (Thurston 1929a).

Scilly: Lousley 1971; T, 20 plants, C.H.; Pentle Bay, plentifully, J.E.L.; bulbfield between Great Pool and Pentle Bay, P.G.; TN, two plants on shore, J.E.L.

BUDDLEJACEAE
BUDDLEJA L.
375/1 * § **B. davidii** Franchet, Butterfly-bush, first appeared after the 1939—1945 war, and has since spread rapidly to all parts of the mainland of Cornwall, but it is still absent from Scilly.

SCROPHULARIACEAE
LIMOSELLA L.
426/1 **L. aquatica** L.   Mudwort
Recorded for W Cornwall and Scilly (Flora), but there are no records later than 1921, when Thurston refound it on Chy-an-hal Moor, near Penzance, and Downes saw it in Abbey Pool, Tresco.

MIMULUS L.
425/1   § **M. guttatus** DC.   Monkeyflower
(*M. langsdorfii* Donn)
Frequent and widespread in W Cornwall, rare in the East. It should be noted that the records in the Flora may also include records for the hybrid, with which it is often confused.
West: 32, Nanquidno, St Just, B.M.S.; 43, Nancledra, G.L.; Boskednan, B.M.S.; 62, Chypons, Mullion (Suppt), 1967, C.W.; 73, Perranwell, L.J.M.; 86, Rialton, St Columb Minor, C.W.
East: 08, Trebarwith (Flora), 1966, J.A.P.; Rocky Valley (Flora), 1966, J.A.P.; Tintagel (Flora), 1960, B.Sh.; 15, Lostwithiel (Flora), 1967, L.J.M.
Scilly: Lousley 1971; T, in profusion in field near the barn between Great Pool and Pentle Bay, recorder unknown.

[425/2 § **M. luteus** L.   Blood-drop-emlets
A specimen from Maenporth, 1901, F.H.D., Herb. Davey, **(TRU)**, labelled this, is clearly *M. guttatus*. Six post—1950 records have been erroneously attributed to this species, but in all cases they should be referred to the hybrid (see below).]

425/1 § **M. guttatus x luteus**
x 2   Only recently recognised in Britain, this hybrid Mimulus is frequent in parts of Cornwall. The following records include those wrongly ascribed to *M. luteus*.

*West: 33, Bojewyan to Portheras Cove, various recorders; 43, Pendour Cove, Zennor, M.B.G.; 64, Porthtowan Valley, J.G.T.; 71, Coverack, various recorders; 73, Carvedras Valley, Constantine, R.B.G.; 74, Manor Parsley, near Porthtowan, J.G.T.; 86, Quintrell Downs, 1903, C.R.

*East: 97, Lundy Bay, L.W.; 08, Tintagel area, 1947, L.L., (BM); 16, Treslea Water, E of Bodmin, K.P.; 26, Tremar Coombe, Liskeard, J.L.; 36, Pillatonmill, I.N.

425/3 § **M. moschatus** Douglas ex Lindley   Musk
No longer grown in gardens since it lost its scent. It has thus become very rare as an escape.

West: 63, Releath, near Wendron, B.M.S.; garden weed, Treskillard, L.J.M.; 85, Penhallow Moor, Newlyn East, C.C.V. (Thurston and Vigurs 1926).

East: 83, St Anthony, Herb. Tech. Coll.; 95, marsh near Burngullow Station, W.T. (Thurston and Vigurs 1926); 05, Penwithick, near St Austell, W.T. (Thurston 1929a); 08 (09), Boscastle, 1901, W.Wi., Herb. W. Wise, (LAUS), (as *M. luteus*); 27, NE bank of R Lynher, Rilla Mill, N.J.F.

VERBASCUM L.

416/1 **V. thapsus** L., Great Mullein, is of frequent occurrence throughout Cornwall, in a variety of dry habitats, especially on blown sand.

416/9 § **V. blattaria** L.   Moth Mullein
A rare introduction, formerly known throughout the county, now almost gone.

West: no recent records.

East: 96, NE of St Columb Major (Suppt), still there, post—1950, J.A.P.; 25, Looe dust-heaps, F.H.P. (Thurston 1928).

Scilly: no recent records, Lousley 1971.

416/10 V. virgatum Stokes   Twiggy Mullein

A very rare British plant, constant in a few localities, especially in the Lower Tamar area, casual elsewhere.
West: 43, casual in garden, Penzance, G.B.M.; 53 Phillack Towans (Suppt), and Upton Towans, 1970, B.M.S.; 64, casual on old mine-workings, Tuckingmill, J.S.R.; 73, Falmouth (Flora), frequent near Penmere Halt, 1961, L.J.M.; 86, casual at Tregunnel Road, Newquay, L.G.
East: 83, one plant, St Anthony Head, B.E.M.G.; 84, near Boscawen Park, Truro, W.Bo. (Thurston and Vigurs 1925); 95, St Dennis Junction, B.B.; 97, near Wadebridge, J.A.P.; 05, Charlestown, W.T. (Thurston and Vigurs 1927); 25, Looe dust-heaps, F.H.P. (Thurston 1928); 35, Trevollard (Flora), post—1950, I.N.; Tideford (Flora), post—1950, S.M.; 45, St Johns, S.M.; Torpoint (Flora), post—1950, S.M.; H.M.S. Raleigh, 1976, E.G.; Southdown Quarry, Millbrook, L.J.M.; Wearde, near Saltash, I.N.; Antony Passage, I.N.; St Stephens, Saltash (Flora), post—1950, I.N.; Coombe Farm, Saltash, I.N., 25 plants, 1978, E.G.; (44), one plant in clover-field, Rame, S.M.; 46, Clifton Farm, I.N.
Scilly: Lousley 1971; T, Rose Field, D.Hu.

416/3 § V. phlomoides L.   Orange Mullein

Casual, possibly on the increase.
*West: 53, plentiful on waste ground, Lelant, 1974, reported independently by G.B.M. and B.M.S.; mine-waste, Halamanning, St Hilary, K.P.
East: 20, old railway station, Bude, 1974, L.J.M.
Scilly: one station, Lousley 1971.

416/7 V. nigrum L.   Dark Mullein

Frequent in parts of Mid-Cornwall, but absent from large areas, and in the E only on the south coasts.
West: 62, Poldhu, near golf-links, R.H.; Cury (Flora), post—1950, J.B.; 72, church-wall, Constantine, R.H.; 73, Falmouth Reservoir, L.J.M.; near Treluswell cross-roads, K.P.; Ponsanooth (Flora), near Viaduct, 1962, J.G.T.; Kennel Vale, Ponsanooth, L.J.M.; Mabe (Flora), post—1950, R.H.; 74, Gwennap (Flora), at United Mines, L.J.M.; 83, Falmouth (Flora), by the station, 1974, K.P.; Swanpool, L.J.M.; 84, old Kea Churchyard, C.W.

East: 83, St Anthony Head, J.R.; Percuil, J.R.; Pendower Beach, J.G.T.; quarry, Philleigh, B.E.M.G.; 84, Ruan Lanihorne churchyard, and Trelonk Farm, C.W.; 93, three places in Veryan Parish, C.W.; Nare Head, J.A.P.; 95, St Dennis Junction, B.B.; 96, railway embankment, Goss Moor, J.G.; 04, Pentewan (Suppt), post—1950, J.A.P.; 05, Par (Flora), post—1950, J.A.P.; mine-waste E of St Blazey, J.A.P.; 15, Fowey, H.W.P. (Thurston 1935); 25, Looe (Flora), Bodigga Cliff, E of Looe, K.H.; 35, several places between Wacker and Antony, S.M.; Seaton (Flora), 1966, L.J.M.; 45, Lower Anderton, Millbrook, and between Wolsdon and St Johns, S.M.

Scilly: no recent records, Lousley 1971.

var. **tomentosum** Bab.

East: 35, Seaton (Flora, as *V. nigrum x thapsus*), 7 or 8 plants, 1967, S.M. (as the hybrid, but probably this).

SCROPHULARIA L.

424/1 **S. nodosa** L., Common Figwort, is common and widespread on the mainland.

Scilly: rare, Lousley 1971; B, between Southward and Samson Hill, 1969, J.P.B.

424/2 **S. auriculata** L. (*S. aquatica* L.), Water Figwort, is frequent and widely distributed in damp places throughout the mainland. Rejected for Scilly, Lousley 1971.

424/5 § **S. vernalis** L.   Yellow Figwort

A very rare but persistent introduction.

West: 83, Falmouth (Flora and Suppt), Kimberley Park, 1954—65, R.H.; three plants in grounds of hotel off Stracey Road, Falmouth, 1974, L.J.M.

  *East: 84, amongst ruins, grounds of Trehane, NE of Truro, 1976, B.E.M.G.

424/4 **S. scorodonia** L.   Balm-leaved Figwort

Rather local and rare, but often frequent in areas where it does occur. Absent from the extreme E of the county.

West: 42, between Kemyel Wood and Mousehole, G.B.M.; Buryas Bridge, near Penzance, G.B.M.; 43, Penlee Park, Penzance, J.B.; 53, Marazion Marsh (Flora),

G.C.D. (Thurston 1935); Canons Town, B.M.S.; Hayle, B.M.S.; Phillack Towans, W.B. (Thurston 1935); Upton Towans, 1977, L.J.M.; (54), St Ives (Flora), near railway station, R.H.; 75, Perranporth (Flora and Suppt), three places around Perranporth, 1964—78, L.J.M.; Holywell Bay, L.J.M.; Chyverton Woods, near Zelah, L.J.M.; 83, Flushing (Flora), post—1950, R.H.; 85, Shepherds, near Goonhavern, L.J.M.; 86, Newquay (Flora), The Gannel, 1967, L.J.M.

East: 94, wood near Caerhays Castle, L.J.M.; 95, St Dennis Junction, B.B.; 96, railway, Goss Moor, L.J.M.; 97, Rock (Flora), 1946—77, R.W.D.; 05, Carlyon Bay, R.H.; Charlestown (Suppt), overlooking harbour, 1977, E.A.; Par (Flora), near harbour, 1962, L.J.M.; 15, Fowey (Flora), 1977, L.J.M.; by railway, Golant, L.J.M. Scilly: common, Lousley 1971; TN, 1972, J.P.B.

[424/3 **S. umbrosa** Dumort. (*S. alata* Gilib.), Green Figwort. We have not been able to trace a specimen to support the record in the Flora, and, as the locality is outside the known distribution of this species, we have no hesitation in removing it from the Cornish list.]

MISOPATES RAFIN.

417/1 **M. orontium** (L.) Rafin.   Lesser Snapdragon
(*Antirrhinum orontium* L.)

Cultivated ground and waste places. Still quite frequent in parts of W Cornwall, much less so in the East.

West: 32, Lands End (Flora), 1978, J.S.R.; Boscregan, B.M.S.; Porthgwarra, S.M.; Sennen, J.B.; 33, St Just (Flora), three places around St Just, 1973, M.C.; 43, near Tremithick Cross, Penzance, B.M.S.; 62, Breage, 1949, G.B.M.; Porthleven, H.B.S.; 64, garden weed, Camborne, J.S.R.; 71, Lizard (Flora), 1964, J.B.; Kennack, H.F.D. (Thurston 1928), 1959—77, J.Fo.; Poltesco, and Grade, H.F.D. (Thurston 1928); 73, near Mabe, L.J.M.; Golden Bank, Falmouth (Flora), Rosecarrack, Swanvale, and Newporth Head, 1961, L.J.M.; 75, Ventongimps, H.F.D. (Thurston 1928); 83, Penpol, Devoran, L.J.M.; 84, old railway near Truro, J.S.R.; 87, Treburick, St Eval, R.D.P.; Porthmeor, Porthcothan, J.B.; near Gunver Head, Padstow, J.A.P.; 96, Winnards Perch, L.J.M.

East: 83, garden weed, St Mawes, B.E.M.G.; near Portscatho, J.S.R.; 96, near Goss Moor, L.J.M.; 97, Polzeath (Suppt), 1951, R.W.D.; cornfield, Greenaways, and Pentire Peninsula, R.W.D.; 05, Polkerris, B.Sh.; 08 (09), Forrabury, Boscastle (Flora), 1960, E.A.; 27, garden weed, Rilla Mill, N.J.F.; 35, Wivelscombe (Flora), post—1950, I.N.; 36, Callington, B.Sh.; 38, Launceston (Flora) 1970, G.L.K.; Saltash, Coombe, Wearde, and St Stephens, post—1950, I.N.; Thanckes, Torpoint, S.M. Scilly: Lousley 1971.

CHAENORHINUM (DC.) REICHENB.

421/1 **C. minus** (L.) Lange (*Linaria minor* (L.) Desf.), Small Toadflax, is common and widespread along the railways. Also occasionally in arable fields and waste places. Absent from Scilly.

LINARIA MILLER

420/4 **L. vulgaris** Miller, Common Toadflax, is very common and widespread, but there are no recent records from Scilly.

420/5 § **L. genistifolia** (L.) Miller   Balkan Toadflax
subsp. **dalmatica** (L.) Maire & Petitmengin
(Suppt as *L. dalmatica* Mill.)

Slowly increasing as a railway alien.

*West: 53, railway ballast, Angarrack, 1967, B.M.S. East: 95, St Dennis Junction, 1976, B.B.; 05, Par Sands (Suppt), by railway, Par, 1972, B.G.; 26, railway between Liskeard and Coombe, 1922—3, C.P.F. (Thurston and Vigurs 1925).

420/2 § **L. purpurea** (L.) Miller   Purple Toadflax
Originally a rare garden escape, now frequent as a colonist of waste places throughout the county. Several colour-forms are found.

West: 43, Trevarrack, Penzance, B.M.S.; 53, near Power-station, Hayle, L.J.M.; 64, Tuckingmill, Camborne, L.J.M.; 74, Redruth (Flora), Sparnon Close, 1977, K.P.; United Mines, Gwennap, L.J.M.; 75, Perranporth, and Bolingey, J.A.P.; 83, Falmouth (Flora), 1977, J.S.R.; Swanpool, L.J.M.; Mylor Bridge, F.G.F.; 84, Truro (Flora), by railway station, 1963, L.J.M.

217

East: 84, near Boscawen Park, Truro, A.Gr. (Thurston and Vigurs 1924); 97, near Polmorla, St Breock, K.P.; roadside Reserve above Wadebridge, L.J.M.; 05, Par (Flora), post—1950, J.A.P.; 26, railway between Liskeard and Coombe, 1922—3, C.P.F. (Thurston and Vigurs 1925); waste ground, Liskeard, N.J.F.; 27, Rillaton, N.J.F.; 35, Tideford, J.A.P.; Downderry, S.M.; Polbathic, and Trerulefoot, S.M.; 38, Launceston, B.Sh.; 45, Saltash (Flora), post—1950, D.B.; Torpoint, St Johns, and Millbrook, S.M.

420/3 **L. repens** (L.) Miller   Pale Toadflax
Scattered throughout Mid and East Cornwall, absent from West Penwith and Scilly. This species is particularly frequent around Mabe, near Falmouth.

West: 63, by railway near Gwinear Road Station, L.J.M.; 64, hedge, Reskadinnick, Camborne, R.J.M.; 73, Penryn (Flora), 1974, L.J.M.; Treluswell, near Penryn, R.M.; Budock (Flora), Crill Hill, post—1950, L.J.M.; Mabe (Flora), still frequent around Mabe, and near the reservoir, 1950 onwards, various recorders; Pulla Cross, Gwennap (Flora), 1961, L.J.M.; Longdowns (Flora), 1977, K.P.; on wall, Stithians, L.J.M.; 74, near Wheal Bassett, Porthtowan, L.J.M.; 83, Falmouth (Flora), 1962, L.J.M.; 86, Newquay, G.C.D. (Thurston 1935).

East: 97, Rock, 1945, R.W.D.; wall, Polzeath Hill, R.W.D.; 05, Par (Flora), still there, 1950 onwards, various recorders; 08 (09), Boscastle, B.E.M.G.; 15, railway between Lostwithiel and Fowey, J.B.; 25, opposite Sandplace Station, J.L.; Polperro, H.W.P. (Thurston 1935), 1964, L.J.M.; 26, railway E of Liskeard Station (Thurston and Vigurs 1925); 27, Rilla Mill, N.J.F.; 36 or 37, garden weed, Haye, Callington, 1923, H.Pa.; 45, old railway line near Wivelscombe, and on siding, Wearde Quay, I.N.

420/3 **L. repens x vulgaris** = *L. x sepium* Allman
x 4   A rather rare hybrid, but possibly overlooked.
West: 73, Falmouth Reservoir (Flora), refound 1961, R.B.G., has appeared in most years since; 74, lane at Trevince Moor, Gwennap, L.J.M.
East: 05, Par, 1923, L.T.M. (Thurston and Vigurs 1924), refound 1972, B.G.; 25, near Polperro, L.J.M.

218

420/3 **L. repens x supina** = *L. x cornubiensis* Druce
x 6 Confined to Cornwall, this very rare hybrid could still survive in its sole locality.

  *East: 05, Par Harbour, L.T.M. (B.E.C. 1925, p. 998).

420/6 § **L. supina** (L.) Chaz.   Prostrate Toadflax
  Very local and rare, but sometimes in quantity. Davey thought it to be native, but this is not the general opnion today.

  West: 43, railway, Ponsadene, Penzance, E.A.R. (Thurston 1935), still there, 1950, BRC; 83, railway waste-ground, Falmouth Station, 1972, L.J.M.; 84, plentifully on old railway track, Newham, Truro, 1966, L.J.M.; 87, Mother Ivey's Bay, near Trevose Head, H.F.D. (Thurston 1928).

  East: 95, St Dennis Junction, 1976, B.B.; 05, Par Sands (Flora), still there in fair quantity, various recorders; 45, old railway track, Wearde, near Saltash, 1966, I.N., 1971, S.M.

CYMBALARIA HILL

423/1 § C. **muralis** P. Gaertner, B. Meyer & Scherb. (*Linaria cymbalaria* (L.) Mill.), Ivy-leaved Toadflax, is common on walls throughout the county (rare in Scilly).

KICKXIA DUMORT.

422/2 **K. elatine** (L.) Dumort. (*Linaria elatine* Mill.), Sharp-leaved Fluellin, is frequent and widely distributed as a weed of arable land and waste places (rare in Scilly).

422/1 **K. spuria** (L.) Dumort.   Round-leaved Fluellin
  (*Linaria spuria* Mill.)

  A rare and local weed of coastal arable, mainly in the W.
  West: 62, Gunwalloe (Flora), post—1950, R.H.; Porthleven, H.B.S.; 71, Lizard (Flora), N of Lizard Town, 1970, B.M.S.; 74, by A 30 near Nanteague Farm, G.A.; 75, Rejerrah, L.J.M.; 85, council tip, Newlyn East, L.J.M.; 86, Newquay (Flora), post—1950, R.L.G.L.; (76), Crantock, and West Pentire, R.H.; 87, field near Gunver Head, Padstow, J.A.P.

  East: 83, St Anthony (Flora), post—1950, Herb. Tech. Coll.; 97, St Enodoc, frequent in cornfield, R.W.D.; cornfield, Pentireglaze, R.W.D.; 05, Charlestown, W.T.

(Thurston 1928).
Scilly: no recent records, Lousley 1971.

DIGITALIS L.

429/1 **D. purpurea** L., Foxglove, is a common plant of roadsides, cliffs, and hedgebanks.

ERINUS L.

428/1 § **E. alpinus** L. Fairy Foxglove
A fairly recent garden escape.
*West: 53 (54), 183 plants naturalised on car-park wall, St Ives, L.J.M.; 72, naturalised on wall by main entrance to Lanarth House, St Keverne, 1970, G.B.M.

VERONICA L.

Common species: 430/13a V. **serpyllifolia** L., Thyme-leaved Speedwell (rare in Scilly), 430/5 V. **officinalis** L., Heath Speedwell, 430/7 V. **chamaedrys** L., Germander Speedwell, 430/6 V. **montana** L., Wood Speedwell (very rare in Scilly), 430/1 V. **beccabunga** L., Brooklime (no recent record for Scilly), 430/15 V. **arvensis** L., Wall Speedwell, and 430/21 § V. **persica** Poiret (V. *tournefortii* C. Gmel.), Common Field-speedwell.

430/4 **V. scutellata** L. Marsh Speedwell
Scattered throughout the county, but rather local. West: 32, near Polgigga, Lands End, P.J.R.; 42, Chyan-hal (Flora), Paul, post—1950, B.M.S.; Kerris Moor, B.M.S.; 53, Long Rock, B.M.S.; Marazion Marsh (Flora), 1966, A.B.; 61, Ruan Pool, Lizard, J.A.P.; Hayle Kimbro Pool, M.C.H., T.M. and L.J.M.; 63, Crowan, B.M.S.; Carnmenellis Moor (Flora), 1964, L.J.M.; 73, Polmarth Moor, L.J.M.; near Stithians (Flora), by the reservoir, 1976, J.S.R.; Halvossa Bog, Long Downs, L.J.M.
East: 95, Trenoweth Wood, CNT; Goss Moor, J.B.; 96, bog at Ruthvoes; near Goss Moor, L.J.M.; 05, Luxulyan, B.Sh.; 06, Helmentor (Flora), Red Moor, 1964, L.J.M.; 21, Wrasford Moor, J.A.P.; 26, Coombe, Liskeard (Flora), 1967, J.A.P.; 27, Smallacombe, Fowey Valley, R.Go. and L.J.M.; Siblyback Reservoir, E.G.; 29, Greena Moor (Flora), near Greenamoor

Bridge, 1977, C.C.; 38, near Launceston (Flora), St Stephens, 1970, G.L.K.

430/2 **V. anagallis-aquatica** L.   Blue Water-speedwell

The account in the Flora contains records for this species and the next. The following is possibly the only extant station.

East: 47, by the Tamar near Weir Head (Flora), refound 1958, I.N.

430/3 **V. catenata** Pennell   Pink Water-speedwell

Apparently only in one station.

*East: 97, Rock (Flora, as last species), still there, 1950 onwards, various recorders, 1979, R.W.D.

430/14 § **V. peregrina** L.   American Speedwell

An increasing colonist of the larger estates.

West: 42, Trewidden, Penzance, B.E.M.G.; 43, Gulval, G.L.; Penlee Park, Penzance, J.B.; Morrab Gardens, Penzance, B.M.S.; 73, Penwarne, near Mawnan Smith, R.H.; Devoran, R.H.; 84, Treseder's Nursery, Truro, B.E.M.G.

*East: 84, garden weed, St Clement, Truro, 1923, K.M.S. (Thurston and Vigurs 1924).

430/23 **V. agrestis** L.   Green Field-speedwell

'A very common and abundant weed' (Flora). Now rare and local.

West: 33, St Just, M.C.; 62, Porthleven, H.B.S.; 75, frequent as a weed in Zelah Nurseries, L.J.M.; 86 (76), Kelsey Head, near Newquay, A.B.

East: 97, in two cornfields on Pentire Farm, R.W.D.; (98), cornfield above Compit, R.W.D. (both stations on Pentire Peninsula); 38, St Stephens, Launceston, G.L.K.; 45, still common in Torpoint area, S.M.

Scilly: Lousley 1971; M, garden, Star Castle, D.E.A.

430/22 **V. polita** Fries   Grey Field-speedwell

(*V. didyma* Ten.)

This species is also now much reduced, but perhaps it is more frequent than the last.

West: 43, Penzance, B.M.S.; 62, Porthleven, H.B.S.; 63, Treskillard, L.J.M.; 64, Penhallick, and Council tip, Tolvaddon, L.J.M.; garden weed, Tehidy, J.S.R.; 75,

frequent, Zelah Nurseries, L.J.M.; 87, Trevone, J.A.P.
East: 83, garden weed, Philleigh, B.E.M.G.; 97, corn-
field, Shilla Valley, Polzeath, R.W.D.; cornfield, Com
Head, Pentire Peninsula, R.W.D.; 45, common in
Torpoint area, S.M.
Scilly: Lousley 1971.

430/24 § **V. filiformis** Sm.   Slender Speedwell
The sudden appearance and rapid spread of this species
in the county has paralleled its spectacular advance in
the British Isles as a whole. Now frequent and widespread in Cornwall.

First records:
*West: 75, Perranzabuloe Churchyard, 1945, F.R.
(B.E.C. 1945).
*East: 97, Chapel Amble, 1954, R.I.S.
Scilly: M, 1955, R.C.L.H., Lousley 1971.

430/20 **V. hederifolia** L.   Ivy-leaved Speedwell
subsp. **lucorum** (Klett and Richter) Hartl
This is the common taxon, with pale lilac flowers.
Throughout the county.

subsp. **hederifolia**
A recently-recognised taxon in Britain, with blue
flowers and anthers. Common and widespread. We are
grateful to Mrs K.E. Higgs for first drawing our attention
to this subspecies.

First records:
*West: 72, Trenance, Porthoustock, 1971, A.Si.
*East: 15, Fowey, 1978, L.J.M.
*Scilly: M, Porthloo, Content, and Holy Vale, 1971,
A.Si.; T, Dolphin Town, and Towns Hill, 1971, A.Si.;
MN, Middle Town, and Higher Town, 1971, A.Si.

HEBE COMMERSON

431/1   § **H. elliptica x speciosa** = *H. x franciscana* (Eastwood)
Souster
= *H. lewisii* auct.

This common garden shrub of the mild SW counties is
naturalised on cliffs, usually not far from houses.
*West: 53, Marazion cliffs, L.J.M.; 61, Lizard Point,

1964, J.A.P.; 62, cliff near Gunwalloe, L.J.M.; 64
frequent on cliffs, Portreath, L.J.M.; wall at Truro
L.J.M.

*East: 15, Fowey cliffs, N.J.F.; 45, near Anton
Passage, 1966, J.A.P.

Scilly: Lousley 1971, as *H. lewisii.*

SIBTHORPIA L.

427/1 **S. europaea** L. Cornish Moneywort
Frequent and widespread in suitable habitats. Recorded
since 1950 in 19 of the stations listed in the Flora and
Suppt. The following records are additional to those
West: 33, Portheras stream, Pendeen, M.C.; 42
Trevelloe, W of Mousehole, J.A.P.; 42 or 43, N of
Sancreed, J.A.P.; 43, near New Mill, N of Penzance
B.M.S.; Porthmeor, J.S.R.; 53 (54), Gwealavellan, near
Godrevy, R.J.M.; 62, Porthleven, H.B.S.; 63, Trelubba
Farm, Wendron, G.B.M.; Bolenowe Valley, Troon
L.J.M.; 72, Glendurgan Gardens, B.E.M.G.; Mengearne
Brill, L.J.M.; 73, on shady lawn, Greenwith House
Perranwell, L.J.M.; Eathorne Valley, near Constantine
L.J.M.; Penjerrick, near Falmouth, L.J.M.; 74
Tregavethan, near Truro, L.J.M.; 75, Ventongimps
(B.E.C. 1935, p. 180); 83, Pendower Valley, Roseland
L.J.M.; 84, lane by Treliske Hospital, Truro, G.B.M
East: 85, reclaimed bog near Ladock, L.J.M.; 94
Tregoney, J.A.P.; 04, Colonna, S of Mevagissey, L.J.M.
05, Tregorrick, near St Austell, L.J.M.; damp wood
near St Austell, L.J.M.; 07, near Gam Bridge, N of S
Breward, J.A.P.; 16, Fletchers Bridge, near Bodmin
E.A. and L.J.M.; Cabilla Wood, Fowey Valley, L.J.M.
17, Pendrift, Blisland, E.A.; near Penstroda, Blisland
J.G.; 18, Camel Valley W of Pencarrow, and S of Camel
ford, J.A.P.; 27, near Caradon Town, R.W.D. and
L.J.M.; 28, by R. Kensey, near Red Down, L.J.M.
35, Seaton Valley, S.M.; 36, drive of Newton Ferrers
Pillaton, I.N.; 37, near Kerney Bridge, Golberdon, I.N.
above Horsebridge, J.A.P.; 45 (44), Rame, S.M.; 46
Danescombe Valley, I.N.; above Norris Green, I.N.
woods at Cotehele, N.J.F.

Scilly: Lousley 1971; T, Castle Down, A.Y.

MELAMPYRUM L.

[434/4 **M. sylvaticum** L., Small Cow-wheat, is rejected by Davey (Flora). This is a far northern species, and the record must have been a mistake.]

434/3 **M. pratense** L.   Common Cow-wheat
Rather frequent and widespread in the wooded parts of the county, but local in the West, and absent from much of West Penwith, and from Scilly.

var. **hians** Druce
Scattered throughout Mid and East Cornwall.
West: 84, woods near Truro (Flora), Bishops Wood, 1979, L.J.M.
East: 84, Lamorran Woods, R.J.M. and L.J.M.; 95, Trenowth Wood, Grampound, CNT; 16, St Neot, L.J.M.; 36, Cadsonbury, L.J.M.; 37, Luckett Reserve, CNT; Carthamartha Wood, 1970, L.J.M.

EUPHRASIA L.   EYEBRIGHT

Recent work on this genus has shown that some of the species listed in the Flora, and, indeed, in the Suppt, cannot be maintained.

Common species: 435/1/12 **E. tetraquetra** (Berb.) Arrondeau (*E. occidentalis* Wettst.),   435/1/13 **E. nemorosa** (Pers.) Wallr. (incl. *E. curta* (Fries) Wettst.) (absent from Scilly), and   435/1/15 **E. confusa** Pugsley.

[435/
1/19   **E. rostkoviana** Hayne is not found S of the Bristol Channel.   The records in the Flora and Suppt refer to the next two species.]

435/
1/22   **E. anglica** Pugsley
Rather local and rare, but found throughout the county.
West: 33, Bostraze Moor, St Just, J.A.P.; 42 or 43, Penzance, H.W.P. (Thurston 1935); 43, Higher Kerrowe, Try Valley, B.M.S.; Carn Galva, L.J.M.; 53, Upton Towans, L.J.M.; 63, Carnmenellis, L.J.M.; 73, Polmarth Bog, near Carnmenellis, L.J.M.; granite quarries, Mabe, L.J.M.; 74, old quarry, Carn Marth, Redruth, L.J.M.
East: 06, Red Moor, E.A. and L.J.M.; 17, De Lank Quarry, R.W.D.; Dozmary Pool, R.W.D.; 21, Wrasford Moor, R.W.D.; 27, moors near the Cheesewring, R.W.D.;

Smallacombe, Fowey Valley, R.Go. and L.J.M.; 29
Greena Moor, R.W.D.
Scilly: Lousley 1971.

435/ **E. vigursii** Davey
1/23 This well-marked species was described as new to
science by Davey in 1907 (*J. Bot. London*, 45: 219)
and is found only in Devon and Cornwall. Here, it is
a characteristic plant of dwarf heathland.

West: 61, Predannack Downs, CNT; 64, Connor Down
(Flora), between Connor Downs and Nancemellin
Farm, L.J.M.; Porthtowan (Flora), 1966, L.J.M.
Reskajeague Downs, between Portreath and Godrevy
L.J.M.; Gooden Heane Point, Portreath, L.J.M.; 71
Goonhilly Downs, W.R.H.; 75, St Agnes Head, A.C.L.
W of Cligga Head, CNT; Ventongimps (Suppt), F.R.
(Thurston 1929), still there, 1967, G.A., R.Go., and
L.J.M.; 85, Quintrell Downs (Flora), 1952, BRC
East: 96, Rosenannon, St Breock, R.W.D.; St Breock
Downs, R.W.D.; 06, Retire Common, L.J.M.; Race
course Downs, near Bodmin, L.J.M.; 16, Treslea Downs
St Neot, L.J.M.; 17, Cardinham Downs, J.B.; Blisland
R.W.D.; 18, Wilsey Down, J.E.L. (Thurston and Vigurs
1926, as *E. rostkoviana*); 25, Longcoombe, P.F.Y.; 26
Pensilva and St Cleer, P.F.Y.; 28, Kittows Moor
Treneglos, J.E.L. (Thurston and Vigurs 1926, as *E.
rostkoviana*); Badgall Downs, L.J.M.; Laneast Downs
R.G.; 36, Viverdon Down, and 37, Hingston Down
R.W.D.; Kit Hill, P.F.Y.; Silver Valley, and valley E of
this, Harrowbarrow, E.G.; valley N of Haye, Callington
E.G.

[**E. kerneri** auct., and **E. stricta** auct. (both in Suppt)
were, in our opinion, erroneous names given to other
species.]

435/ **E. arctica** Lange ex Rostrup subsp. **borealis** (Townsend)
1/18 Yeo
(*E. brevipila* of Flora and Suppt)

A very rare eyebright in Cornwall. Some of the earlier
records may apply to other species. The following
appear to be correct.

West: 53, Carbis Bay (Flora), 1912, E.T.; 63, near
Condurrow, Camborne, L.J.M.; 64, Tregajorran, near
Carn Brea, L.J.M.

East: 17, Bolventor, 1918, F.R.; 18, by stream N of Doney's Shop, M.A.
Scilly: Lousley 1971.

[E. borealis auct. was recorded in the Flora and Suppt, but it is not clear which species was intended. Davey's specimen from Carnkief, Herb. Davey, (TRU), looks much like *E. nemorosa*.]

435/   E. micrantha Reichenb.
1/1   (*E. gracilis* Fr.)
Frequent on moors and old mine-workings, but often overlooked.

West: 33, St Just, J.B.; Carn Galva, L.J.M.; 61, heath near Hayle Kimbro, L.J.M.; 62, near the cliffs, Gunwalloe, CNT; 63, Porkellis Moor, L.J.M.; 64, old mine-workings, Lanner, L.J.M.; 74, moor S of Mt Hawke, L.J.M.; mine-waste, Gwennap, R.W.D. and L.J.M.; near Chacewater Station, L.J.M.; 75, Rees Wood, Chyverton, C.J.; near St Agnes Beacon, F.R. (Thurston 1928); 84, Bishops Wood, near Truro, W.H.F. (Thurston and Vigurs 1923); 85, Penhallow Moor, Newlyn East, L.J.M.

East: 96, Tregonetha Downs, St Columb, L.J.M.; near Hustyn Gate, St Breock, R.W.D.; 05, Trethurgy, near St Austell, B.E.M.G. and L.J.M.; 06, Red Moor, E.A. and L.J.M.; 18, Bodmin Moor, near Watergate, L.J.M.; Wilsey Down, J.E.L. (Thurston and Vigurs 1926); 21, Wrasford Moor, R.W.D.; 28, Laneast Downs, G.L.K.; Kittows Moor, J.E.L. (Thurston and Vigurs 1926); 37, Hingston Down, R.W.D.
Scilly: one station, Lousley 1971.

Euphrasia hybrids are frequent in Cornwall, but their parentage is often open to dispute. The putative hybrid below, however, is a common and widespread taxon, often in the absence of both parents.

435/   E. confusa x nemorosa
1/15   First record:
x 13   *East: 18, Davidstow, J.E.L. (Thurston 1935)

ODONTITES LUDWIG

436/1a **O. verna** (Bellardi) Dumort.   Red Bartsia
subsp. **verna**

Rare in Cornwall, though possibly overlooked.

West: 62, Cowanna Fen, 1962, R.H.

East: 84, arable fields, Fentongollan, 1969, B.E.M.G.;
45, St Johns, T.A.B., **BM**.

436/1b subsp. **serotina** (Dumort.) Corb., is common and widespread throughout the county.   Rejected for Scilly,
Lousley 1971.

PARENTUCELLIA VIV.

437/1 **P. viscosa** (L.) Caruel   Yellow Bartisa
Damp edges of fields and waste places.   Quite frequent
throughout the county, sometimes in quantity.

West: 32, in two places near St Just, M.C.; 33, Wheal
Hernon Hill, St Just, M.C.; 42, near St Buryan, R.L.G.L.;
near Drift Reservoir, G.B.M.; 43, Embla Farm,
Towednack, C.W.; Morvah, H.B.S.; 52, Praa Sands,
B.B.; 53, Upton Towans, L.J.M.; St Erth (Flora), near
the church, H.B.S.; 61, Predannack Downs, E.A.; above
Kynance Cove, H.B.S.; 62, Porthleven, H.B.S.; Wheal
Grey, Ashton, F.G.F.; 71, Coverack (Suppt), Black
Head, H.B.S.; West Kennack Sands, D.S.D.; 72, Rose-
mullion Head, L.J.M.; near St Keverne, P.D.W. (Thurston
and Vigurs 1926); Gweek, J.Fo.; Mawnan Glebe, K.H.;
Frenchman's Creek, Helford River, C.H.F.; 73,
Newporth Head, near Maenporth, L.J.M.; Polmarth
Moor, Carnmenellis, L.J.M.; Mabe (Flora), post—1950,
L.J.M.; Swanvale, Falmouth, L.J.M.; near Stithians,
J.S.R.; marshy field, Mabe Reservoir, L.J.M.; 74, Five
Acres, Allet, G.A.; Silverwell Moor, L.J.M.; 75,
Ventongimps Quarry, B.M.S. *et al;* Penwartha Coombe,
Perranporth, B.B.; 83, Falmouth, L.J.M.; Trefusis Point,
near Flushing, L.J.M.; 86, S side of the Gannel,
Newquay, K.Ha.; 97, near Stepper Point, Padstow,
J.S.R.

East: 97, Treworrnan salt-marsh, C.W.; cliff-flush,
Pentire Peninsula, R.W.D.; 05, Polkerris, B.Sh.; Par
(Flora), post—1950, L.J.M.; 08, meadow at Trebarwith,
R.L.G.L.; 25, Looe (Flora), 1978, L.J.M.
Scilly: common, Lousley 1971.

PEDICULARIS L.

432/2 **P. sylvatica** L., Lousewort, is common on damp soils throughout the county.

432/1 **P. palustris** L.   Marsh Lousewort

This species has declined somewhat since the Flora, reflecting the increasing drainage of wet places.

West: 32, Sennen (Flora), 1971, B.M.S.; 33, Bostraze Moor, J.A.P.; 42, Chy-an-hal Moor (Flora), 1948, J.B.; Kerris Moor, 1948, J.B.; Paul (Flora), 1971, B.M.S.; 53, Marazion Marsh, A.B.; (54), Gwealavellan Marsh, near Godrevy, R.J.M.; 71, N of Gwendreath, J.A.P.; Crousa Downs, J.Fo.; 72, near Leech Pool, Goonhilly, J.A.P.; 73, Budock, near Falmouth, L.J.M.; Rame (Flora), post—1950, L.J.M.; 75, Penhale Sands (Flora), 1977, L.J.M.

East: 95, Goss Moor, L.J.M.; N of St Dennis, J.A.P.; 05, Par (Flora), near the Station, J.A.P.; Starrick Moor (Suppt), 1954, J.B.; 08, De Lank at Bradford, 1939, R.W.D.; 26, Draynes Valley, F.H.C. and J.L.; 27, Upper Fowey Valley, J.B.

Scilly: no recent records, early records doubtful, Lousley 1971.

RHINANTHUS L.

433/2 **R. minor** L.   Yellow Rattle
(*R. crista-gallii* L.)

Common and widespread in grassy places on the mainland but absent from Scilly.

var. **stenophyllus** Schur (*R. stenophyllus* Schur), is a late-flowering form found in a number of scattered localities.

[433/1 **R. angustifolius** C.C. Gmelin (*R. major* Ehrh.), Greater Yellow Rattle, was dismissed by Davey (Flora), as an obvious mistake. It has no place in the Cornish list.]

LATHRAEA L.

[439/1 **Lathraea squamaria** L.   Toothwort

An unlocalised record for V.C.I. was accepted by Davey (Flora), but in the absence of further evidence this is best rejected.]

ACANTHACEAE

ACANTHUS L.

443/1 § **A. mollis** L. Bear's-breech

An increasing garden throw-out, often forming large colonies.

West: 53, Lelant, J.A.P.; 62, Porthleven, H.B.S.; 64, Portreath, J.T.B. (Thurston 1935), now a large colony, 1977, J.S.R.; waste ground, Tolvaddon, J.S.R.; 71, Pistol Lane, Lizard, 1959—77, J.Fo.; Ruan Minor (Flora), near Kuggar, H.M.B. (*Proc. B.S.B.I.*, **3**: 60), 72, Mawnan, L.J.M.; 74, United Mines, Gwennap, L.J.M.; 83, Madiera Walk, Falmouth, L.J.M.; Pennance Point, near Falmouth, L.J.M.

*East: 83, Portscatho, J.S.R.; 97, roadside near Lundy Bay, R.W.D.; 15, Menabilly, near Fowey (B.E.C. 1933), 35, Downderry, J.A.P.; 45, near Carbeile Mill, Torpoint, S.M.

Scilly: Lousley 1971.

OROBANCHACEAE

OROBANCHE L.

[440/2 **O. purpurea** Jacq., Yarrow Broomrape. We support Davey (Flora) in rejecting this species for Cornwall.]

440/4 **O. alba** Stephen ex Willd. Thyme Broomrape
(*O. rubra* Sm.)

Locally frequent on the Lizard, extremely rare elsewhere in Cornwall.

West: 61, Carn Caerthillian, D.S.D.; Kynance (Flora), still there, 1950 onwards, various recorders; Mullion (Suppt), 1947, J.B.; 62, Gunwalloe (Suppt), still there, 1950—76, various recorders; Halsferran Cliff, J.A.P. (possibly the same station); 71, Church Cove, Landewednack, J.A.P.; Kennack, 1956—64, J.B.; Beagle Point, near Black Head, 1950—60, R.B.G.; Downas Valley, CNT.

East: 94, Port Holland (Suppt), refound 1963, L.J.M., but not since.

440/8 **O. minor** Sm. Common Broomrape

Scattered throughout the county, though mainly near the sea, on a variety of host plants.

West: 53, Marazion (Flora), 1968, J.B.; Lelant Downs, L.J.M.; Hayle Causeway, S.M.; near Hayle Power-Station, L.J.M.; Angarrack Bridge, J.M.M., R.P., and L.J.M.; 62, Porthleven, H.B.S.; 71, Kennack Sands, J.B.; 75, St Agnes, F.G.F.; 85, new road verge, Rejerrah, in great quantity, L.G.; 87, dunes, Constantine Bay, L.J.M.; 97, near Padstow (Suppt), Stepper Point, J.A.P.

East: 83, cliffs near castle, St Mawes, B.E.M.G.; Towan Beach, St Anthony, L.J.M.; abundant in pasture between Bohortha and St Anthony, L.J.M.; Portscatho, L.J.M.; 85, roadside, Ladock, L.J.M.; 94, Hemmick Bay, J.B.; 05, Charlestown, W.T. (Thurston 1929a); Par (Flora), 1951—54, J.B.; 15, Lantivet Bay, K.H.; 35, Seaton, N J.F.; Portwrinkle, S.M.; Wacker, near Antony, S.M.; 45, Carbeile Mill, Torpoint, S.M.; (44), Penlee Battery, near Cawsand, S.M.

Scilly: Lousley 1971.

This species occurs frequently in gardens on cultivated plants. It has a particular liking for *Senecio greyi* auct. The following are all post—1950 records for this host:

West: 42, Alexandra Gardens, Penzance, G.B.M.; 53, St Ives Secondary School, R.Sm.; 83, Point, Devoran, L.J.M.; 87, Trevone, Padstow, E.G.M., comm. N.D.W.

Scilly: Lousley 1971.

On other hosts:

West: 43, in greenhouse, Penlee Gardens, Penzance, G.B.M. (on *Clianthus puniceus*).

East: 15, garden, Fowey, L.J.M. (on *Parahebe catarrhactae*).

440/11 **O. maritima** Pugsley   Carrot Broomrape
(*O. amethystea* auct.)

It is by no means certain that the above is the correct name for this plant, as it has been given by various authorities to what may be different taxa. We have therefore listed the records here under their host plants.

On *Daucus carota* subsp. *gummifer* or *Plantago* sp.:
West: 53, Marazion (Flora), 1975, B.M.S.; 62, Porth-leven, H.B.S.; 87, Porthcothan, T.H.A.

East: 25, Looe (Flora), E Looe cliffs, 1966, J.A.P.; 35, from Seaton to Tregantle (Flora), Eglarooze Cliff,

1978, D.Ha.; Long Sands, Tregantle, post—1950, S.M.; Sharrow, 1967, S.M.; 45, from Tregantle to Rame (Flora), E end of Whitsand Bay, 1979, E.G.; (44), Rame Head, 1968, J.M.W. and L.J.M.; Penlee Point, L.J.M.

On *Eryngium maritimum* : (this is probably a form of *O. minor*).

West: 53, near Marazion Station, various recorders; 64, Porthtowan (Flora), 1971, B.M.S.; Portreath, L.J.M., now gone; 87, Treyarnon, T.H.A.; Mother Ivey's Bay, C.G.L. (Thurston and Vigurs 1926).
Scilly: Lousley 1971.

440/10 **O. hederae** Duby   Ivy Broomrape

Rather rare and local, but very persistent in most of its stations.

West: 52, Prussia Cove (Suppt), still there, 1973, R.M.P.; Keneggy Cliffs, L.J.M.; 53, Carbis Bay (Flora), at Hawks Point, post—1950, B.M.S.; Lelant Golf-links, A.T. (Thurston 1935), 1971, B.M.S.; Hayle, B.M.S.; Copperhouse, Hayle, J.A.P.; near Lelant Station, S.M.; 63, near Leedstown, comm. J.B.B.; 64, in three places around Portreath, L.J.M.; 86, Newquay (Flora), still there, post—1950, J.B.

East: 93, Camels Cove, Portloe, A.T.; 05, Polkerris, near Par (Suppt), 1965, R.D.P.; 08, Trebarwith (Flora), 1962, D.S.D.; 15, Fowey (Flora), abundant below St Catherines Point, 1968, comm, T.O.D.; Lantic Bay, J.C.D.; Lantivet Bay (Suppt), 1966, L.J.M.
Scilly: Lousley 1971.

[440/6 **O. elatior** Sutton, Knapweed Broomrape. We agree with Davey (Flora) in removing this species from the Cornish list.]

440/3   **O. rapum-genistae** Thuill.   Greater Broomrape
(*O. major* L.)

Always rare in Cornwall, this Broomrape has further decreased in the last fifty years, echoing its general decline in Britain.

West: 72, between Durgan and Helford Passage, during the 'thirties', R.B.G.
East: 84, three plants in garden, Nansgwithick,

Tresillian, C.N. (Thurston 1935); 07, wood along Allen Valley, 1955, R.W.S.; 21, woodland rise, Coombe Valley, 1972, L.J.M.

LENTIBULARIACEAE

PINGUICULA L.

441/1 **P. lusitanica** L. Pale Butterwort

Still present in a large number of stations; but in view of the ever-growing drainage of wet areas, we think it advisable to list all the post—1950 records.

West: 32, Sennen, and Lands End (Flora), between the two, R.L.G.L.; Skewjack Moor, Sennen (Flora), 1966, R.W.D. and L.J.M.; Porthgwarra, E.G.; Nanjizal, B.M.S.; Carnyorth Farm, Pendeen, M.C.; 42, Chy-an-hal Moor (Flora), 1971, B.M.S.; cliff-slopes W of Lamorna Cove, J.A.P.; 43, Trevean Cliffs, near Porthmoina Cove, K.H.; Morvah, J.B.; Zennor (Flora), post—1950, L.J.M.; Marazion Marsh, L.J.M.; 61, Goonhilly Reserve, LFC; Kynance, B.M.S.; 63, Black Rock, near Crowan, J.B.; 64, marsh, Red River Valley, R.J.M. and L.J.M.; 71, Coverack (Suppt), between here and Lowland Point, L.C.F.; Crousa Downs, J.Fo.; Croft Pascoe Pool, L.J.M.; 73, Chywoon Moor, near Long Downs (Flora), 1962, L.J.M.; Polmarth Bog, Carnmenellis, L.J.M.; 74, Menagissey, Mt Hawke (Flora), post—1950, L.J.M.; Trevince Moor, Gwennap (Flora), 1966, L.J.M.; Carrine Common, L.J.M.; bog at Allet, G.A.; 75, Ventongimps (Flora), post—1950, B.M.S.; 85, top of Newlyn Downs, L.J.M.; Penhallow Moor, Newlyn East (Flora), 1966, L.J.M.; 86, St Eval (Flora), bog S of here, J.A.P.

East: 95, Goss Moor (Flora), 1954, J.B.; Rosenannon Bog, N.J.F.; 07, De Lank, E.A. and E.W.M.; 16, S of Middle Taphouse, J.A.P.; 17, near Temple Bridge, Bodmin Moor, L.J.M.; 18, below Rough Tor, J.G.T.; Bowithick, J.A.P.; Crowdy Marsh, E.W.M.; 27, Lamelgate, Fowey Valley, L.G.; marsh below Fox Tor, B.B.

441/4 § **P. grandiflora** Lam. Large-flowered Butterwort

Once naturalised in West and East Cornwall. Edgar Rees witnessed its decline and final demise in the West Penwith moors, first at Skewjack, next at Tremethick, and lastly at Trungle Moor. There have been no subsequent records.

West: 42, Trungle Moor, Paul (Flora), 1928, E.A.R.; 43, Tremethick Moor (Flora), 1925, E.A.R.

441/3 **P. vulgaris** L.   Common Butterwort

An important addition to the Cornish Flora. The plant is extremely rare in S Britain, and this is the most southerly station in the British Isles.

*West: 71, Crousa Downs, near Coverack, 1965, J.A.P.

UTRICULARIA L.

442/4 **U. minor** L.   Lesser Bladderwort

Very rare and local, though occasionally in quantity on Bodmin Moor.

West: 53, Long Rock Marsh, B.M.S.; Marazion Marsh (Flora), 1949, J.B. (these two stations are more-or-less contiguous); 62, Loe Pool, 1927, C.H.F.; 63, Porkellis Moor (Flora), still there, 1962, L.J.M.

East: 96, Goss Moor, with *U. neglecta*, L.J.M.; 17, Bradford, R.W.D.; plentiful on Redhill Marsh, Bodmin Moor, R.Go. and L.J.M.; 18, Crowdy Marsh, R.Go. and L.J.M.; 27, pool near Higher Langdon Farm, Fowey Valley, E.G.; Smallacombe, Fowey Valley, R.Go. and L.J.M.

(A specimen from 53, Marazion Marsh, in Herb. Bannister **(TRU)**, labelled *U. intermedia* Hayne, collected in 1948, does have somewhat toothed leaf-segments, with solitary bristles, and needs further investigation).

442/1 **U. vulgaris** L.   Greater Bladderwort

This species has been much confused with the next, and the records in the Flora and Suppt contain errors. It is known with certainty only from the following station:

West: 75, Carnkief Pond, Perranzabuloe (Suppt as *U. major*), still there in quantity, 1950—80, various recorders.

442/2 **U. australis** R.Br.   Western Bladderwort
(*U. major* Schmidel)

Very rare and local, but possibly overlooked to some extent.

West: 53, Marazion Marsh (Flora), still there 1948, S.B.

East: 96, Goss Moor (Flora), still there, 1950—70, various recorders; 06, moor near Helmentor (Red Moor, Flora), still there, 1950 onwards, CNT.

PLANTAGINACEAE
PLANTAGO L.

Common species: 472/1 **P. major** L., Greater Plantain, 472/5 **P. coronopus** L., Buck's-horn Plantain, 472/4 **P. maritima** L., Sea Plantain (rare in Scilly), and 472/3 **P. lanceolata** L., Ribwort Plantain.

472/2   **P. media** L.   Hoary Plantain

Unaccountably rare in Cornwall, and often confused with a short-petioled form of *P. lanceolata.*

West: 53, Carbis Bay (Flora), 1949, J.B.; 62, Porthleven, H.B.S.; 75, Gear Sands, Perranporth, L.J.M.; 86, abundant in Newquay Churchyard, 1923 (Thurston and Vigurs 1924); St Columb Minor churchyard, C.W.

East: 05, near post-office, Holmbush, St Austell, 1922—5, W.T. (Thurston and Vigurs 1926); pasture, Charlestown, W.T. (Thurston 1929a); 38, in two places near Launceston, G.L.K.; 45, grounds of Antony House, S.M.

Scilly: rejected, Lousley 1971.

LITTORELLA BERGIUS

473/1   **L. uniflora** (L.) Ascherson   Shoreweed

Scattered throughout the county in pools and reservoirs. Usually plentiful where it does occur.

West: 32, Tredinney, near Crows-an-wra, B.M.S.; 42, Drift Reservoir, B.M.S.; 61, Lizard Downs (Flora), post—1950, E.A.; near Mullion, E.J.P. (Thurston and Vigurs 1927); Ruan Pool, T.M.; Hayle Kimbro Pool, L.J.M.; 62, Loe Pool (Flora), still plentiful, 1968, T.M. and L.J.M.; 63, Crowan Reservoir (Flora), 1966, reported independently by J.B., B.M.S., and S.B.; 71, Croft Pascoe Pool, J.M.M. and R.P.; 73, Mabe Reservoir (Flora), post—1950, R.H.; Stithians Reservoir, L.J.M.; 75, Penhale Sands, NCS.

East: 05, Crinnis Beach, St Austell, R.D.P.; 17, Dozmary Pool (Flora), 1953, R.W.D.; 21, Tamar Lake (Flora), still there, 1950 onwards, various recorders. Scilly: Lousley 1971.

CAPRIFOLIACEAE
SAMBUCUS L.
487/1 § **S. ebulus L.** Dwarf Elder
Very rare, but persistent in a few localities.
West: 53, St Erth (Flora), 1965, H.B.S.
East: 97, St Minver (Flora), Rock, G.C.D. (B.E.C. 1931); 38, Launceston (Flora), still there, 1961, E.A.

487/2 **S. nigra L.** Elder
Common and widely distributed throughout the county.

var. **aurea** Sweet Golden Elder
East: 29, near Week St Mary, 1979, L.J.M.

var. **laciniata** Mill. Cut-leaved Elder
East: 84, near Pencalenick, L.J.M.

VIBURNUM L.
488/3 **V. opulus L.**, Guelder-rose, is too frequent in the county to warrant listing of localities, but it is much less so in the West, and is absent from West Penwith, and from Scilly.

488/1 § **V. lantana L.** Wayfaring-tree
Best regarded as an introduction here. It has not been refound in Davey's two localities (Flora).
West: 53, one bush, no doubt introduced, Trencrom, near St Ives, L.J.M.

SYMPHORICARPOS DUH.
489/1 § **S. albus** (L.) S.F. Blake (*S. racemosus* Michx), Snowberry, is now frequent and widespread in the county (absent from Scilly).

LEYCESTERIA WALL.
492/1 § **L. formosa** Wall. Himalayan Honeysuckle
Widely grown in gardens, and becoming frequently reported as a bird-sown introduction in hedges and waste places, on walls, and in woodland.
West: 63, Pendarves Wood, L.J.M.; Godolphin, H.B.S.; 64, Nance Wood, Portreath, R.J.M. and L.J.M.; 73, by stream, Devoran, L.J.M.; 83, Swanpool, L.J.M.; 84, old rubbish tip, Newham, Truro, L.J.M.
East: 84, Pencalenick, L.J.M.; 05, St Austell, B.Sh.

LONICERA L.

491/3 **L. periclymenum** L., Honeysuckle, is common and widespread.

§ **L. nitida** Wilson   Chinese Honeysuckle
The familiar hedging-plant, now frequently reported as a naturalised garden throw-out.

*West: 64, near Reskadinnick, Camborne, R.J.M.; Tolvaddon, Camborne, R.J.M. and L.J.M.; 74, Bissoe Valley, L.J.M.; 84, Kea, 1962, L.J.M.; 86, Carnanton Woods, Vale of Lanherne, CNT.

*East: 19, gully near Tresparrett Posts, R.W.D. and L.J.M.; 36, by disused quarry, Hepwell Bridge, Quethiock, 1971, I.N.

491/2 § **L. japonica** Thunb.   Japanese Honeysuckle
An increasing garden introduction, often forming extensive patches.

*West: 42, sea-shore near Newlyn Harbour, L.J.M.; 83, a large mass on face of quarry car-park, Falmouth, 1967, L.J.M.

*East: 15, near Readymoney, Fowey, L.J.M.

cv. **aureo-reticulata**
West: 64, near Reskadinnick, Camborne, R.J.M.; 72, between Helford Passage and Durgan, 1960 onwards, R.B.G.

ADOXACEAE

ADOXA L.

493/1 **A. moschatellina** L.   Moschatel
Still very local, this species has increased considerably in the last seventy years.

West: 63, between Roseworthy and Roseworthy Farm, T.J.P. (Thurston and Vigurs 1923), still there, 1980, R.M.; 86, St Mawgan-in-Pydar (Suppt), refound 1975, L.G.

East: 05, between Tywardreath and Par (Thurston 1935); near stream, Polpey, Par, B.G.; 06, near Grogley Halt, J.A.P.; 07, Dinham's Bridge, E.A.; Allen Valley near Trelill, St Kew, C.W.; Hellandbridge, K.H.J.; Shell Woods, Helland, E.A.; Wenfordbridge, E.A.; St Breward, E.A.; 08, roadside, Helstone, L.J.M.; between Trewarmett and Treknow, E.B. (Thurston and Vigurs 1925); 18, near Advent Church, J.G. and C.W.; 19, Valency Valley, E.B. (Thurston and Vigurs 1925), Peters Wood, 1966, J.A.P.; near Minster Church, E.A.; hedges between Minster and Lesnewth, I.N.; 20, coppice near Bude Canal, H.H.H. (Thurston and Vigurs 1925); 21, Coombe Valley, R.O. (Thurston and Vigurs 1925), still there, 1976, R.D.; 25, W. Looe Valley, J.A.P.; above Sowdens Bridge, W. Looe Valley, W.B.P. (Thurston and Vigurs 1924); near Duloe Rectory, 1923, G.G. (Thurston and Vigurs 1924); Sandplace, E. Looe Valley, F.H.C. and J.L.; 26, near Liskeard, C.P.F. (Thurston and Vigurs 1927); 35, Seaton Valley, 1922, D. and W.M. (Thurston and Vigurs 1924), 1966, I.N.; Pillaton Mill, I.N.; Lydcott Wood, J.A.P.; 37, Tamar Valley, near Greystone Bridge, J.A.P.

VALERIANACEAE
VALERIANELLA MILLER

494/1 **V. locusta** (L.) Laterrade Common Cornsalad
(*V. olitoria* Poll.)
Frequent, though rarely common, in suitable habitats.

subsp. **dunensis** (D.E. Allen) P.D. Sell
This recently described taxon is frequent on fixed dunes.
West: 53, Upton Towans; (54), Gwithian Towans, and Godrevy Towans, L.J.M.; 71, Kennack Sands, L.J.M.; 75, Reen Sands, Perranporth, 1926, B.T.L., K (*Watsonia*, 5: 45—46); 87, dunes at Constantine Bay, L.J.M.; Harlyn Bay, L.J.M.
East: 20, Bude dunes, 1925, E.T., K (*Watsonia*, 5: 45—46).
Scilly: Lousley 1971.

494/2 **V. carinata** Loisel. Keeled-fruited Cornsalad
Listed in the Flora as rather rare, this species has increased to the extent that it is now a frequent plant in many parts of the county, except in Scilly, where it is still rare.

494/5 **V. dentata** (L.) Pollich Narrow-fruited Cornsalad
Formerly a common cornfield weed like the next, this species has now virtually disappeared from the county.

West: 71, recorded without locality, 1950 onwards,
BRC.

East: 97, cornfield W of Shilla Wood, Polzeath, 1940,
R.W.D.; 45, recorded without locality, 1950 onwards,
BRC.

Scilly: one record, Lousley 1971.

494/3 **V. rimosa** Bast.   Broad-fruited Cornsalad
Like the preceding, almost extinct.

West: 87, recorded without locality for this square,
1950 onwards, BRC.

East: 97, Trebetherick, 1940, R.W.D.; 05, Par, L.T.M.
(Thurston 1930); 08 and 26, recorded without locality,
1950 onwards, BRC.

494/4 § **V. eriocarpa** Desv.   Hairy-fruited Cornsalad
Very rare and local, but sometimes present in large
populations.

West: 53, Hayle, L.M. (B.E.C. 1927), Phillack 1951,
BRC, abundant there, 1977, L.J.M.; 87, sand-dunes,
Constantine Bay, three large colonies, 1971—77, L.J.M.;
between Windmill and Harlyn Bay, 1965, J.A.P.

East: 97, grassy slope above Ship Inn, Wadebridge,
1977, L.J.M.; 45, Rame (Flora), 1950, BRC.

VALERIANA L.

495/1 **V. officinalis** L. (incl. *V. sambucifolia* Mikan), Common
Valerian, is common and widespread (absent from
Scilly).

CENTRANTHUS DC.

496/1 § **C. ruber** (L.) DC., Red Valerian, is frequent throughout the county, mainly on walls.   Scarlet, pink, and
white forms commonly occur.

DIPSACACEAE

DIPSACUS L.

497/1 **D. fullonum** L. (*D. sylvestris* Huds.), Teasel, is of
frequent occurrence throughout Cornwall.

§ **D. sativus** (L.) Honckeny   Fuller's Teasel
Only as a very rare casual.

West: 62, hedge-top, Porthleven, H.B.S.; 63, waste

ground, Treskillard, Redruth, J.M.; 85, Council tip, Newlyn East, L.J.M.

East: 05, Crinnis, near Par, W.T. (Thurston and Vigurs 1926); Tregorrick, near St Austell, W.T. (Thurston and Vigurs 1926); 15, waste ground, Fowey, W.T. (Thurston and Vigurs 1926).

SUCCISA HALLER

500/1 **S. pratensis** Moench (*Scabiosa succisa* L.), Devil's-bit Scabious, is a very common plant on the mainland of Cornwall, in a variety of habitats. Rejected for Scilly (Lousley 1971).

KNAUTIA L.

498/1 **K. arvensis** (L.) Coulter (*Scabiosa arvensis* L.), Field Scabious, is frequent and widespread on the less acid soils. Extinct in Scilly, Lousley 1971.

SCABIOSA L.

499/2 § **S. atropurpurea** L. Sweet Scabious
(*S. maritima* L.)

A very local but persistent casual.

West: 86, above Newquay Harbour (Flora), still there, 1972, L.G.

499/1 **S. columbaria** L. Small Scabious

Unaccountably rare in Cornwall. All the records require confirmation.

West: 53, Marazion Marsh, W end, 1962—3, J.R.P.; Carbis Bay, B.M.S.; 87, Constantine Bay, 1965, W.G.

East: 83, field between St Mawes and Percuil, W.T. (Thurston 1930); 05, Polmear, near Par (Suppt): the specimen in Herb. Thurston, **K,** may be correctly determined, but it could be an introduced species.

CAMPANULACEAE

CAMPANULA L.

475/10 § **C. alliariifolia** Willd. Cornish Bellflower

An increasing railway alien, sometimes present in quantity.

*West: 53, Angarrack railway bank, 1967, B.M.S.; Phillack Towans, B.M.S.; by railway at level-crossing, Hayle, L.J.M.

*East: 05, railway, Par, B.G.; 05 or 15, between Lostwithiel and Par, J.B.; 07, Port Isaac Station, 1943, **K**, still there, L.B., 1976, R.W.D.; 26, Liskeard (B.E.C. 1945); 45, railway embankment, Wearde, Saltash, 1966, I.N.

[475/1 **C. latifolia** L., Giant Bellflower. We agree with Davey (Flora), that this record was an obvious error.]

475/2   § **C. trachelium** L.   Nettle-leaved Bellflower
One station only, where it may have been introduced.
East: 45, farm at Coombe, Saltash (Flora), refound 1973, I.N. and E.R.

475/3   § **C. rapunculoides** L.   Creeping Bellflower
East: 97, N of Trenain Farm, St Enodoc, a large patch, c 1975, J.A., comm. E.W.M., det. R.W.D.

475/7   **C. rotundifolia** L.   Harebell
In contrast with its frequent occurrence in most British counties, the Harebell is noticeably rare in the SW peninsula, and especially so in Cornwall.
West: 53,   one   plant,   Lelant   Golf   Links,   T.J.P. (Thurston 1930); Phillack Towans, A.T. (Thurston 1930); Gwithian Towans, W.R.H.; 61, Kynance, and between Kynance and Gew Graze (Flora), still there, 1950 onwards, various recorders; 87, Constantine Bay, W.G.; 97, Tregirls Farm, Padstow, W.S.
East: 97, Pentire Peninsula (Flora), still there, 1950—80, R.W.D.

LEGOUSIA DURANDE

476/1   **L. hybrida** (L.) Delarbe   Venus'-looking-glass
Always rare in Cornwall, this cornfield weed is now virtually extinct.
East: 97, field near St Enodoc Church, E.T. and W.T. (Thurston and Vigurs 1925); Polzeath, 1940, R.W.D.

WAHLENBERGIA SCHRADER EX ROTH

474/1   **W. hederacea** (L.) Reichenb.   Ivy-leaved Bellflower
Frequent and widespread in damp places, especially on the granite.   In view of the increased drainage and

ploughing of such habitats, we have thought it advisable to list all its known stations.

West: 32, near Crows-an-wra, P.J.R.; Nanquidno Valley, M.C.; 33, Bostraze, E of St Just, J.A.P.; 42, Chy-an-hal Moor, G.L.; Clodgy Moor, Paul, S.B.; Kerris Moor, 1948, J.B.; woodland reserve, Drift Reservoir, G.B.M.; 43, Zennor (Suppt), Trewey Common, 1966, J.A.P.; Lanyon Farm, Morvah, J.A.P.; Towednack, B.M.S.; Nancledra, A.T. (Thurston 1935); 63, Porkellis Moor (Flora), 1976, J.R.D.; Crowan, J.B.; Bolenowe Valley, near Troon, L.J.M.; Brea Valley, R.J.M.; 72, near Constantine, L.J.M.; 73, Crosmeneggus, near Frogpool, L.J.M.; Stithians Reservoir, S.M.; Polmarth Bog, L.J.M.; near Stithians village (Flora), post—1950, L.J.M.; Menerlue, near Rame, L.J.M.; Budock Bottom, L.J.M.

East: 85, marshy field near Ladock, L.J.M.; 95, Goss Moor (Flora), 1971, CNT; 05, damp wood near St Austell, L.J.M.; Stenalees, 1952—4, J.B.; Luxulyan (Flora), 1962, B.Sh.; 06, Criggan Moor, L.J.M.; Red Moor (Flora), 1971, CNT; 17, Cardinham Moor, R.Go.; Penstroda, Blisland, D.D.; Bradford Bridge, CNT; near Penkestle Moor, S of Dozmary Pool, C.W.; De Lank River, R.W.D.; Bowithick, C.J.; 27, Smallacombe, Fowey Valley, R.Go. and L.J.M.; Fowey Valley, J.L.; marsh near Caradon Town, R.W.D. and L.J.M.; wood at Rillaton, N.J.F.; 28, near Red Down, Egloskerry, J.A.P.; 37, in fir wood, Stare Bridge, Linkinhorne, I.N. Scilly: Lousley 1971.

JASIONE L.

479/1 **J. montana** L., Sheep's-bit, is common and widely distributed. Several varieties, of doubtful validity, have been recorded.

LOBELIA L.

480/1 **L. urens** L.   Heath Lobelia

Still present in quantity in its original station, where it is now protected.

East: 15, damp moorland SE of Lostwithiel, covering several acres (Flora), still plentiful, 1950—79, various recorders; in small area to the E of the main site, still present, 1969, R.W.D.

COMPOSITAE

EUPATORIUM L.

525/1 **E. cannabinum** L., Hemp-agrimony, is common and widespread on the mainland (absent from Scilly).

BELLIS L.

524/1 **B. perennis** L., Daisy, is very common in suitable habitats throughout the county.

SOLIDAGO L.

518/1 **S. virgaurea** L., Goldenrod, is frequent and widespread throughout the county.

518/2 § **S. canadensis** L.   Canadian Goldenrod
Occasional, on waste ground and roadsides.
*West: 53, St Erth, 1962, L.J.M.; 63, Treskillard, L.J.M.; 64, between Portreath and Redruth, L.J.M.

518/3 § **S. gigantea** Aiton
*West: 53, Copperhouse, Hayle, 1966, L.J.M.; 63, Carnarthen, near Carn Brea, L.J.M.; Troon Hill, L.J.M.

ASTER L.

519/6 § **A. novi-belgii** L.   Michaelmas-daisy
Michaelmas Daisies are widely naturalised in Cornwall, and are more common than the following records indicate.
West: 33, Cot Valley, and Carn Gloose, St Just, M.C.; 53, Long Rock, L.J.M.; Copperhouse, Hayle, L.J.M.; 63, Troon Hill, L.J.M.; 73, Devoran Creek, L.J.M.; 87, Porthcothan, L.J.M.
East: 46, by R Tamar between Calstock and Harewood, R.W.D.

519/9 § **A. lanceolatus x novi-belgii** = *A. x salignus* Willd.
East: 05, Par (Flora and Suppt), still there, post—1950, L.J.M.

519/7 § **A. laevis x novi-belgii** = *A. x versicolor* Willd.
x 6   *West: 63, Newton Moor, Treskillard, L.J.M.; 75, Perranporth, L.J.M.

519/1 **A. tripolium** L. Sea Aster

Frequent and widespread in salt-marshes around the coasts, rarely on sea-cliffs (rejected for Scilly, Lousley 1971).

var. **discoideus** Reichenb.

West: 53, salt-marsh, Lelant (Thurston and Vigurs 1925).

East: 97, Camel Estuary, C.J.

ERIGERON L.

521/5 § **E. karvinskianus** DC. = *E. mucronatus* DC.

Mexican Fleabane

In the last twenty years or so, this introduced daisy has spread with remarkable speed into many parts of the county, and is now a frequent wall-plant.

*West: 42, walls, Newlyn, J.S.R.; 43, Penzance, R.L.G.L.; 52, near Pengersick, Praa Sands, H.B.S.; St Michael's Mount, J.A.P.; 53, Marazion, R.L.G.L.; by A30 between Hayle and Penzance, J.A.P.; Lelant, J.A.P.; (54), St Ives, L.J.M.; 63, Troon, J.S.R.; Pendarves, near Camborne, L.J.M.; 71, Ruan Minor, J.A.P.; 72, St Keverne, J.H. and L.J.M.; Helford Passage, near the Post Office, K.E.H.; Porthoustock, RNHS; Mawnan Church End, J.S.R.; near Polgidden Cove, Helford River, L.J.M.; 73, old walls, Marlborough House, Falmouth, 1960, L.J.M.; abundant on wall, Falmouth Hospital; 83, near Devoran, J.S.R.

*East: 83, St Mawes, B.E.M.G.; St Just-in-Roseland, L.J.M.; 84, Malpas, and St Clement, J.A.P.; 94, Grampound Bridge, 1962, L.J.M.; 05, wall near St Austell Station, L.J.M.; Par, L.J.M.; 15, Fowey, L.J.M.; 25, E Looe, and Hannafore, L.J.M.; 35, Hessenford, S.M.; Downderry, J.A.P.; 45, Saltash, S.M.; Cawsand, J.A.P.; 47, Gunnislake, J.S.R.

*Scilly: Lousley 1971.

521/1 **E. acer** L. Blue Fleabane

Still very local, as it has always been, but sometimes present in quantity.

West: 53, Phillack Towans, G.A. and R.Go.; 75, in several parts of Penhale Sands, L.J.M.; 87, in small quantity on Golf Course, Constantine Bay, L.J.M.; 97, old railway, Wadebridge, R.D.

East: 97, Rock (Suppt), still there, 1950—71, various recorders.

521/4   § **E. glaucus** Ker-Gawler   Beach Aster
Widely grown on garden-walls in coastal areas, and becoming increasingly naturalised.

*West: 32, well-established at Sennen Cove, 1967, L.J.M.; 53, Carbis Bay, L.J.M.; 83, on sea-cliffs, Falmouth, L.J.M.; 84, on wall by leat, Truro, L.J.M.; 86, in quarry, Watergate Bay, L.J.M.

*East: 83, walls of St Mawes Castle, 1968, L.J.M.; 97, sandy bank on sea-front, Rock, J.M.M. and R.P.

CONYZA LESS.

522/1   § **C. canadensis** (L.) Cronq.   Canadian Fleabane
(*Erigeron canadense* L.)

Not the common alien here that it is in many Southern counties, but very rare and local.

West: 97, garden weed, Padstow, E.H.

East: 05, ballast-heap, Charlestown, W.T. (Thurston and Vigurs 1926); 45, Wearde, near Saltash, 'in good numbers', E.G.; Saltash, one plant, E.G. and I.N.

FILAGO L.

514/1   **F. vulgaris** Lam.   Common Cudweed
(*F. germanica* L.)

No longer a frequent plant, but still in a number of localities.

West: 72, Merthen Point, Helford River, J.A.P.; cliffs between Mawnan and Durgan, L.J.M.; Maenporth (Flora), post—1950, R.H.; 84, Treliske, Truro, D.D.

East: 96, Tregamere Quarry, St Columb, T.H.A.; 04, Pentewan (Flora), 1954, J.B.; 07, old railway, Slades-bridge, L.J.M.; 26, Liskeard (Flora), 1965, J.L.; St Cleer, J.L.; N of Menheniot, J.A.P.; 35, Bake, between Trerulefoot and Hessenford, S.M.; Trevollard, I.N.; Wivelscombe, I.N.; 38, near Launceston (Flora), W of Launceston, G.L.K.; 45, Wearde Camp, I.N.; Erth Island, I.N.

Scilly: Lousley 1971.

[514/2 **F. lutescens** Jordan (*F. apiculata* G.E.Sm.), Red-tipped Cudweed, was rejected by Davey (Flora) as an error. It should be removed from the Cornish list.]

514/3 **F. pyramidata** L.   Broad-leaved Cudweed
(*F. spathulata* Presl.)

Restricted in Cornwall to the following locality.

*East: 97, in three distinct stations on Pentire Peninsula: field above Miniver Hill, field W of Markham's Quay, and field above Com Head, post—1950, R.W.D. Scilly: rejected, Lousley 1971.

LOGFIA CASS.

514/5 **L. minima** (Sm.) Dumort.   Small Cudweed
(*Filago minima* Fr.)

Still present in a number of localities, and a feature of some of the china-clay tips.

West: 43, near Georgia, Nancledra, B.M.S.; 73, Long-downs (Flora), post—1950, R.H.; Eathorne, near Constantine, L.J.M.; 74, United Mines (Flora), Croft Handy, R.H.

East: 95, Trerice, St Dennis, L.G.; Nanpean, E.T. (Thurston and Vigurs 1925); Meledor, near St Stephens, L.J.M.; Bugle, J.B.; Goonamarth, near St Austell, J.B.; 96, Goss Moor, N.J.F.; 05, Crinnis Beach, near St Austell, R.D.P.; Par Sands (Flora), 1966, L.A.B.; Treverbyn, near Stenalees, 1951—4, J.B.; Carbis Common, J.A.P.; 06, Helmentor (Flora), Red Moor, 1963, E.A. and L.J.M.; 07, De Lank quarries, E.A.; 08, Trebarwith, 1920, R.W.D.

Scilly: of doubtful occurrence, Lousley 1971.

OMALOTHECA CASS.

515/1 **O. sylvatica** (L.) Schultz Bip & F.W. Schultz
                                      Heath Cudweed

(*Gnaphalium sylvaticum* L.)

Listed in the Flora without definite locality; the following is therefore the only defined station.

East: 38, one plant in woodland, Trebursye, W of Launceston, A.V. (Thurston 1929a).

FILAGINELLA OPIZ

515/4 **F. uliginosa** (L.) Opiz (*Gnaphalium uliginosum* L.), Marsh Cudweed, is frequent throughout the county in suitable habitats.

GNAPHALIUM L.

[515/5 **G. luteo-album** L., Jersey Cudweed, found its way into the Cornish list by mistake, and was rejected by Davey (Flora).]

ANTENNARIA GAERTNER

517/1 **A. dioica** (L.) Gaertner   Mountain Everlasting

Still relatively plentiful in two Cornish stations.

West: 53, Connor Downs (Flora), still there, 1949, S.B., but since gone; 64, edge of cliff, Portreath, 1932, H.H. (Thurston 1935), since gone; 75, St Agnes (Flora), refound, 1969, CNT, the actual station being a stretch of maritime heath between Cross Coombe and Cligga Head; Budnick, near Perranporth (Flora), still present in quantity over ¾ mile of blown sand between the top of Budnick Hill and the path to the Lost Church; 86 (76), one small patch on Crantock Sands, 1971—5, M.N., comm. E.A.

ANAPHALIS DC.

516/1 § **A. margaritacea** (L.) Bentham   Pearly Everlasting

East: 95, McClaren's Dry, near Treviscoe, St Dennis, 1974, R.W.D. and L.J.M.

INULA L.

512/1 § **I. helenium** L.   Elecampane

A long-established introduction, rare and very local. West: 32, St Levan (Flora), Roskestal, post—1950, G.L.; 43, Zennor (Flora), post—1950, B.M.S.; Tremithick Cross, B.M.S.; Boswarva, near Trengwainton, S.Bu.; 53, St Ives (Thurston 1929a), 1968, J.B.B.; 61, Trevitho Farm, near Penhale, E.J.P. (Thurston and Vigurs 1927); 62, Poldhu Valley near Chypons, E.J.P. (Thurston and Vigurs 1927); 71, Kennack (Flora), 1952, S.B.; 73, near Penryn Station, R.H.; 86, Trerair Farm, St Eval (Flora), six plants, 1967, C.W.

East: 17, near Penstroda, Blisland, J.G.; 20, Mere,

Bude (Suppt), still there, 1974, R.D.; Northcott Mouth, N of Bude, H.H.H. (Thurston and Vigurs 1926); 21, Coombe Valley, J.L.P. (Thurston and Vigurs 1924), 1979, K.H.; 35, Trevollard (Flora), still there, post—1950, I.N.; 36, Callington, E.T. (Thurston 1928); 38, plentiful in orchard, Lawhitton, near Launceston, W.W. (Thurston and Vigurs 1926); 46, Halton Quay, 1923 (Thurston and Vigurs 1924).

Scilly: probably extinct, Lousley 1971.

512/4 **I. conyza** DC. Ploughman's-spikenard

Locally frequent and remarkably persistent in coastal areas, very rare elsewhere.

West: 52, hedge near Perranuthnoe, J.A.P.; 53, Carbis Bay (Flora), 1949, J.B.; Lelant (Flora), post—1950, L.J.M.; Hayle (Flora), 1959, G.B.M.; Carnsew Spit, Hayle, 1972, L.B.; near St Erth, B.M.S.; Upton Towans, N.J.F. and B.M.S.; (54), Gwithian Towans, 1949, J.B.; between Gwithian and Lower Nanterrow Farm, L.J.M.; Godrevy Towans, R.J.M. and L.J.M.; near Gwealavellan, L.J.M.; 64, Portreath, L.J.M.; Porthtowan (Suppt), 1976, L.J.M.; 72, St Anthony-in-Meneage (Flora), 1967, C.W.; 75, Perranporth (Flora), Mount, 1967, C.W.; Holywell Bay, L.J.M.; 83, Maenporth (Flora), post—1950, L.J.M.; 84, Newham, Truro, L.J.M.; 85, Newlyn East (Suppt), 1977, L.J.M.; 97, near Stepper Point, L.G.

East: 84, Fentongollan, B.E.M.G.; 97, Amble Dam, Camel Estuary, S.M.; St Enodoc (Flora), Rock Dunes, 1966, J.A.P.; 1980, R.W.D.; Pentireglaze, R.W.D.; 07, Helland (Flora), by railway at Hellandbridge, post—1950, K.H.J.; 15, Lantic Bay, K.H.; 35, Seaton (Flora), 1966, L.J.M.; Antony, S.M.; 45, Wearde, Saltash, S.M.; Torpoint (Flora), 1966, S.M.

512/5 **I. crithmoides** L. Golden Samphire

Local and rather rare, but still in most of its old stations.

West: 32, Porthcurno, E.A.R. (Thurston and Vigurs 1927); 33, Pendeen Watch, B.M.S.; Botallack Cliffs, R.D.P.; 64, Chapel Porth, B.M.S.; 71, Downas Cliffs, near Black Head, H.F.D. (Thurston 1928), still there, comm. D.E.C., 1977; 75, St Agnes Head (Suppt), 1976, L.J.M.; Perranporth (Flora), Droskyn Point, 1976, C.J.; 86, Griffin's Point, near Mawgan Porth, S.M.; 87, Park

Head (Flora), 1979, K.H.; abundant at Dinas Head, Constantine Bay, L.J.M.; Trevose Head (Flora), 1965, K.E.H.; Trevone (Flora), 1965, W.G.; Guddna Common, Crugmeer, L.G. (?=Tregudda Cliff, Flora); 97, Stepper Point, J.A.P.

East: 97, Pentire, and Polzeath (Flora), still at Pentire Cove and The Rumps, 1950—80, R.W.D.; 08, Tintagel (Flora), 1960, B.Sh.; Rocky Valley (Flora), post—1950, R.J.M. *et al;* (09), Boscastle (Flora), 1979, L.J.M.; 35, various parts of Whitsand Bay (Flora), between Tregantle and Portwrinkle, 1966, and on cliffs at Sharrow and Freathy, post—1950, S.M.

PULICARIA GAERTNER

513/1 **P. dysenterica** (L.) Bernh., Common Fleabane, is common and widespread (very rare in Scilly).

513/2 **P. vulgaris** Gaertner, Small Fleabane. 'Extinct' (Flora). We have been unable to trace a specimen to support Ralf's record, and have no hesitation in excluding it from the Cornish list.]

BIDENS L.

502/2 **B. tripartita** L. Trifid Bur-marigold

Scattered over much of the county, but very local. West: 53, Long Rock marsh (Flora), 1970, B.M.S.; Marazion Marsh, A.B.; (54), one plant St Ives, L.B.; 62, Poldhu Marsh, L.J.M.; Gunwalloe Marsh, LFC; Loe Pool (Flora), post—1950, H.B.S.; 71, Erisey, The Lizard, E.J.P. (Thurston and Vigurs 1927); 72, near Manaccan, 1926, C.H.F.; 86, Porth Reservoir, B.B.

East: 95, Goss Moor, CNT; 97, Amble Marshes (Flora), post—1950, R.W.D.; 05, Par Harbour, L.T.M. (Thurston 1929a); 07, Hellandbridge, K.H.J.; 21, Tamar Lake, R.D.; 36, tributary of R. Lynher near Herod Wood, Clapper Bridge, I.N.; 46, Kingsmill, Landulph, C.P.H. (Thurston 1935); Clifton farmyard, I.N.

502/1 **B. cernua** L. Nodding Bur-marigold

Now extremely rare in the county.

West: no recent records.

East: 95, Goss Moor (Flora), refound 1971, CNT; 05, near Par Station (Flora), refound 1966, J.A.P.

HELIANTHUS L.

§ **H. annuus** L.   Sunflower

A frequent garden escape, mainly on rubbish tips.
West: 63, Council tip, Treskillard, L.J.M.; 64, Council
tip, Tolvaddon, Redruth, L.J.M.; 74, old tip, Bissoe,
L.J.M.; 85, Council tip, Newlyn East, L.J.M.

§ **H. tuberosus** L.   Jerusalem Artichoke

More or less confined to rubbish tips, rarely established
on waste ground.
West: 63, Council tip, Treskillard, L.J.M.; West Basset
Mine, Carnkie, L.J.M.; 73, Council tip, Falmouth,
L.J.M.; 74, old tip, Bissoe, L.J.M.

XANTHIUM L.

505/2 § **X. spinosum** L.   Spiny Cocklebur

A very rare casual.
West: 43, in arable field below Gulval Carn, 1962,
G.B.M.; 63, reclaimed rubbish tip, Carnkie, Redruth,
L.J.M.

GALINSOGA RUIZ & PAVÓN

503/1 § **G. parviflora** Cav.   Gallant Soldier

Not the common alien that it is in many Southern
counties, and increasing only very slowly here.

*West: 84, waste ground, Moresk Road, Truro, B.E.M.G.;
86, one plant in seed-tray of bedding plants, Little
Trethiggey Nursery, near Newquay, 1965, L.J.M.
*East: 45, weed in nursery at Saltash, 1971, E.G.

503/2 § **G. quadriradiata** Luiz. & Pav.   Shaggy Soldier

An earlier arrival than the preceding species, and thus
slightly more widespread.

*West: 43, plentiful in nursery, Gulval, B.M.S.; 73,
nursery at Kernick, Penryn, 1959, R.B.G.; bailiff's
garden, Falmouth Reservoir, L.J.M.; 83, garden, Wood
Lane, Falmouth, G.Wh.; 84, waste ground, Moresk
Road, Truro, B.E.M.G.
*East: 45, nursery at Saltash, 1971, E.G.

SANTOLINA L.

530/1 § **S. chamaecyparissus** L. Lavender Cotton

The well-known garden shrub, now becoming naturalised in sandy places.

*West: 53, two large patches, Upton Towans, R.M. and L.J.M.; 87, a large patch on blown sand, Constantine Bay, L.J.M.

ANTHEMIS L.

§ **A. punctata** Vahl Italian Mayweed

subsp. **cupaniana** (Tod. ex Hyman) R. Fernandes

A tender plant, often grown in seaside gardens, and sometimes escaping.

*West: 53, many plants by railway, Angarrack Bridge, 1975, E.S.E., R.J.M., and L.J.M. (though introduced, this is probably the true wild plant here, differing slightly from the garden cultivar); 86, low cliff near Newquay Harbour, L.J.M.

*East: 20, road-bank, Stratton, near Bude, 1978, L.J.M.

526/3 **A. arvensis** L. Corn Chamomile

Always rare in Cornwall, it is now even more so, and difficult to find.

West: 61, Mullion, R.O. (Thurston and Vigurs 1925); 62, Helston, R.O. (Thurston and Vigurs 1925); 72, near Maenporth Beach, L.J.M.; 75, Sandy field, Mount, Penhale, L.J.M.

East: 83, roadside, Philleigh, B.E.M.G.; 84, Fentongollan, B.E.M.G.; 97, Bodieve, near Wadebridge, J.A.P.; 20, Widemouth Bay, R.O. (Thurston and Vigurs 1925).

526/2 **A. cotula** L. Stinking Chamomile

Not the common plant it once was (Flora), but probably more frequent than the following records indicate.

West: 53, mine waste, Halamanning, St Hilary, K.P.; 63, Clowance, L.J.M.; Penhale Moor, near Camborne, L.J.M.; 73, Penryn Creek, L.J.M.

East: 19, Beeny Cliff, Boscastle, J.A.P.; 25, Polperro (Flora), 1978, L.J.M.; 27, Henwood, Bodmin Moor, R.W.D. and L.J.M.; 45, between Torpoint and St Johns (Flora), 1966, S.M.

Scilly: Lousley 1971.

526/1 § **A. tinctoria** L. Yellow Chamomile

*West: 73, Council tip, Falmouth, 1970, L.J.M.

East: 83, Council tip, Gerrans, B.E.M.G.; 05, one plant, waste ground, Par, E.B. (Thurston and Vigurs 1923); Par Harbour, L.T.M. (Thurston and Vigurs 1926).

ACHILLEA L.

528/3 **A. ptarmica** L., Sneezewort (absent from Scilly), and 528/1 **A. millefolium** L., Yarrow, are frequent and widespread.

CHAMAEMELUM MILLER

527/1 **C. nobile** (L.) All. (*Anthemis nobilis* L.), Chamomile, is frequent and widespread, but scarce in the Lower Tamar area.

MATRICARIA L.

531/1a **M. maritima** L. (*M. inodora* L. var. *salina* Bab.), and 531/1b **M. perforata** Merat (*M. inodora* L. *sensu stricto*), Scentless Mayweed, are both common and widespread species.

CHAMOMILLA S.F. GRAY

532/2 § **C. suaveolens** (Pursh) Rydb. (*Matricaria suaveolens* Buchenau), Pineappleweed, is common and widespread.

532/1 **C. recutita** (L.) Rauschert Scented Mayweed
(*Matricaria chamomilla* L.)

Uncommon and rather local, but perhaps increasing. West: 43, Penzance, B.M.S.; 53, Phillack Towans, G.A. and L.J.M.; 61, cliffs at Polurrian, The Lizard, 1959—77, J.Fo.; 62, waste ground, Helston, R.O. (Thurston and Vigurs 1925), 1978, L.J.M.; 63, fowl-run, Treskillard, L.J.M.; 64, Tolvaddon, Redruth, J.S.R.; 74, Bissoe (Suppt), Council tip, 1970, B.E.M.G.; 75, Wheal Kitty, St Agnes, L.J.M.; 85, Council tip, Newlyn East, L.J.M.

East: 35, Trematon, near Saltash, J.A.P.; 38, Launceston (Flora), 1970, G.L.K.; 45, Council tip, St Johns, S.M.

OTANTHUS HOFFMANNS. & LINK

529/1 O. maritimus (L.) Hoffmanns. & Link   Cottonweed
(*Diotis maritima* Cass.)

Though cited by Davey as extinct (Flora), this extremely rare species was subsequently found in two mainland stations. It is possibly now extinct, but its reappearance cannot be entirely ruled out. The last three recorded occurrences are listed below.

West: 42 or 43, Penzance (B.E.C. 1927).
East: 05, Par Sands (Suppt), refound 1933, L.T.M. and H.W.P.
Scilly: MN, 1916–1936, Lousley 1971.

CHRYSANTHEMUM L.

533/1 C. segetum L., Corn Marigold, is too frequent and widespread for listing of localities, but it is now beginning to decline in numbers.

TANACETUM L.

533/5 T. vulgare L., Tansy, is of frequent occurrence throughout the mainland of Cornwall, but its status as a native plant is open to doubt, as it is usually found not far from houses.
Scilly: A, one plant by W side of lighthouse, 1974–9, E.G.

533/4 § T. parthenium (L.) Schultz Bip (*Chrysanthemum parthenium* Bernh.), Feverfew, is a common denizen of waste ground throughout the county.

LEUCANTHEMUM MILLER

533/2 L. vulgare Lam. (*Chrysanthemum leucanthemum* L.), Oxeye Daisy, is a common and widely distributed plant of dry places, especially on cliff-tops.

533/3 § L. maximum (Ramond) DC.   Shasta Daisy
This common garden perennial is well-naturalised in several places.
West: 53, waste ground, Hayle, L.J.M.; 63, old tip, Carnkie, Redruth, L.J.M.; old mine workings, Treskillard, L.J.M.; 64, between Nancekuke and Porthtowan, R.J.M. and L.J.M.; 75, near Treago, near Newquay, L.J.M.; Holywell Bay, L.J.M.; 86, The Gannel, R.J.M.; Water-

gate Bay (Suppt), still there, 1967, L.J.M.

*East: 20, well-established at Northcott Mouth, N of Bude, 1972, L.J.M.

ARTEMISIA L.

535/1 **A. vulgaris** L., Mugwort, is common and widespread in Cornwall.

535/6 **A. absinthium** L.   Wormwood
Once widely distributed in the county, this species has become unaccountably rare in the last 60 years.
West: no recent records.
East: 97 (98), Roscarrock, Portquin, 1946, R.W.D.; 19, Boscastle (Flora), E.A., comm. 1960; St Gennys (Suppt), post—1960, L.J.M.; 21, field S of Morwenstow, 1968, J.A.P.

535/4 § **A. stellerana** Besser   Hoary Mugwort
This silvery-leaved garden plant was naturalised for many years on Marazion Beach, but has now gone.
West: 53, near Marazion (Flora), last recording c 1965, B.M.S.

[535/7 **A. maritima** L., Sea Wormwood, was recorded from two localities in the Flora. One of these, from Scilly, was rejected by Lousley (1971), and the other record, made by F. Pascoe, cannot be accepted without a voucher specimen, in view of the great unreliability of the 'Pascoe List'.]

TUSSILAGO L.

508/1 **T. farfara** L., Colt's-foot, is quite frequent throughout the county (rare in Scilly).

PETASITES MILLER

509/4 § **P. fragrans** (Vill.) C. Presl, Winter Heliotrope, is a long-standing introduction found commonly throughout the county, often as an ineradicable garden weed.

509/1 **P. hybridus** (L.) P. Gaertner, B. Meyer & Scherb.
                                                          Butterbur
In scattered localities in E Cornwall, rare in the West.
West: 42, Lariggan Stream, Penzance (Flora), 1968, G.B.M.; 72, Porthoustock, R.H.; 75, Holywell Bay,

L.J.M.; 83, Mylor Bridge (Flora), post—1950, R.H.; 87, Trevone, A.B.

East: 93, Pendower Valley, L.J.M.; Portloe, M.E.B.; 06, Washaway, near Bodmin, S.M.; Brocton, near Grogley Halt, S.M.; 08, Lanteglos Church (Suppt), still there, post—1950, various recorders; 15, Lansallos, S.M.; 25, Sandplace Station, F.H.C. and J.L.; 26, Seaton Valley, at Roseland, and near Menheniot Station, J.A.P.; 35, Hessenford (Flora), 1967, S.M.; 38, Launceston (Flora), 1960, B.Sh.; W of Launceston, G.L.K.; 45, orchard at St Johns (Flora), post—1950, I.N., about the Well, 1967, S.M.

509/3 § **P. japonicus** (Siebold & Zucc.) Maxim.

Giant Butterbur

A rare introduction, rapidly forming large masses.
*West: 53, near Bowl Rock, Trencrom, 1970, recorded independently by E.M.H. and H.M.; 62, Nancemerrin Farm, near Helston, D.M.S., comm. S.M.T.; 86, by stream, Watergate Bay, post—1950, M.M.W., spreading fast, 1977, R.W.D. and L.J.M.

DORONICUM L.

507/1 § **D. pardalianches** L.   Leopard's-bane

A rather persistent garden throw-out.

West: 71, Kennack Valley, E.T. and A.J.H. (Thurston and Vigurs 1926); 86, deserted garden, Colan, near Newquay, L.G.

East: 84, hedge between St Clement and Pencalenick, K.M.S. (Thurston and Vigurs 1926); 25, Looe, S.R.

SENECIO L.

Common species: 506/1 S. **jacobaea** L., Common Ragwort, 506/2 S. **aquaticus** Hill, Marsh Ragwort (absent from Scilly), 506/6 S. **sylvaticus** L., Heath Groundsel, and 506/8 S. **vulgaris** L., Groundsel.

§ **S. cruentus** DC.   Cineraria

This is the familiar greenhouse pot-plant. It sometimes occurs in large numbers on walls and waste places in St Ives, having seeded itself from plants in the nearby Municipal Park.

*West: 53 (54), St Ives, 1971, L.B.

506/15 § **S. mikanioides** Otto ex Walpers   German Ivy

An introduction of unknown origin, sometimes forming huge, scrambling masses.

*West: 43, Gulval churchyard, 1973, B.M.S.

*East: 83, field border, Rosevine, near Portscatho, 1974, B.E.M.G.

Scilly: common, Lousley 1971.

506/18 § **S. bicolor** (Willd.) Tod.   Silver Ragwort
subsp. **cineraria** (DC.) Chater
(*S. cineraria* DC.)

Commonly grown in seaside parks and gardens, and often escaping into wild situations, especially on cliffs.

West: 62, Porthleven, H.B.S.; 86, slopes above Newquay Harbour (Flora), still present in quantity, 1976, L.J.M.; abundant on Trenance Cliffs, Mawgan Porth, 1968, R.F.

East: 15, sparingly at Polruan, S.M.; 20, roadside, Widemouth Bay (B.E.C. 1935); sea-cliffs at Bude, L.J.M.

506/18 **S. bicolor** subsp. **cineraria** x **jacobaea** = *S. x albescens*
x 1   Burbidge & Colgan
(*S. cineraria x jacobaea*)

Whenever the preceding species 'escapes', it readily hybridises with the Common Ragwort.

West: 53, three plants by old ferry, Lelant, J.M.M., L.J.M. and R.P.; 74, one plant, Redruth, L.J.M.

*East: 08 (09), one plant, Boscastle village, L.J.M.; 15, one plant by car-park, Fowey, L.J.M.; 20, Efford Down, Bude, 1970, L.J.M.; 35, Downderry, L.J.M.

[506/   **S. congestus** (R.Br.) DC. (*S. palustris* Hook.), Marsh
16   Fleawort, has no place in the Cornish flora. The sole record was another of Pascoe's mistakes, rejected by Davey (Flora).]

506/3 **S. erucifolius** L.   Hoary Ragwort

Generally very rare and local, reflecting the lack of calcareous soils in Cornwall, but frequent on the culm measures around Bude.

West: 61, Mullion (Flora), post—1950, R.H.; 62, Gunwalloe (Flora), post—1950, R.H.; Cury (Flora), between Cury and Poldhu, 1968, M.C.H. *et al;* Poldhu car-park, L.J.M.; 72, road-verge, Trelowarren, one plant, J.S.R.

East: 05, Par Harbour, L.T.M. (Thurston 1935); 20, by railway, Bude, L.J.M.; ride of plantation N of Bude, L.J.M.; frequent from Sandymouth to Widemouth (Flora), plentiful at Northcott Mouth, and between there and Maer Lake, 1972, L.J.M.; 35, one or two plants at Wacker, Antony, S.M.; 45, disused railway siding, Wearde Quay, Saltash, I.N.

506/4 § S. squalidus L.   Oxford Ragwort

Widespread along the main railway line, rare elsewhere. Rejected for Cornwall by Davey (Flora), but reinstated by Thurston and Vigurs (Suppt).

West: 42, road-verge, Raginnis, Mousehole, J.S.R.; 42 or 43, Morrab Road, Penzance, E.A.R. (Thurston 1935); 43, railway, Penzance, to 53, Longrock, post—1950, various recorders; 53, near Power Station, Hayle, L.J.M.; 63, Connor Downs, J.S.R.; 64, Camborne by-pass, J.S.R.; 83, Marlborough Crescent, Falmouth, L.J.M.; 84, Cowlands Creek, S of Truro, C.W.

East: 95, railway, Goss Moor, L.J.M.; Burngullow Station, near St Austell, W.T. (Thurston 1935); 05, Par Harbour (Suppt), 1966, J.A.P.; 15, between Golant and Milltown, J.A.P.; 26, Liskeard Station, L.J.M.; 37, Kelly Bray, near Callington, E.G.; 45, Torpoint, S.M.; Saltash Goodsyard, E.Wh.; Southdown Quarry, Millbrook, E.G.

506/7 S. viscosus L.   Sticky Groundsel

An extremely rare plant in Cornwall, and probably an introduction.

East: 05, railway bank, Par (B.E.C. 1946); 08, Trebarwith, 1920, R.W.D.; 19, Millook, near Crackington Haven, E.G.; 20, disused railway station, Bude, L.J.M.; 45, Saltash Goodsyard, E.G.

506/8+ S. vulgaris L.

var. hibernicus Syme (var. *radiatus* auct.)

The radiate form of groundsel is very rare and sporadic here, but it may be overlooked to some extent.

West: 62, Ashton, F.G.F.; 63, garden weed, Treskillard,

L.J.M.; 85, railway track, Shepherds Halt, near Goon-havern, L.J.M.

subsp. **denticulatus** (O.F. Mueller)P.D. Sell

A distinct radiate form, thought to be native. Briggs' record has not been refound.

East: 35, Tregantle, Whitsand Bay, T.A.B. (Briggs 1880).

CARLINA L.

537/1 **C. vulgaris** L., Carline Thistle, is frequent in suitable habitats throughout Cornwall (? extinct in Scilly).

ARCTIUM L.

538/4 **A. minus** Bernh., Lesser Burdock, is frequent and widely distributed.

538/1 **A. lappa** L.   Greater Burdock
(*A. majus* Bernh.)

Rather rare and local, as it has always been.

West: 53, Marazion Marsh, J.R.P.; 75, Perranporth (Flora), Penhale Sands, 1965, NCS.

East: 06, Polmorla Bridge, Camel Valley, C.J.; 08, Rocky Valley, J.A.P.; 20, Bude (Flora), near the canal, 1972, L.J.M.; 27, near Pensilva, R.F.W.; 35, near Hessenford, by the road to the coast (Flora), Seaton Valley, 1966, J.A.P.

Scilly: rejected, Lousley 1971.

538/2 **A. nemorosum** Lej.   Wood Burdock
and 3 (incl. *A. pubens* Bab.)

A complex species, not easily separated from *A. pubens.* Little recent work has been done on these two taxa in Cornwall, and we are not confident as to the precise distribution of each, or if, indeed, both occur. We have therefore placed recent records for both species together here.

West: 63, near the water-works, Baripper, L.J.M.; 64, Portreath Harbour, F.H.P.; 75, Lambourne, Perranzabuloe (B.E.C. 1938, p.194).

East: 25, near Sandplace, D.B.; near Duloe, D.B.; 26, SE of Liskeard, D.B.; 45, 'common in Torpoint area', S.M.

Scilly: Lousley 1971.

CARDUUS L.

539/1 **C. tenuiflorus** Curtis *(C. pycnocephalus* L. var. *tenuiflorus)*, Slender Thistle, is common and widespread along the Cornish coastline.

539/3 **C. nutans L.**   Musk Thistle
Scattered throughout the county, and rather local, but more frequent in the extreme SE.

West: 32, St Just (Flora), Nanquidno Farm, M.C.; 42, Penzance, G.B.M.; 43, Zennor (Flora), 1949, J.B.; 52, Trewavas Head, G.B.M.; 53, Lelant (Flora), 1949, J.B.; mine-workings, Gwinear, L.J.M.; Upton Towans, L.J.M.; 61, Mullion (Flora), post—1950, B.M.S.; 71, Cadgwith, J.B.; Coverack (Suppt), between there and Ruan Minor, 1960, G.B.M.; Downas Valley, CNT; 75, Perranporth (Flora), near Bolingey, 1966, J.A.P.; 86 (76), Cubert, K.H.; Pentire Head, Newquay (Flora), post—1950, L.J.M.; 97, Stepper Point, L.G.

East: 97, Miniver Hill, and in pastures, Pentire, 1922—80, R.W.D.; 04, Gribbin Head, J.B.; Pentewan (Flora), 1954, J.B.; 08 (09), Trevalga (Flora), 1965, J.B.; Boscastle, J.B.; 15, Lantic Bay, R.W.D. and L.J.M.; 19, Pencarrow Point, L.J.M.; 20, Bude (Flora), 1966, J.A.P.; 21, Marsland, J.A.P.; 35, St Germans Hut (Flora), post—1950, S.M.; Pillaton (Flora), Holwood Quarry, 1975, L.J.M.; 45, near Empacombe, J.A.P.; Wiggle Cliff, and above Ninney, S.M.; (44), Penlee Point (Flora), 1972, L.G.

Scilly: with doubt, Lousley 1971.

539/4 **C. acanthoides L.**   Welted Thistle
(C. crispus auct.)

Extremely rare and local.

West: no recent records.

East: 21, Stanbury Mouth, N of Bude, O.G., comm. 1965; 45, outskirts of Torpoint, I.N.

CIRSIUM MILLER

Common species: 540/2 **C. vulgare** (Savi) Ten. *(Cnicus lanceolatus* Willd.), Spear Thistle,   540/3 **C. palustre** (L.) Scop. *(Cnicus palustris* Willd.), Marsh Thistle, and 540/4 **C. arvense** (L.) Scop. *(Cnicus arvensis* Hoffm.), Creeping Thistle.

[540/1 **C. eriophorum** (L.) Scop. (*Cnicus eriophorus* Roth), Woolly Thistle. An early record for this species was rejected by Davey, and as the plant is most unlikely to occur here, we have no hesitation in doing the same.]

540/8 **C. dissectum** (L.) Hill   Meadow Thistle
(*Cnicus pratensis* Willd.)
Confined in Cornwall to the culm measures of the NE of the county, with an outlier in the Lower Tamar area. Recent work by C. Crooke has shown this species to be fairly common in parts of the Upper Tamar Valley. East: 19, near Otterham Mill, C.C.; Newham, N of Otterham, R.W.D. and L.J.M.; 20, S of Moreton Mill, C.C.; 21, Kilkhampton (Flora), near Alderbeer, 1977, C.C.; Wrasford Moor, R.W.D.; Tamar Lake (Flora), 1970, L.J.M.; near W Youlstone, C.C.; Woolley Barrows, L.J.M.; 28, Laneast Downs, G.L.K.; 29, Greena Moor (Flora), post—1950, R.W.D.; near Greenamoor Bridge, C.C.; near Hendra, Canworthy Water, C.C.; several places between E Balsdon and N Tamerton, C.C.; 36, Viverdon Down, I.N.; 39, between E Balsdon and N Tamerton, C.C.

540/6 **C. acaule** Scop.   Dwarf Thistle
(*Cnicus acaulis* Willd.)
Extremely rare, and confined to one locality.
East: 20, Efford Down, Bude (Flora), still plentiful in a limited area, 1970, L.J.M.; one patch on golf-links, Bude, R.O. (Thurston and Vigurs 1925).

540/4+ **C. arvense** (L.) Scop.
var. setosum C.A. Mey
West: 73, Oldhill, Falmouth, W.T. (Thurston 1935).
East: 05, Par Sands, L.T.M.; Charlestown, W.T. (both Thurston 1929a).

540/4 **C. arvense x palustre** = *C. x celakovskianum* Knaf
x 3 *East: 05, Par, L.T.M. (B.E.C. 1929).

ONOPORDON L.

542/1 § **O. acanthium** L.   Cotton Thistle

A very rare introduction, usually a garden escape.
West: 53 (54), one plant, Godrevy Hill, B.J.; 86, S side
of The Gannel, Newquay, L.G.

*East: 26, W of Liskeard, D.B.

SILYBUM ADANSON

541/1 § **S. marianum** (L.) Gaertner   Milk Thistle

A local but persistent introduction.
West: 86 (76), Gannel side of E Pentire (Flora) ? =
Crantock, 1970, L.G.; 87, Porthcothan (Flora), 1977,
B.B.
East: 97, near Polzeath (Flora), 1948—80, R.W.D.; 05,
Crinnis (Suppt), edge of golf-course, 1958, C.S.; one
plant, Par Harbour, L.T.M. (Thurston and Vigurs 1925);
garden, Charlestown, W.T. (Thurston and Vigurs 1927);
15, garden, Lostwithiel, E.T. (Thurston and Vigurs
1927).

SERRATULA L.

545/1 **S. tinctoria** L., Saw-wort, is frequent and widespread,
especially on hedgebanks and cliff-tops (absent from
Scilly).

CENTAUREA L.

544/1 **C. scabiosa** L., Greater Knapweed (absent from
Scilly), and 544/6 **C. nigra** L., Common Knapweed
(apparently absent from Scilly), are both frequent and
widespread on the mainland.

544/9 § **C. calcitrapa** L.   Red Star-thistle

A very rare casual, now almost gone.
West: 71, by track from Lizard Town to Bass Point,
one plant, 1976, J.Fo.

544/10 § **C. solstitialis** L.   Yellow Star-thistle

Similarly rare and casual.

West: 64, Tehidy, Camborne, 1974, J.S.R.; 86 (76), weed in garden, Crantock, A.H.

East: 84, waste ground near Boscawen Park, Truro, W.H.F. (Thurston and Vigurs 1923); 15, garden weed, Lostwithiel, E.T. (Thurston and Vigurs 1927).

Scilly: Lousley 1971.

544/6+ **C. nigra** L.

var. **radiata** Koch

This form of Common Knapweed with conspicuous ray-florets is a characteristic plant of maritime heaths, rarely inland.

West: 43, Bosigran, near Porthmeor, M.C.; 61, Kynance Downs (Suppt), 1979, J.H.; Mullion Cliffs, J.H.; 64, Gooden Heane Point, Portreath, L.J.M.; 71, quarry S of Enys Head, Cadgwith, J.H.; 87, between Dinas Head and Constantine Bay, L.J.M.

East: 08 (09), W side of Boscastle Haven, L.J.M.; 21, Duckpool slopes, and Coombe Valley, L.J.M.

544/7 **C. debeauxii** Gren. & Godron   Slender Knapweed
subsp. **nemoralis** (Jordan) Dostal
(*C. nemoralis* Jordan)

Not easily separated from *C. nigra*. Probably rare in Cornwall. The following appear to be reliable records:

East: 97, Polzeath, H.E.F. (Thurston 1929a); Pentire Cove, 1979, R.W.D.; 04, Mevagissey Bay (Marsden-Jones and Turrill, 1954, p.52); 05, Par, K; 25, Polperro, 1924, F.R. (Thurston and Vigurs 1925).

Scilly: Lousley 1971. In our opinion the Scilly records should be re-examined, as it is unlikely that this species should be present in the absence of *C. nigra*.

C. nemoralis/nigra

Intermediate plants occur at

West: 63, near Four Lanes, Redruth, L.J.M.

East: 25, Polperro (Marsden-Jones and Turrill, 1954, p.52).

544/2 § **C. montana** L.   Perennial Cornflower
This well-known cottage-garden plant is becoming
increasingly naturalised in the county.

*West: 74, railway, Mt Hawke Station, L.J.M.

*East: 08, between Port Isaac and Port Gaverne,
L.J.M.; 20 (10), Widemouth Bay, 1967, L.J.M.; 26,
Merrymeet, near Liskeard, S.M.; 28, Polyphant, L.J.M.;
35, Polbathic, S.M.; 37, Bray Shop, Linkinhorne, N.J.F.;
38, one plant, Launceston, L.J.M.

544/3 **C. cyanus** L.   Cornflower
Once a common cornfield weed in many Southern
counties, but always rare in Cornwall, and now only
casual.

West: 53 or 63, Connor Downs, B.M.S.; 63, field at
Godolphin Cross, W.H.F. (Thurston and Vigurs 1926);
72, near Mawnan Smith, 1969, R.B.G.; 73, near
Falmouth Hospital, 1962, L.J.M.

East: 05, in two places along the by-pass, St Austell,
W.T. (Thurston 1935); 36 or 46, cornfield, St Dominick,
1923, W.Ch. (Thurston and Vigurs 1924).

*Scilly: A, one plant near Covean, St Agnes, 1970, E.G.;
T, bulbfield near Great Pool, Tresco, 1967, J.A.P.

CICHORIUM L.

546/1 § **C. intybus** L., Chicory, is frequent throughout the
county, though rarely in quantity.

ARNOSERIS GAERTNER

[548/1 **A. minima** Schweigger & Koerte, Lamb's Succory.
Another of Pascoe's mistakes. We support Davey in his
rejection of this species from the Cornish list.]

HYPOCHAERIS L.

549/1 **H. radicata** L., Cat's-ear, is a very common plant of dry
places throughout Cornwall.

549/3 **H. maculata** L.   Spotted Cat's-ear
Still present in both of its Cornish stations. The
Porthtowan colony is one of the two largest in the
British Isles.

West: 61, Lizard (Flora) — the record refers to
Kynance, still there, 1950—79, various recorders; 64,

turfy slope between Perranporth and Portreath (Flora) — the actual site is Porthtowan, still there in quantity, 1950—80, various recorders.

549/2 **H. glabra** L.   Smooth Cat's-ear

Not subsequently refound in either of its two stations at 05, Par, or 20, Bude. We refrain, however, from marking this species as extinct, as it is easily overlooked, and could still be present.

LEONTODON L.

550/1 **L. autumnalis** L., Autumn Hawkbit (rare in Scilly), and   550/3 **L. taraxacoides** (Vill.) Mérat (*L. nudicaule* Banks & Soland.), Lesser Hawkbit, are both common species throughout the county.

550/1+ **L. autumnalis** L.

var. **sordidus** Bab.

West: 63, near Bolenowe, Troon, R.J.M.; 64, near Camborne, R.J.M.; North Cliffs, Portreath, R.J.M.
East: 15, near Lerryn, R.J.M.

550/2 **L. hispidus** L.   Rough Hawkbit

Very rare over most of the county, but more frequent in the Lower Tamar area.
West: 75, Perranzabuloe churchyard, F.R. (Thurston 1935); Gear Sands, Perranporth, L.J.M.
East: recorded post—1950, without locality, for squares 25, 29, 35—38, 45, 46, and 20.
Scilly: Lousley 1971.

PICRIS L.

551/1 **P. echioides** L., Bristly Oxtongue, is a frequent plant of mainly coastal areas throughout the county.

551/2 **P. hieracioides** L.   Hawkweed Oxtongue

Very rare and local.
West: 53, near Lelant Church, B.M.S.; 75, Perranporth (Suppt), 1964, L.J.M.; in hedgebanks near Gear Sands, Penhale, L.J.M.
East: 05, waste ground, Charlestown, W.T. (Thurston 1929a); 19, abundant on hill above Crackington Haven, T.N.S.P. (Thurston 1929a); 37, in ruins of old building below Kit Hill, BSBI.
Scilly: rejected, Lousley 1971.

TRAGOPOGON L.

552/2 § **T. porrifolius** L.   Salsify

An ancient but persistent introduction, still increasing. West: 52, Praa Sands, B.B.; 53, Lelant, T.J.P. (Thurston and Vigurs 1924), 1966, L.A.B.; (54), Gwithian Towans, L.J.M.; 62, between Cury and Poldhu Cove, R.O. (Thurston and Vigurs 1925); 71, Church Cove, Landewednack, H.F.D. (Thurston 1928), post—1950, F.W.A. (*Proc. B.S.B.I.*, 1: 56); Kuggar, Ruan Minor, R.B.G.; 72, Budock Vean, R.B.G.; 73, Devoran (Flora), 1966, C.W.; 75, between Penhale and Holywell Bay, C.W.; 83, Falmouth (Flora), post—1950, L.J.M.; 86, The Gannel, B.J. and E.J.; near St Eval airfield, comm. T.O.D.; 87, Constantine Bay, W.G.; 97, Padstow (Flora), Hawkers Cove, post—1950, J.A.P.

East: 83, Gerrans (Suppt), Trewince Quay, 1968, L.J.M.; 08, Port Gaverne (B.E.C. 1945); 15, Fowey, N.J.F.; 25, E Cliff, Polperro, M.M.P.; 35, Downderry, I.N.; 36, Hatt, near Saltash, E.G.; 45, Saltash Station, I.N.; 46, Calstock churchyard, 1923, E.T. (Thurston and Vigurs 1924).

552/1b **T. pratensis** L.   Goat's-beard

subsp. **minor** (Miller) Wahlenb.

Very rare in the West, local in the East, but frequent in the Lower Tamar area.

West: 53, Lelant (Suppt), 1964, G.L.; 83, Mylor churchyard, E.T. and L.T.M. (Thurston 1930); 84, railway at Newham, Truro, W.H.F. (Thurston and Vigurs 1926).

East: 97, Rock (Suppt), 1966, J.A.P.; 20, Helebridge, near Bude, J.A.P.; Widemouth Bay, L.J.M.; 26, three places near Liskeard, D.B.; Doublebois, H.P.; 35, near Tideford, L.J.M.; E of Portwrinkle, S.M.; Wacker, near Antony, S.M.; Wivelscombe, I.N.; 36, Hatt, Saltash (Flora), 1966, I.N.; 37, Horsebridge, R.Tamar, I.N.; 38, Launceston (Flora), 1960, B.Sh.; Polson Bridge, Launceston, L.J.M.; near Sheers Barton, Lawhitton, S.M.; railway bank, Coombe, Saltash, I.N.; viaduct, Saltash, I.N.; Torpoint, S.M.; near Empacombe, J.A.P.; Edgcumbe Park, L.J.M.; Maker Heights (Flora), 1965, L.J.M.; 46, Calstock (Flora), 1966, J.A.P.; 47, Weir Head (Flora), post—1950, I.N.

subsp. **minor/pratensis**

We are grateful to S.C. Madge for drawing our attention to this taxon, which is intermediate between the two subspecies. True subsp. *pratensis* does not seem to occur in Cornwall.

West: 97, railway near Edmonton, Wadebridge, S.M.

East: 35, cliff road, Sharrow, S.M.; Polscoe, Sheviock, S.M.; Tregantle Cliff, L.J.M.; 38, Polson Bridge, Launceston, L.J.M.; 45, car-park at Tregonhawke, S.M.; three places around Torpoint, S.M.; (44), lane to Polhawn Cove, Rame Head, S.M.; 46, Danescombe Valley Hotel, B.E.M.G. (as subsp. *pratensis*).

SONCHUS L.

556/4 S. **asper** (L.) Hill, Prickly Sow-thistle, 556/3 S. **oleraceus** L., Smooth Sow-thistle, and 556/2 S. **arvensis** L., Perennial Sow-thistle, are all common and widespread species.

[556/1 S. **palustris** L.   Marsh Sow-thistle

Rejected for Cornwall by Davey (Flora). A very recent record from East: 08, Sandyway Wood, near Lostwithiel, June 1980, J. Hartshorne, requires confirmation.]

LACTUCA L.

554/1 § **L. serriola** L.   Prickly Lettuce

Occurs only as a very rare casual.

East: 45, one plant on waste ground, Saltash, 1979, E.G.

554/3 § **L. saligna** L.   Least Lettuce

The merest casual in Cornwall.

*West: 42, by the boating-lake, Lariggan, Penzance, 1979, B.M.S.

*East: 05, ballast-heap, Charlestown, W.T. (Thurston and Vigurs 1926).

554/2 § **L. virosa** L.   Great Lettuce

Very rare and casual.

East: 84, near Boscawen Park, Truro, W.Bo. (Thurston and Vigurs 1925); 45, Wearde, Saltash, 1971, I.N. and E.R.

MYCELIS CASS.

555/1 **M. muralis** (L.) Dumort.   Wall Lettuce
(*Lactuca muralis* Gaertn.)

Very local and rare. Possibly introduced.

*West: 83, Point, Restronguet, 1968, F.G.F.

East: 19, Minster Churchyard (Suppt), still there, 1964, E.A. and L.J.M.; 38, Launceston, 1957, P.C.H.

TARAXACUM WEBER
Dandelion

We are indebted to Dr A.J. Richards for naming much of our material. Without his masterly account of the British Dandelions (Richards, 1972), this section would not have been possible. All records are those of L.J.M. unless otherwise attributed.

Section Spectabilia

560/33 **T. unguilobum** Dahlst.

Rather local, but more frequent in the East.

West: 43, near Wicca Pool, Zennor; 84, St Clement Wood, Idless.

*East: 95, Treviscoe, St Dennis, 1976; 97, Pentire Peninsula; 17, Blisland, Dozmary Pool, F.H.; 27, Siblyback Reservoir; 28, Altarnun; between Warbstow and Trenear.

34   **T. fulvicarpum** Dahlst.

*West: 75, Holywell Bay, 1977.

36   **T. faeroense** (Dahlst.) Dahlst.

Widespread in old pastures, especially in upland areas.

West: 75, dune-marsh, Penhale Sands.

East: 96, Goss Moor; 05, Par Beach, 1973; 17, Dozmary Pool, F.H.; 19, Newham, near Otterham; 26, moorland, St Cleer; 28, by R.Inny near Laneast.

37   **T. spectabile** Dahlst.

*East: 27, Siblyback Reservoir, 1979.

42   **T. euryphyllum** (Dahlst.) M.P. Christiansen

A characteristic species of dunes, rarely inland.

*West: 32, Whitsand Bay, Sennen; 53, Upton Towans; 75, Penhale Sands, 1973.

*East: 95, Treviscoe, St Dennis, 1976; 97, Pentire Peninsula; 16, Bofarnel Downs, near Lostwithiel; 18 old railway, Otterham; near Rough Tor, Bodmin Moor 27, Siblyback Reservoir.

43   **T. maculosum** A.J. Richards, (1981) = *T. maculigerum* auct.

A well-marked species, widespread in W Cornwall, less so in the East. Most Cornish plants differ from the type in possessing pollen.

West: 42, Lamorna Valley; 53, Carbis Bay; in two places at Lelant; base of Trink Hill, Towednack; 63, Porkellis Moor; 64, Connor Downs; Tehidy, Camborne; 75, near Perranzabuloe Church; 83, orchard at Penpol House, Devoran.

*East: 94, Tregoney, 1976; 25, Shutta Hill, Looe.

T. cornubiense A.J. Richards, (1981)

A distinct taxon, with lightly marked leaves, probably widespread in the county.

*West: 42, Lamorna Valley; 63, plentiful at Roseworthy,   near   Camborne;   garden,   Treskillard;   74, plentiful on old railway track near St Agnes, 1974, BM; 84, St Clement Wood, Idless.

*East: 15, Fowey; 46, Cotehele, Tamar Valley.

51   **T. laetifrons** Dahlst.

*West: 75, Penhale Sands, 1976.

61   **T. nordstedtii** Dahlst.

The most common member of this section in Cornwall. Recorded for nearly every 10 km. square in a total of 106 individual stations, but not yet recorded for Scilly.

64   **T. adamii** Claire

Rather variable in Cornwall, and perhaps confused with other species, but certainly of frequent occurrence throughout the county.

West: 33, Crookhorn, St Just; 53, Upton Towans.

East: 05, Par Beach; 08, Trebarwith; (09), Boscastle; 18, Otterham Station; 25, Fowey; 28, Altarnun; Tresmeer Church; 29, Week St Mary.

Scilly: Lousley 1971.

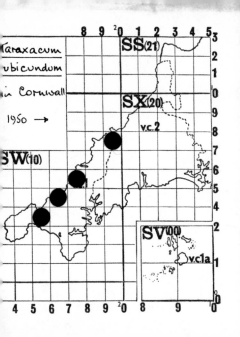

Taraxacum
rubicundum

in Cornwall

1950 →

T. britannicum Dahlst.

*An elegant species, easily recognised, with bright green leaves, reddish petioles, and patent outer bracts. It is one of the most common species in Cornwall, with 22 listed stations.

Section Erythrosperma

1   **T. brachyglossum** (Dahlst.) Dahlst.

One of the most common dune species, rarely found inland.

West: 32, Gwendra Beach, Sennen; 53, Marazion Dunes; 62, Gunwalloe Church Cove; 71, Chynalls Point, Coverack; 75, Penhale Sands; Holywell Bay.

East: 83, Pendower Beach; 05, Trethurgy, near St Austell, F.H.; Par Beach; 20, Crooklets, Bude; 36, Westcott Farm, near Callington, E.T. (B.E.C. 1924).

1 x 64   **T. brachyglossum x adamii**

West: 75, near Perranzabuloe Church, 1976.

3   **T. lacistophyllum** (Dahlst.) Raunk.

Mainly on fixed dunes.

West: 61 or 71, Lizard, G.C.D. (B.E.C. 1929); 87, Constantine Bay.

East: 97, Pentire Peninsula; 20, Crooklets, Bude; 36, Haye Lane, Callington, E.T. (B.E.C. 1924); 45, on low wall, Mt Edgcumbe.

4   **T. rubicundum** (Dahlst.) Dahlst.

Apparently confined to the coast, in Cornwall.

West: 53, Upton Towans, F.H.; 64, Hells Mouth, R.J.M.; 75, Perranporth, M.M.W., **BM**; Penhale Sands.

East: 97, Pentire Peninsula.

6   **T. silesiacum** Dahlst. ex G. Hagl.

On fixed dunes, rather local.

*West: 53, Upton Towans; (54), Godrevy Towans; 75, Penhale Sands, 1973.

T. arenastrum A.J. Richards, (1981)

*Scilly: MN, 1978, C.Li.

10   **T. hispanicum** H. Lindb. fil.
      *West: 75, Liskey Hill, Perranporth, 1969, R.C.P.
      OXF.

12   **T. laetum** (Dahlst.) Dahlst.
      West: 75, Penhale Sands.

13   **T. laetiforme** Dahlst.
      *East: 97 (98), Pentire Peninsula, 1977.

15   **T. fulvum** Raunk.
      West: 32, Whitsand Bay, Sennen; 42 or 43, Penzance,
      G.C.D. (B.E.C. 1929); 53, Upton Towans.

16   **T. fulviforme** Dahlst.
      Mainly on the coast, rarely inland.
      West: 32, Gwenver Beach, Sennen; 33, Carn Gloose,
      St Just; 53, Upton Towans; (54), Godrevy Towans; 63,
      hedgebank, Bolenowe, Troon; 64, Porth Towan; 75,
      Penhale Sands.

17   **T. oxoniense** Dahlst.
      Frequent and widespread in W Cornwall, less so in the
      East. Often on fixed dunes, but also on walls, waste
      ground, etc.
      West: 53, Lelant Dunes; Carnsew Spit, Hayle, P.J.R.;
      Angarrack Bridge; Upton Towans; (54), Gwithian and
      Godrevy Towans; 72, Maenporth; 75, Penhale Sands;
      Holywell Bay; 83, Point, Devoran; 87, Constantine Bay;
      97, Petherick crossroads, near Padstow.
      *East: 83, Pendower Beach; 84, Sett Bridge, Ruan
      Lanihorne, R.J.M. and L.J.M.; 05, Par Beach, 1973; 20,
      Efford Down, Bude; 35, Tregantle Cliff, Whitesand Bay.
      Scilly: Lousley 1971.

19   **T. glauciniforme** Dahlst.
      West: 75, Penhale Sands.

[20   **T. proximum** (Dahlst.) Dahlst.,   was   erroneously
      recorded for v.c.1. *fide* A.J. Richards (1972).]

21   **T. simile** Raunk.
      Mainly coastal, on cliff-tops and rocky places.
      *West: 32, Sennen, 1976; 64, cliff-path, Porthtowan;
      87, Constantine Bay.

*East: 97, Pentire Peninsula, 1977; 08 (09), rock-face, Boscastle; 20, Marhamchurch, near Bude.

23   **T. degelii** G. Hagl.

*West: 53, Upton Towans, 1977.

25   **T. pseudolacistophyllum** van Soest

*West: 53, Upton Towans, 1977.

26   **T. canulum** G. Hagl.

*East: 28, in churchyard, Treneglos, 1979.

Section Taraxacum (Vulgaria)

67   **T. subcyanolepis** M.P. Christiansen

Probably frequent, but overlooked.

*West: 63, waste ground, Treskillard, Redruth; 83, Penpol House, Devoran, 1974.

*East: 06, Ruthernbridge, 1977.

68   **T. cyanolepis** Dahlst.

*West: 63, waste ground, Treskillard, Redruth, 1976.

69   **T. sellandii** Dahlst.

*East: 95, near Treviscoe, St Dennis, 1976.

70   **T. ancistrolobum** Dahlst.

*West: 73, by Falmouth Reservoir, 1974; 83, garden weed, Falmouth.

71   **T. mericyclum** A.J. Richards in ed.

= *T. sublaciniosum* auct. angl. non Dahlst. & H. Lindb. fil.

*West: 63, garden, Treskillard, Redruth, 1974.

72   **T. stenacrum** Dahlst.

Frequent and widespread by roadsides.

*West: 63, Stennack, near Camborne, 1975; Treskillard; 72, roadside near Earth Station, Goonhilly Downs; 75, Holywell Bay; 86, near Newquay Harbour; 87, golf-links, Constantine Bay; 97, Padstow.

*East: 06, Menadue, near Lanlivery, 1977; 08, near Helstone, Camelford; 26, St Cleer.

74   **T. procerisquameum** H. Ollg. = *T. procerum* auct. angl. non Hagl.

*West: 72, by roadside, Gweek, 1974.

75   **T. pannucium** Dahlst.

Mainly in rich pastures near the coast.

*West: 53, Copperhouse, Hayle; Upton Towans; 75, Penhale Sands, 1973.

78   **T. alatum** H. Lindb. fil.

A common roadside species in W Cornwall, less so in the East.

*West: 63, Troon Hill, near Camborne; 64, Bel Lake, near Camborne; 72, Gillan Creek, Helford River; Maenporth; 73, garden near Perranwell Station; Stithians, 1974; 74, nursery, Redruth; 83, Penpol House, Devoran; 86, Vale of Lanherne, near Newquay.

*East: 95, Trefullock, near Summercourt; 07, Sladesbridge, near Wadebridge; 25, Looe.

79   **T. lingulatum** Marklund

A common and widespread species, in waste land and by roadsides.

*West: 33, Cot Valley, St Just; 53, Angarrack, near Hayle; 63, Stennack, near Camborne; 64, Portreath, 1973; 75, Penhale Sands.

*East: 84, Pencalenick, 1976; 06, Ruthernbridge; 28, churchyard, Treneglos; 29, Week St Mary.

81   **T. croceiflorum** Dahlst.

Probably widespread in Cornwall, but not always easily separable from other species.

*West: 42, roadside, Chy-an-hal, Penzance; 53, Copperhouse, Hale, 1974; 64, near Treswithian roundabout, Camborne; Porthtowan.

*East: 05, waste ground, Par Beach, 1973; 08, St Teath; 18, Camelford; 20, Crooklets, Bude.

83   **T. expallidiforme** Dahlst.

Probably frequent throughout the county.

*West: 52, garden, Perranuthnoe; 63, hedgebank, Treskillard, Redruth; Bolenowe, 1973; 74, nursery, Redruth; 87, Harlyn Bay.

*East: 06, Respryn Bridge, Lanhydrock; 17, Blisland village-green; 20, Crooklets, Bude; 28, churchyard, Treneglos.

84   **T. insigne** E.L. Ekman ex Wiinst. & K. Jessen
       Sandy places near the sea.
       *West: 53 (54), fixed dunes, Gwithian; 64, blown sand,
       Porthtowan; 72, Rosemullion Head, 1973.

91   **T. laciniosum** Dahlst.
       *West: 63, old Council tip, Treskillard, Redruth, 1976.

100   **T. xanthostigma** H. Lindb. fil.
       *East: 05, by pool near Par Station, 1977.

103   **T. cordatum** Palmgren
       *West: 53, Copperhouse, Hayle, 1974.
       *East: 05, Par Beach, 1977.

106   **T. dahlstedtii** H. Lindb. fil.
       *West: 72, roadside near Earth Station, Goonhilly
       Downs; 75, Penhale Sands; 87, Harlyn Bay, near
       Padstow, 1974.

107   **T. ostenfeldii** Raunk. = *T. duplidens* H. Lindb. fil.
       *West: 62, Gunwalloe Church Cove, 1974; 87,
       Constantine Bay.

110   **T. fulgidum** G. Hagl.
       Damp pasture on edge of fixed dunes. An outlier much
       removed from its main area of distribution in Britain.
       *West: 75, Penhale Sands, 1976.

114   **T. hamatum** Raunk.
       Apparently very local, but possibly overlooked.
       West: 61 or 71, Lizard, 1956, A.H.G.A., BM, comm.
       A.J.R.
       *East: 95, near Treviscoe, St Dennis, 1976; 18, old
       railway, Otterham.

115   **T. hamatiforme** Dahlst.
       Widespread in fields and by roadsides.
       West: 32, Sennen Cove; 42, Penberth Valley; 61,
       Caerthillian Cove; 63, pasture, Treskillard, Redruth;
       73, sandy ground, Porthtowan.
       *East: 06, Ruthernbridge, 1977; 07, Wenford Dries,
       near Blisland; 08, near Helstone, Camelford; (09),
       Boscastle; 18, near Rough Tor, Bodmin Moor; 28,
       between Warbstow and Treneer.   Scilly: Lousley 1971.

[116 **T. marklundii** Palmgren, is wrongly recorded in Britain, fide A.J.R. The plants previously recorded under this name are among the most common dandelions in the county, and no doubt refer to the next two species.]

T. quadrans H. Ollg.

Probably common throughout the county. The following records are det. A.J.R.

*West: 63, Treskillard, Redruth, 1973.

*East: 05, Trethurgy, near St Austell, F.H.

T. subhamatum M.P. Chrstiansen

*East: 05, Par Beach, 1977.

T. polyhamatum H. Ollg.

*East: 06, Ruthernbridge, 1977.

T. pseudohamatum Dahlst.

*West: 72, roadside near Earth Station, Goonhilly Downs, 1979.

118 **T. oblongatum** Dahlst.

Usually a plant of shady lanes in Cornwall, but also in upland grassland.

West: 53, cliff-top, Carbis Bay; 64, Bel Lake, Camborne; 84, Coombe Creek, near Truro.

*East: 94, Lamorran, 1976; 08, near Helstone, Camelford; 16, Bofarnel Downs, near Lostwithiel; 17, edge of moorland, Trencreek, near Blisland; 19, St Juliot, Boscastle; 26, St Cleer; 28, between Warbstow and Treneer.

119 **T. lamprophyllum** M.P. Christiansen = *T. maculatum* auct. angl. non Jordan

A very common and widespread species, recorded for 23 stations throughout the county, but not yet recorded for Scilly. First records:

*West: 64, South Drive, Tehidy, Camborne, 1974.

*East: 83, St Mawes, 1975.

121 **T. raunkiaeri** Wiinst. = *T. duplidentifrons* Dahlst. ex Druce

Scattered throughout the county, but rarely found in quantity.

*West: 62, Gunwalloe Valley; 75, Holywell Bay, 1977.
·*East: 94, Tregony, 1976; 06, Ruthernbridge; 08, Port Gaverne Valley; 19, Tresparrett Posts; 20, Crooklets, Bude; 27, Siblyback Rservoir; 28, near Tresmeer Church; 38, old railway, Launceston.

125 **T. polyodon** Dahlst.
Frequent and widespread in Cornwall.
*West: 63, Condurrow, Camborne, 1973; 64, Reskadinnick Turn, Camborne; 73, Perranwharf, Devoran; Ponsanooth; Chyvogue, Perranwell Station; 75, near Perranzabuloe Church; 83, Swanpool, Falmouth; Penpol House, Devoran; 84, near Nancevellan, Truro.
*East: 84, Pencalenick, near Truro; 94, West Portholland, 1975.

132 **T. cophocentrum** Dahlst.
*East: 05, Par Beach, 1977.

T. laciniosifrons Wiinst. = *T. sinuatum* auct. angl. non Dahlst.
*West: 53, Marazion, 1976, E.Ch.

T. exsertum Hagendijk, Van Soest & Zevenbergen
*East: 95, Treviscoe, St Dennis, 1976, OXF.

LAPSANA L.

547/1 **L. communis** L., Nipplewort, is common and widespread throughout Cornwall.

CREPIS L.

559/6 **C. capillaris** (L.) Wallr., Smooth Hawk's-beard, and 559/2 § **C. vesicaria** L., subsp. **haenseleri** (Boiss. ex DC.) P.D. Sell (*C. taraxacifolia* Thuill.), Beaked Hawk's-beard, are common and widely distributed throughout the county.

559/5 § **C. biennis** L.   Rough Hawk's-beard
Once found as a rare casual (Flora and Suppt). There are no subsequent records.

HIERACIUM L.

Subgenus Pilosella

558/2/ **H. pilosella** L., Mouse-ear Hawkweed, is common and
1   widespread on the mainland, but rare in Scilly.

subsp. **micradenium** Naegeli & Peter
(var. *concinnatum* F.J. Hanb.)
Recorded in the past for both vice-counties (Flora), but
there are no recent records.

subsp. **trichosoma** Peter = subsp. *nigrescens* (Fries)
Naegeli & Peter
*West: 53 (54), Godrevy Towans, 1976, L.J.M.

[2   **H. peleteranum** Mérat has been recorded in the past
(Suppt), but, in the absence of a confirmatory specimen,
we feel it is best to reject it as a Cornish species until
further evidence becomes available.]

8   § **H. aurantiacum** L.   Fox and Cubs.
subsp. **carpathicola** Naegeli & Peter
(Suppt as *H. brunneocroceum* Pugsley)
An old-established escape, no longer grown in gardens,
but well-naturalised in a number of sites.
West: 33, St Just, M.C.; 63, Nancegollan Station, I.G.;
64, Trewirgie, Redruth, L.J.M.; 73, wall-top, Devoran,
J.A.P.; 83, Falmouth, L.J.M.; 86, Mawgan, 1903 (B.E.C.
1922).
East: 84, Malpas, J.A.P.; 05, St Austell, J.A.P.; 07,
Port Isaac Road Station, R.W.D.; 05, Carvear Moor,
near St Austell, B.E.M.G.; 25, Sandplace Halt, S.M.; 26,
Moorswater, Liskeard, S.M.; 46, Landulph, B.Sh.

2/8 x 1 **H. aurantiacum** x **pilosella** = *H. x stoloniflorum* Waldst.
& Kit.
*East: 05, Carvear Moor, near St Austell, 1978,
B.E.M.G. and L.J.M.

Subgenus Hieracium

558/1/ **H. exotericum** Jordan ex Boreau agg.
98   More than one species is included here, one of which,
from Holwood Quarry, with prettily-marked leaves, is
very distinct.
West: 83, Falmouth (Flora, as *H. serratifrons* Almq.),
not refound.

*East: 06, in grass and on wall, Lanhydrock, L.J.M.; on waste-heap, Red Moor, 1971, CNT; 36, Holwood Quarry, near Pillaton Mill, E.R.

149   **H. vulgatum** Fries   Wood Hawkweed
The records in the Flora are not supported by specimens, and may refer to other species.   Probably introduced.
East: 38, Launceston (Suppt), common on walls there, 1971, L.J.M.

152   § **H. lepidulum** (Stenstrom) Omang
A railway introduction, now spreading.
*West: 74, old railway track, St Agnes Station, 1972, L.J.M.; 75, railway near Perranporth, L.J.M.; 85, old railway, Newlyn East, L.J.M.
*East: 96, by railway, Goss Moor, L.J.M.

162   § **H. cheriense** Jordan ex Boreau
*West: 73, railway embankment near Penryn viaduct, 1963, L.J.M.

163   **H. strumosum** (W.R. Linton) A. Ley
Possibly native in E Cornwall.
East: 05, wall, St Austell (Suppt), now frequent in St Austell, 1966, L.J.M.; 27, rocky bank, Upton Cross, 1948, N.D.S.; 37, above Landlake Mill, by Lowley Stream, Lezant, T.N.S.P. (Thurston 1928); 36, Callington, W.W. (Pugsley 1948).

[**H. tridentatifolium** (Zahn) P.D. Sell & C. West (*H. corymbosum* Fries), and **H. crocatum** Fries were rejected by Davey (Flora). Neither is known to occur in Britain.]

217   **H. umbellatum** L.   Narrow-leaved Hawkweed
subsp. **umbellatum**
Frequent and widespread throughout the county (absent from Scilly).

218   subsp. **bichlorophyllum** (Druce & Zahn) P.D. Sell & C. West.
Widespread throughout the county, and in most areas more common than the type.

219 **H. perpropinquum** (Zahn) Druce

Broad-leaved Hawkweed

(*H. boreale* auct.)

Extremely rare and local.

East: 36, Cadsonbury, Callington (Flora), refound 1971, L.J.M.

MONOCOTYLEDONES

ALISMATACEAE

BALDELLIA PARL.

561/1 **B. ranunculoides** (L.) Parl.   Lesser Water-plantain

(*Alisma ranunculoides* L.)

Rare and local, but sometimes present in quantity. West: 32, Sennen Moor (Flora), between Sennen and Land's End, J.A.P.; 53, Long Rock Marsh (Flora), 1971, B.M.S.; Marazion (Flora), 1966, A.B.; 61, 'Lizard district' (Flora), still in most pools on the Lizard, as at: Kynance, B.M.S.; W of Holestrow, J.A.P.; Ruan Pool, J.A.P.; near Grochall, J.Fo.; Hayle Kimbro Pool, L.J.M.; 71, Goonhilly Nature Reserve, LFC; Crousa Downs, J.A.P.; Croft Pascoe Pool, L.J.M.; 75, Trebisken Moor—Penhale Sands (Flora), still plentiful in pools on the dunes, 1964—80. L.J.M.; 87, in three cliff-flushes between Constantine Bay and Dinas Head, 1977, L.J.M. East: no recent records.

Scilly: Lousley 1971.

ALISMA L.

563/1 **A. plantago-aquatica** L., Water-plantain, is frequent and widespread in suitable habitats, but absent from West Penwith and Scilly.

HYDROCHARITACEAE

ELODEA MICHX

570/1 § **E. canadensis** Michx   Canadian Waterweed

Compared with many other counties, this introduction has never been as common, but it has increased considerably since the Flora.

West: 42, in boating-pool, Lariggan, Penzance, G.B.M.; 62, Loe Pool (Flora), plentiful 1968, T.M. and L.J.M.; 63, Pendarves Lake, near Camborne, S.M.T.; 72, in old reservoir, Gweek, L.J.M.; 73, Falmouth Reservoir, L.J.M.; 75, Holywell Bay, L.J.M.; 83, Mylor Bridge, W.T. (Thurston 1928); 84, Truro leats (Flora), still there, and also in Moresk Stream, L.J.M.

East: 84, within the grounds of Truro School, A.S.; 20, plentiful in Bude Canal, L.J.M.; 45, Borough Pond, Torpoint, originally planted, S.M.

LAGAROSIPHON HARVEY

571/1 § **L. major** (Ridley) Moss   Curly Water-thyme
An aquarists' throw-out, increasing rapidly once introduced.

*West: 32, N of Sennen village, 1954, B.M.S. (*Proc. B.S.B.I.*, 1: 322); 43, pond at Ding Dong, B.M.S.

*East: 95, abundant in old quarry between Indian Queens and St Dennis, 1965, L.J.M.; 96, Quarry pool, Tregamere, St Columb Major, J.A.P.; 05, Walden Pond, near St Blazey, J.A.P.

JUNCAGINACEAE

TRIGLOCHIN L.

574/2 **T. maritima** L., Sea Arrowgrass, is a constant feature of salt-marshes throughout the county, and thus absent from West Penwith and Scilly.

574/1 **T. palustris** L.   Marsh Arrowgrass
Damp, sandy pastures, usually not far from the coast. Frequent in suitable habitats.

West: 32, pool between Sennen and Land's End, J.A.P.; Brew Moor (Flora), 1970, B.M.S.; 53, Loggans Moor, Hayle, B.M.S.; (54), Gwithian Marsh, L.J.M.; 61, Kynance (Flora), 1970, B.M.S.; Predannick Cliff, B.E.M.G. and J.A.P.; 62, Poldhu (Flora), R.W.D. and L.J.M.; Gunwalloe, R.H.; 75, Carnkief (Flora), 1962, R.W.D. and L.J.M.; Perranporth (Flora), Penhale Sands, 1968, L.J.M.; 85, Trevemper Bridge (Flora), post—1950, B.M.S.; 86 (76), Cubert, K.H.; 87, Booby's Bay, Constantine Bay, T.H.A.; near Gunver Head, J.A.P.

East: 94, Caerhayes, L.J.M.; 97, Amble Marshes, R.W.D.; Pentire Peninsula, R.W.D.; 20, Bude marshes, R.D.; 25, between Sandplace and Looe (Flora), Trenant, post—1950, S.M.; W Looe estuary, S.M.; 35, Tideford,

S.M.; Wacker Creek, S.M.; 45, St John's Lake (Flora), post—1950, S.M.; Yonderberry Point, Torpoint, S.M.; 46, Landulph marsh, E.G.
Scilly: rare, Lousley 1971.

POTAMOGETONACEAE
POTAMOGETON L.

577/2 **P. polygonifolius** Pourret, Bog Pondweed, is common in bogs and acid pools throughout Cornwall. When growing in deep water, it is often wrongly recorded as the next species.

577/1 **P. natans** L. Broad-leaved Pondweed
Rare in the county, and much over-recorded. We have omitted records from very acid localities because of the possibility of confusion with the preceding species.
West: 63, Pendarves Lake, S.M.T.; 71, Goonhilly Downs N of Gwendreath, J.A.P.; 75, Carnkief Pond (Flora), 1976, L.J.M.
East: 85, Arallas, near Mitchell, C.J.; 21, Tamar Lake, D.H.
Scilly: very rare, Lousley 1971.

[577/7 **P. alpinus** Balbis, Red Pondweed, was yet another error on the 'Pascoe List'. We agree with Davey (Flora) in rejecting this species.]

577/9 **P. perfoliatus** L. Perfoliate Pondweed
Very local, though remarkably persistent where it does occur.
West: 62, Loe Pool (Flora), still there, various recorders; in the boating-lake, Municipal Gardens, Helston (Suppt), post—1950, L.J.M.; 63, Clowance Pond, W.T. (Thurston and Vigurs 1927); 73, Falmouth Reservoir (Flora), still there, 1950 onwards, L.J.M.
*East: 21, Tamar Lake, various recorders.
Scilly: very rare, Lousley 1971.

577/13 **P. pusillus** L. Lesser Pondweed
(incl. *R. panormitanus* Biv.)
Probably more frequent than the few records listed here show, but much confused with *P. berchtoldii* Fieber. The account in the Flora and Suppt covers both species.
West: 32, Sennen, B.M.S.

East: 84 or 94, near Probus Halt, W.T. (Thurston 1929a); 96, Goss Moor, L.J.M.; 05, pool on Par Beach, L.J.M.; 21, Tamar Lake, D.H.; 26, pond at Moorswater, Liskeard, C.P.F. (Thurston and Vigurs 1927).
Scilly: Lousley 1971.

[577/ **P. obtusifolius** Mert. & Koch, Blunt-leaved Pondweed,
14 was rejected by Davey (Flora), a decision with which we agree.]

577/15 **P. berchtoldii** Fieber   Small Pondweed
More common than *P. pusillus*, especially in less acid waters.
*West: 53, Marazion Marsh, L.J.M.; along the Hayle River, L.J.M.; 62, Gunwalloe Stream, CNT; Poldhu Stream, R.A.G. (*Proc. B.S.B.I.*, 3: 197); 63, Pendarves Lake, near Camborne, S.M.T.; 64, Tehidy Lake, L.J.M.; 73, Stithians Reservoir, L.J.M.; 75, Carnkief Pond, L.J.M.; Ellenglaze Stream, Penhale Sands, G.A., R.Go. and L.J.M.; 87, stream on golf-course, Constantine Bay, L.J.M.
*East: 05, Walden Pond, near St Blazey, 1970, J.A.P.; 06, pond NW of Bugle, J.A.P.

577/16 **P. trichoides** Cham. and Schlecht.
Known in the county from this one station.
*East: 20, Bude canal, 1919, W.S.D'U., **RAMM**, re-found 1945, C.We., **CGE**.

577/19 **P. crispus** L.   Curled Pondweed
Extremely local, and frequent only in the Upper Tamar area.
West: 83, in streamlet, Queen Mary Gardens, Falmouth, L.J.M.
East: 97, Amble Marshes, R.W.D.; 15, Couch's Mill, near Lerryn, F.R. (Thurston and Vigurs 1927); 20, Bude Canal (Suppt), refound 1961, E.A.; Moreton Mill, J.A.P.; 21, Tamar Lake, 1950 onwards, D.H.; 26, Looe River near Lodge, S of Liskeard, C.P.F. (Thurston and Vigurs 1927).

577/21 **P. pectinatus** L.   Fennel Pondweed
(incl. *P. interruptus* Kit.)
Very local and rare. Absent from E Cornwall.
West: 61, Hayle Kimbro Pool, NCS; 62, Municipal Lake, Helston, R.W.D., R.J.M., and L.J.M.; 64, Bel Lake, Red River Valley, R.J.M.; Tehidy Lake, near Camborne, L.J.M.; 83, Swanpool, Falmouth (Flora), still there in great quantity, 1966, L.J.M.
Scilly: Lousley 1971.

RUPPIACEAE

RUPPIA L.

579/2 **R. maritima** L.   Beaked Tasselweed
(*R. rostellata* Koch)
Brackish pools and ditches. Rather local around the estuaries.
West: no recent records.
East: 84, pool between Tresillian and Malpas, L.J.M.; salt-pan, Ruan Lanihorne, T.M. and L.J.M.; 05, near Par Station (Flora), 1954, J.B.; Par Beach, J.A.P.; 25, West Looe Valley (Flora), 1969, L.J.M.; 46, Clifton, near Landulph, I.N.
Scilly: Lousley 1971.

579/1 **R. cirrhosa** (Petagna) Grande   Spiral Tasselweed
(*R. maritima* auct.)
A very rare and decreasing plant in Britain, but possibly still holding on in Cornwall.
West: 83, Swanpool, Falmouth (Flora), still there in 1951, R.W.D.
East: 97, Amble Marshes, R.W.D.; 05, Par Beach (Suppt), 1966, L.A.B.

ZOSTERACEAE

ZOSTERA L.

576/1 **Z. marina** L.   Eelgrass
Frequent and widespread in the estuaries and sheltered bays of the S coast. Often washed up on the strand-line after storms, even on the N Coast. As the origin of such plants is uncertain, we have marked their occurrences accordingly, with a cross.
West: 32+, Sennen Cove and Whitsand Bay, L.J.M.;

42, Penzance (Flora), post—1950, B.M.S.; 43, Long Rock (Flora), post—1970, S.M.T.; 52+, Perranuthnoe, L.J.M.; 53, between Marazion and St Michael's Mount, S.M.T.; (54)+, near Gwithian, L.J.M.; Godrevy, R.Go.; 62+, Gunwalloe, L.J.M.; 64, Portreath (Flora), 1968+, A.B.; 72, Polpenwith Creek, Helford River, S.M.T.; Gillan Harbour, abundant, J.A.P.; W of Rosemullion Head, S.M.T.; 75, Perranporth (Flora), 1968+, L.J.M.; 83, Falmouth (Flora), post—1970, S.M.T.

East: 83+, between St Just and St Mawes, L.J.M.; near Amsterdam Point, Gerrans, G.M.; + Pendower Beach, L.J.M.; 94+, Hemmick Beach, L.J.M.; 04+, Vault Beach, Gorran, L.J.M.; 05+, Polkerris, H.W.P. (Thurston 1935); 15+, Fowey, H.W.P. (Thurston 1935), colony found 1970, S.M.T.; 25, Looe (Flora), Hannafore Point, post—1970, S.M.T.; 35, Whitsand Bay (Flora), post—1950+, S.M.

Scilly: Lousley 1971.

576/2 **Z. angustifolia** (Hornem.)Reichenb.

Narrow-leaved Eelgrass

(*Z. marina* var. *augustifolia*)

Local and rare.

West: 72, Helford Creek, 1951, R.W.D.

*East: 83, Polvarth Point, St Mawes, 1951, R.W.D.; 45, St John's Lake, Saltash, 1967, J.A.P.

Scilly: rejected, Lousley 1971.

576/3 **Z. noltii** Hornem.

Dwarf Eelgrass

(*Z. nana* Roth)

Local and rare.

West: 72, below Gweek, 1965, J.A.P.; Scotch Quay, Helford River, E.A.R. (Thurston and Vigurs 1927) ?= Calamansack, 1951, R.W.D.; Helford Creek, 1926, C.H.F.

East: 45, St John's, Torpoint (Flora), still there *c* 1930, T.W.; 46, Landulph, C.P.H. (Thurston 1935).

ZANNICHELLIACEAE
ZANNICHELLIA L.
580/1 **Z. palustris** L. Horned Pondweed
(incl. *Z. pedunculata* Reichb.)

Very rare, and only in a few scattered stations, usually near the sea.

West: 62, Poldhu Stream (Flora), 1968, L.J.M.; Gunwalloe Valley (Flora), 1968, LFC; 87, cliff-flush between Dinas Head and Constantine Bay, L.J.M.; in stream on golf-course, Constantine Bay, L.J.M.

East: 97, Amble (Flora), post—1950, R.W.D.; 20, Bude Canal, L.J.M.; 21, Tamar Lake, D.H.; 25, Morvah Pond, near Looe (Suppt), refound 1966, J.A.P.

LILIACEAE
NARTHECIUM HUDSON
584/1 **N. ossifragum** (L.) Hudson, Bog Asphodel, is a conspicuous feature of bogs and wet heaths throughout the county (absent from Scilly).

PHORMIUM J.R. & G. FORSTER
587/1 § **P. tenax** J.R. & G. Forster New Zealand Flax

A common and increasing garden escape in Scilly.

*West: 52, several plants on cliffs, Prussia Cove, L.J.M.; 62, Lower Methleigh Farm, Porthleven, 1963, H.B.S.

Scilly: common, Lousley 1971.

COLCHICUM L.
602/1 **C. autumnale** L. Meadow Saffron

Status unknown, but almost certainly introduced.

*East: 21, Coombe Valley, 1959, J.Tr., above old mill, 1979, R.D.

LILIUM L.
593/2 § **L. pyrenaicum** Gouan Pyrenean Lily

A rare garden outcast, often persisting.

West: 43, roadside between Trendrine and Towednack, G.B.M.; 75, edge of plantation near Chyverton, N.H.; 85 (may be in v.c.2.), near Summercourt, C.H.W.

East: 37, hedgebank, Linkinhorne, N.J.F.; between Callington and Kelly Bray, E.G.; 38, wood near Hexworthy, SE of Launceston, 1933, C.H.F.

ORNITHOGALUM L.

598/1 § **O. umbellatum** L.   Star-of-Bethlehem
Long-naturalised in Cornwall, and thus often appearing native. Though absent from a large portion of central Cornwall, elsewhere this plant is too frequent to warrant listing of localities.

SCILLA L.

599/1 **S. verna** Hudson, Spring Squill, is a common plant of cliffs in N and W Cornwall, but absent from a long stretch of the S coast from Par to Saltash. It is also found in a few places inland.

599/2 **S. autumnalis** L.   Autumn Squill
In scattered localities along the N coast, on the Lizard, and in a few places on the S coast of West Penwith, occasionally in quantity. Two genetic races exist, the hexaploid, known only from Cornwall and the Channel Isles, and the tetraploid race, which is found throughout Europe. In Cornwall, the latter form is restricted to parts of the N coast. We are grateful to Dr J. Parker for allowing us to include this information.

West: 32, Porthgwarra, W.R.H.; 33, Cape Cornwall, W.R.H.; 52, Prussia Cove (Flora), Cudden Point, post—1950, B.M.S.; cliff near Perranuthnoe, A.Th. (Thurston and Vigurs 1927); 53 (54), Gwithian, R.H.; Godrevy, CNT; 61 and 71, from Mullion to Cadgwith (Flora), still frequent on the Lizard, various recorders; 62, Porthleven (Flora) post—1950, H.B.S.; Poldhu Cove, J.G.T.; Gunwalloe Church Cove; 75, Holywell (Flora), 1976, A.T. and L.J.M.; 86 (76), between Porth Joke and Crantock, J.G.T.; 87, Porthcothan (Flora), 1965, J.L.; Constantine Bay, W.G.; Trevose Head, K.E.H.; near Gunver Head, J.A.P.; 97, Padstow (Flora), Harbour Cove, 1964, R.W.D.

East: 97, Pentire Peninsula, R.W.D.; Dinham Creek, C.J.; 08, Tintagel (Flora), 1954, R.I.S.; 20, Bude, J.L. Scilly: rejected, Lousley 1971.

HYACINTHOIDES MEDICUS.

600/1 **H. non-scripta** (L.) Chouard ex Rothm. (*Scilla non-scripta* Hoffmgg. & Link), Bluebell, is abundant and widespread on cliffs, hedges, waysides, and woodland.

600/2 § **H. hispanica** (Miller) Rothm.   Spanish Bluebell
(Suppt as *Scilla campanulata* Ait.)

Now widely naturalised by waysides and in waste places throughout Cornwall.

West: 53, Marazion, L.J.M.; Hayle, and Lethlean Towans, L.J.M.; Upton Towans, L.J.M.; (54), Gwithian Towans, L.J.M.; 63, Wheal Grenville, Troon, L.J.M.; 64, Illogan, R.J.M.; cliff, Portreath, J.S.R.; 71, Goonhilly Nature Reserve, S.M.T. *et al.;* 74, United Mines, Gwennap, L.J.M.; Blackwater Hill, and Scorrier, L.J.M.; 75, Cubert, L.J.M.; Perranzabuloe (Suppt), Perrancombe, 1966, L.J.M.; 83, Swanpool, Falmouth, L.J.M.; by railway, Falmouth Station, L.J.M.

*East: 83, cliff-top, Portscatho, 1965, L.J.M.; Pendower Beach, L.J.M.; 95, New Mills, near Ladock, L.J.M.; 05, Par Sands, and Polkerris, L.J.M.; 20, in two places on the dunes, Bude, L.J.M.; 28, Tresmeer, near the church, L.J.M.; 45, Cremyll, L.J.M.

Scilly: Lousley 1971; T, well-naturalised in several places, 1972, T.R.

600/2   **H. hispanica x non-scripta**
x 1   This hybrid sometimes appears where the parents grow in proximity to each other.

*West: 53, near Phillack church, L.J.M.; (54), Gwithian Towans, L.J.M.; 63, Wheal Grenville, Troon, 1966, L.J.M.; 75, Perrancombe, Perranporth, L.J.M.; 83, by railway near Falmouth Station, L.J.M.

*East: 83, Pendower Beach, 1965, L.J.M.

Scilly: Lousley 1971.

MUSCARI MILLER

601/2 § **M. comosum** (L.) Miller   Tassel Hyacinth

A rare introduction, naturalised on dunes.

*West: 53, Upton Towans, 1971, C.H.W. ?= Lethlean Towans, 64 plants in 1976, T.Mi.

*East: 05, Par Harbour, L.T.M.; (B.E.C. 1925 and 1926).

Scilly: MN, Lousley 1971.

601/1 § **M. neglectum** Guss. ex Ten. Grape Hyacinth
(*M. racemosum* Lam. & DC.)
Garden cultivars of this European species often occur as
throw-outs on hedgebanks and sandy waste places.
West: 53, well-naturalised on low dunes, Long Rock,
L.J.M.; Hayle, and Upton Towans, L.J.M.; 63, old tip
near Four Lanes, L.J.M.; 64, hedgebank, Treswithian,
Camborne, R.M.; 74, Goonbell Halt, L.J.M.
East: 97, bank below Gonvena, Wadebridge, B.E.M.G.;
05, Par Sands, L.J.M.; 36, N of Trematon, D.B.; Paynters
Cross, D.B.

ALLIUM L.

Common species: 607/10 § **A. triquetrum** L., Three-
cornered Leek, 607/12 **A. ursinum** L., Ramsons
(rejected for Scilly, Lousley 1971), and 607/5 **A.
vineale** L., Crow Garlic.

607/8 **A. schoenoprasum** L. Chives
(incl. *A. sibiricum* L.)
A characteristic plant of downs and cliffs on the Lizard,
and also in a small area of N Cornwall.
West: 61, now known from *c* 10 stations, comm.
1979, J.H.; 71, in *c* 5 stations, comm. 1979, J.H.; 72,
in *c* 9 stations, comm. 1979, J.H.
East: 08, Trebarwith, 1978, D.H.; (09), Trevalga
(Flora), still there, 1965, J.B.

607/9 § **A. roseum** L. Rosy Garlic
A European species that has spread rapidly in Cornwall
in the last twenty years, and is now thoroughly
naturalised, especially in the West. The name subsp.
bulbiferum (DC.) E.F. Warburg is often applied to the
form with bulbils that is the prevailing type here.
*West: 42, garden outcast, Mousehole, G.B.M.; weed in
nursery, Penzance, G.B.M.; 43, near Penlee Park, comm.
G.B.M.; 53, Lelant Station, J.B.; near the old ferry,
Lelant, J.M.M. and R.P.; Phillack Towans, B.M.S.; (54),
Gwithian Towans, L.J.M.; 61, road to Kynance, J.Fo.;
63, near Four Lanes, R.M.; Connor Downs, J.S.R.;
64, Porthtowan, L.J.M.; 71, Cadgwith, J.R.; Poltesco,
R.B.G.; 72, Bosahan, Manaccan (B.E.C. 1920); Durgan,
L.J.M.; 75, Perranporth, A.Bi.; 83, Falmouth Cemetary

(B.E.C. 1924), still there, 1960 onwards, L.J.M.; Feock R.H.; Mylor Bridge, R.H.; 84, Old Kea churchyard, K.P.
*East: 04, Gorran, B.Sh.; 05, Carlyon Bay, B.G.; 38, Launceston, 1959, B.Sh.
Scilly: Lousley 1971.

607/1 **A. ampeloprasum** L. Wild Leek
In the strict sense, very rare and local. Probably an ancient introduction.
West: 62, Skyburriowe, near Garras, The Lizard, 1954, R.W.D.; 86, Trevarrian, near Mawgan Porth (Thurston 1930).
East: 93, Pendower Beach, 1958, A.L.P.; 20, Bude, 1966, J.A.P.

607/2 var. **babingtonii** (Borrer) Syme Babington's Leek
(*A. babingtonii* Borrer)
Listed by Davey (Flora) as rather rare, it is not so now, except in the East. It seems to be increasing rapidly in the West. Not now regarded as a species, but only as a bulbiliferous form of the preceding.
West: 42, St Loy, near St Buryan, G.B.M.; near Tater-du, Lamorna, D.St.; three plants, Drift, G.B.M.; 43, Gulval, B.M.S.; 53, St Erth Praze, A.C.L.; near Hayle Station (Flora), 1976, J.M.M., L.J.M., and R.P.; 61, Kynance (Flora), post—1950, various recorders; Mullion, BRC; 62, Gunwalloe (Flora), post—1950, R.H.; copse in Gunwalloe Valley, J.H. and L.J.M.; 63, near Leedstown, comm. J.B.B.; 71, Cadgwith, L.A.B.; Housel Bay, 1959—77, J.Fo.; Poltesco (Flora), 1950, BRC; Arrowan Common, A.C.L.; 72, near Helford, K.H.; between Gweek and St Mawgan (Flora), 1950, BRC; Porthallow, R.H.; 75, Penhale Sands, R.L.G.L.; Holywell Bay, L.J.M.; 85, Trevemper Bridge (Suppt), 1976, L.J.M.; Trewerry Mill, near Newlyn East, L.J.M.; 86, Newquay (Flora), still there, post—1950, various recorders; (76), Cubert, K.H.; 87, Porthcothan (Flora), 1965, J.L.; 97, near Treator, Trevone, S.M.
East: 83, near St Anthony (Flora), 1967, R.B.G.; abundant at Trewince, near Gerrans, L.J.M.; Tolverne, King Harry, B.E.M.G.; Portscatho (Flora), 1951, BRC; 97, Polzeath (Flora), still at Old Polzeath, 1980, and introduced at New Polzeath, R.W.D.; Treneague, Wade-

bridge, A.W.; (98), Port Quin, A.W.; 05, Polpey, Par, B.G.; 08, Boscastle (B.E.C. 1940), 1960, E.A.; 19, Crackington Haven (Flora), 1973, E.G.; 20, Bude, B.Sh. Scilly: Lousley 1971.

[607/3 A. scorodoprasum L., Sand Leek, was rejected by Davey (Flora). We agree that it has no place in the Cornish flora.]

CONVALLARIA L.

588/1 **C. majalis L.** Lily-of-the-Valley
Now extremely rare, and only as an obvious garden throw-out, except possibly in Carthamartha Wood, where it may have been native.

West: 53, Phillack Towans, B.M.S.; 83, under *Salix*, edge of Swanpool, Falmouth, L.J.M.

East: 37, Carthamartha Wood (Flora), not found since, but it could still be there.

POLYGONATUM MILLER

589/3 § **P. multiflorum** (L.) All. x **odoratum** (Miller) Druce
x 2 = *P. x hybridum* Brugger Garden Solomon's-seal
The records for *P. multiflorum* All. and *P. officinale* All. in the Flora belong here. The wild *P. multiflorum* is probably not in Cornwall, though the population in Langford Hill Plantation (Flora), if extant, should be re-examined.

West: 85, old tip, Newlyn East, CNT.

East: 85, hedgebank, Trendeal, near Ladock, L.J.M.; 21, lane leading to Priestacott, Kilkhampton, R.D.; wood at top of Tidna Valley, Morwenstow, R.D.; 36, N of Trematon, D.B.

ASPARAGUS L.

591/1a § **A. officinalis** L. subsp. **officinalis** Asparagus
A rare garden outcast in coastal areas.

West: 75, near Ellenglaze Stream, Penhale Sands, B.M.S. and L.J.M.; 85, The Gannel, Newquay, post— 1950, R.L.G.L., 1977, L.G.

East: 97, by edge of creek, S of bridge, Wadebridge, 1977, L.J.M.

591/1b subsp. **prostratus** (Dumort.) Corb.　　　Sea Asparagus

Well-known as one of the Lizard rarities, but recently found in two places on the N coast.

West:　61, in *c* 6 stations, comm. 1979, J.H.; 71, in 3 stations, comm. 1979, J.H.; 64 (65), 49 plants between Chapel Porth and St Agnes Head, 1976, L.J.M.; 87, 15 plants at Dinas Head, near Constantine Bay, 1977, L.J.M.

RUSCUS L.

592/1　**R. aculeatus** L.　　　Butcher's-broom

Local, though widespread, as a plant of rocky cliffs along the S coast, and also occurring as an introduction elsewhere.

West:　61, Kynance (Flora), still there, and at Pentreath, various recorders; 64, Ashill Farm, near Camborne, L.J.M.; 71, Coverack, and Kennack (Flora), still there, and in between, various recorders; Poltesco (Flora), still there, various recorders; 73, in two places along Swanvale Stream, Falmouth, L.J.M.; Lower Crill, Budock, L.J.M.

East:　83, hedge, Curgurrel, N of Portscatho, B.E.M.G.; 93, Carne, and Nare Head, B.E.M.G.; 94, Tredinnick, near Tregoney, W.A.; 08 (09), Boscastle (Suppt), 1972, N.J.F.; 15, near Fowey, W.T. (Thurston 1935); 29, Week St Mary (Suppt), 1978, L.J.M.; 35, near Sheviock, S.M.; 45 (44), Rame Head (Flora), in two places, post— 1950, S.M.; 46, Cargreen, Landulph (Flora), still there, post—1950, I.N.

Scilly:　Lousley 1971.

AMARYLLIDACEAE
LEUCOJUM L.

611/2　§ **L. aestivum** L.　　　Summer Snowflake
　　　　subsp. **pulchellum** (Salis.) Briq.

This garden plant is becoming increasingly found as a garden escape.

West:　43, Tremethick Cross, near Penzance, B.M.S.; 73, Maen Valley, near Falmouth, L.J.M.; 83, Madeira Walk, Falmouth, L.J.M.; 86 (76), by wood near Penpol Creek, Crantock, B.B.

East:　15, Menabilly Wood, near Fowey (B.E.C. 1931).

Scilly:　Lousley 1971.

GALANTHUS L.

12/1 § **G. nivalis** L. Snowdrop

Naturalised locally throughout the county, occasionally in quantity. Rather variable, as several cultivars are found in addition to the type.

West: 42, woodland, Lamorna Valley, L.J.M.; 43, Treassowe, Ludgvan (Flora), 1971, B.M.S.; 53, Treloyhan Woods, St Ives, L.B.; 62, Withy Bed, Porthleven, 1956—62, H.B.S.; 72, Merthen, R.H.; Constantine, R.H.; plentiful at Mill Mehal, near St Keverne, A. and F.G.; 75, Ventongimps Reserve, N.R.; Perranwell Woods, C.J.; 86 (76), Vugga Cove, Crantock, B.B.

East: 83, abundant in copse above Porthbean Beach, Gerrans, L.J.M.; 93, Pendower Valley, L.J.M.; 08, Tintagel, L.J.M.; 25, near Sandplace, D.B.; 26, Coombe, and Lodge, S of Liskeard, D.B.; between Merrymeet and St Ive, D.B.; 27, Rillaton, N.J.F.; 35, Hessenford (Flora), 1966, J.A.P.; 36, in two places S of Callington, D.B.; N of Trematon, and near Hatt, D.B.; 37, near Linkinhorne Church, L.J.M.; Bicton Wood, E of Pensilva, J.A.P.; 45, Ferry Lane, Antony Estate, S.M.; Borough, and Thanckes Wood, Torpoint, S.M.

NARCISSUS L.

Daffodils are a feature of hedgebanks and waste places in the spring, as relics of former cultivation. Most of them are hybrids of complex origin, and therefore difficult to place. Many of the records for *N. pseudonarcissus* belong here.

§ **N. tazetta** L., subsp. **italicus** (Ker-Gawler) Baker

*West: 42, Boskenna, St Buryan (Thurston 1929). Scilly: Lousley 1971.

14/6 § **N. poeticus** L. Pheasant's Eye

West: 53, Hayle Towans, G.C.D. (B.E.C. 1929). Scilly: Lousley 1971.

14/1 **N. pseudonarcissus** L. Wild Daffodil
subsp. **pseudonarcissus**

Native in the wooded valleys of E Cornwall. Owing to the ease with which Narcissus cultivars become naturalised, it is difficult to separate the records of these from those of the genuine native. The following stations, however, appear to be correct.

West: 64, Tehidy Woods, J.G.T.

East: 05, Luxulyan, B.Sh.; 06, Lanhydrock, J.B.; 07 Allen Valley below Kelly Green, J.A.P.; 16, near Bodmin Road Station, J.A.P.; 25, Looe (Flora), Sandplace 1966, J.L.; Sowdens Bridge, J.A.P.; 26, Liskeard (Flora) near Trussel Bridge, D.B.; W of St Ive, D.B.; 28, Treneglos churchyard, introduced; 35, St Germans (Flora), Port Eliot, I.N.; 37, SE of Luckett, J.A.P. Carthamartha Wood, L.J.M.; 38, near Launceston (Flora), below Launceston, post—1950, J.A.P.

Scilly: introduced, Lousley 1971.

614/3 § subsp. **major** (Curtis) Baker   Spanish Daffodil
A long-standing introduction.

West: 32, well-naturalised in Penberth Valley, 1979 L.J.M.; 42, abundantly in wooded valley near Boskenna, St Buryan, L.J.M.; in woodland by stream, Lamorna Valley, L.J.M.

Scilly: Lousley 1971.

614/5 § N. **jonquilla** L. x **pseudonarcissus** = *N. x odorus* L
East: 04, between London Apprentice and Sticker (Flora), refound 1972, B.E.M.G.

Scilly: Lousley 1971.

614/7 § N. **poeticus** x **tazetta** = *N. x medioluteus* Miller
                                                    Primrose-peerless
(*N. biflorus* Curt.)
A frequent garden escape, much under-recorded.

West: 72, near the Crag, Maenporth, E.B. (Thurston and Vigurs 1927); 75, Mount, Perranzabuloe, L.J.M.

East: 45, Wearde Quay, Saltash, S.M.

Scilly: Lousley 1971.

Several other species and cultivars are listed by Lousley 1971.

DIOSCOREACEAE

TAMUS L.

622/1 **T. communis** L., Black Bryony, is common and widespread in Cornwall (absent from Scilly).

IRIDACEAE
HERMODACTYLUS MILLER

617/1 § **H. tuberosus** (L.) Miller   Snake's-head Iris
(*Iris tuberosa* L.)

Very rare, but persistent where naturalised.
West: 43, near Ludgvan (Suppt), still there, 1971,
B.M.S.; 61, Clahar Farm, Mullion, E.J.P. (Thurston
1928), still there, 1959, R.W.D.; 74, Scorrier Woods,
naturalised for 50 years, H.B.

IRIS L.

616/3 **I. foetidissima** L., Stinking Iris, and 616/4 **I.
pseudacorus** L., Yellow Iris, are frequent and widely
distributed in suitable habitats.

ROMULEA MARATTI

[619/1 **R. columnae** Sebastiani and Mauri   Sand Crocus
The only station for this rare plant was at 15, Polruan
(Flora), where it has not been refound, and must there-
fore now be regarded as extinct.]

TRITONIA KER-GAWLER

620/1 § **T. x crocosmiflora** (Lemoine) Nicholson   Montbretia
Commonly established throughout the county in a
variety of habitats, especially by roadsides and on
waste ground near the sea.

GLADIOLUS L.

621/2 § **G. communis** L.   Jack
subsp. **byzantinus** (Miller) A.P. Hamilton

Once widely grown commercially and in gardens, now
naturalised in hedges and waste places. Tellam's record
of *G. illyricus* from Par (Flora) no doubt belongs here.
*West: 32, Gwenver, Sennen, M.C.; 42, Mousehole,
G.B.M.; 52, Prussia Cove, B.M.S.; Hoe Point, B.B.; 53,
Crowlas, J.A.P.; near Canonstown, B.M.S.; Phillack
Towans, CRNHS; 64, Bridge, Portreath, L.J.M.; 71,
around Lizard Town, 1959—77, J.Fo.; 86, Towan
Headland, Newquay, B.B.

East: 83, Trewince Quay, Gerrans, in cornfield,
L.J.M.; Portscatho, L.J.M.; 35, Downderry, L.J.M.
Scilly: common, Lousley 1971.

JUNCACEAE

JUNCUS L.

Common species: 605/8 **J. inflexus** L., Hard Rush (absent from Scilly), 605/9 **J. effusus** L., Soft Rush, 605/10 **J. conglomeratus** L., Compact Rush, 605/7 **J bufonius** L., *sensu stricto*, Toad Rush, 605/22 **J bulbosus** L., *sensu lato*, Bulbous Rush, 605/18 **J acutiflorus** Ehrh. ex Hoffm., Sharp-flowered Rush, and 605/19 **J. articulatus** L., Jointed Rush.

605/14 **J. maritimus** Lam.   Sea Rush

Locally frequent throughout the county in salt-marshes and on raised beaches.

West: 53, Hayle (Flora), 1970, B.M.S.; Phillack (Flora), post—1950, B.M.S.; Upton Towans, L.J.M.; 72, Maenporth (Flora), post—1950, R.H.; 73, Newporth Head, near Falmouth, L.J.M.; 75, Perranporth, W.T. (Thurston and Vigurs 1927); 83, near Falmouth (Flora), Pennance Point, post—1950, L.J.M.; 87, Constantine Bay, W.G.; 97, Padstow (Flora), Harbour Cove, 1964, R.W.D. East: 84, Lamorran, L.J.M.; Ruan Lanihorne, D.R.; 93, Pendower Beach, B.E.M.G.; Camels Cove, Portloe, L.J.M.; 25, Looe (Suppt), Sandplace, and Looe, 1966, J.A.P.; 35, Grove, S of Trematon, J.A.P.; Erth Island, K.H.; Wivelscombe (Flora), post—1950, I.N.; 45, Ince, I.N.; Yonderberry Point, Torpoint, S.M.; Antony Passage, J.A.P.; Rame Head (Flora), E end of Whitsand Bay, post—1950, I.N.; (44), Penlee Point, L.J.M.; 46, above Cargreen, I.N.; Salt Mill, Saltash, I.N.; Halton Quay, I.N.
Scilly: Lousley 1971.

var. **atlanticus** J.W. White
Scilly: a distinct variety found only on St Mary's, Lousley 1971.

605/15 **J. acutus** L.   Sharp Rush

Extremely rare, and known from only one extant station.

*West: 97, Harbour Cove, near Padstow, 1964, R.W.D
*East: 05, Par, E.S.T. (B.E.C. 1933), not found since.

605/9 **J. effusus x inflexus** = *J. x diffusus* Hoppe
x 8 Probably more frequent than the few records would seem to show.

West: 53, Upton Towans, L.J.M.; 75, moor, Goonhavern, L.J.M.; Carnkief (Suppt), still there, 1976, L.J.M.; Mount, Penhale Sands, L.J.M.

605/1 **J. squarrosus** L. Heath Rush
A characteristic plant of damp moorland on granite rock, rarely elsewhere. Frequent on Bodmin Moor, but very rare in the West.

West: 63, Polgear Moor, Carnmenellis, L.J.M.; 73, Polmarth Bog, Carnmenellis, L.J.M.; Rame (Flora), near Polangrain, 1961, L.J.M.; Budock, near Falmouth (Flora), post—1950, L.J.M.

East: 95, Hensbarrow Downs, W.T. (Thurston 1929a); moor by Roche Rock, L.J.M.; 06, Helmentor, and Red Moor (Flora), still there, 1963, E.A.; 17, near Temple Bridge, L.J.M.; Blisland (Flora), post—1950, R.W.D.; Dozmary Pool (Flora), post—1950, R.W.D.; 18, Rough Tor (Flora), 1979, K.H.; N of Bray Down (Flora), Bowithick, C.J.; 27, Hawk's Tor, Northill, W.H.F. (Thurston and Vigurs 1923); Trewortha Tor, I.N.; Cheesewring (Flora), post—1950, I.N.; Harrowbridge, and Smallacombe Downs, S.M.; 28, Laneast Downs (Suppt), 1970, G.L.K.; 36, Viverdon Down (Flora), post—1950, R.W.D.

605/4 **J. compressus** Jacq. Round-fruited Rush
Extremely local, but possibly overlooked. It may be still in more of its old stations.

West: 53, in reed-bed near Black Bridge, Copperhouse, Hayle, 1970, L.J.M.; 73, between Penryn and Flushing (Flora), refound 1979, L.J.M.
Scilly: rejected, Lousley 1971.

605/5 **J. gerardi** Loisel. Salt-marsh Rush
Frequent in salt-marshes, but also on raised beaches.
West: 53, Hayle, and Phillack (Flora), post—1950, B.M.S.; 72, Gillan Creek, Helford River, L.A.B.; 73, between Penryn and Flushing, L.J.M.; 83, between Penarrow and Trefusis Point, S.M.T.; 84, Calenick Creek, L.J.M.

East: 83, Portscatho (Flora), 1978, J.S.R.; Froe Lake
B.E.M.G.; Turnaware Creek, B.E.M.G.; 84, between
Pencalenick and St Clements (Flora), 1966, L.J.M.; 97
Amble Marshes, R.W.D.; 25, Looe (Flora), post—1950
S.M.; 35, Sconner Creek, Shevoick, S.M.; St Germans
J.A.P.; Wivelscombe, I.N.; 45, in several places about
Saltash, I.N.; St Johns Lake (Flora), post—1950, I.N.
Yonderberry Point, Torpoint, S.M.; (44), Whitsand Bay
(Flora), post—1950, I.N.; 46, Cargreen (Flora), post—
1950, I.N.
Scilly: Lousley, 1971.

605/2 § **J. tenuis** Willd.   Slender Rush
This American Rush was first recorded as naturalised at
Tywardreath by Mrs W. Graham in the *Journal of
Botany*, 1894 (Flora). Since then, it has spread with
great rapidity into many parts of the county.

West: 43, near Rosemorran, Gulval, H.S.T. (Thurston
1930); 63, old Council tip, Treskillard, L.J.M.; 64, old
mine, Seligan, Redruth, L.J.M.; 73, Cosawes Wood
Ponsanooth, L.J.M.; Ponsanooth, E.S.T. (Thurston
1935); near Carclew, W.T. and A.J.H. (Thurston and
Vigurs 1926); 74, Silverwell Moor, F.R. (Thurston
1935); edge of Carrine Common, L.J.M.; 75, gliding
school, Perranporth, B.M.S.; Jericho Valley, Mithian
C.J.; 84, Bishops Wood, Idless, G.A. and L.J.M.

East: 93, Veryan, B.E.M.G.; 95, old railway line
Treviscoe, St Dennis, L.J.M.; 04, Pentewan Valley
A.C.J. *et al.*; 04 or 05, near Penrice, St Austell, W.T
(Thurston 1929a); 05, Charlestown, W.T. (Thurston
1935); between Trethurgy and Luxulyan, L.J.M.
Carvear, St Blazey, H.W.P. (Thurston 1935); Starrick
Moor, W.T. (Thurston and Vigurs 1927); 06, Red Moor
CNT; Criggan Moor, A.C.J. *et al.;* lane to Margate Wood
L.T.M. and F.R. (Thurston and Vigurs 1927); 07
Hellandbridge — in Helligan and Shell Woods, E.A.
16, in wood near Glyn Bridge, L.J.M.; 19, Valency
Valley, Boscastle, J.G.D.; 26, between Lamellion and
Moorswater, Liskeard, C.P.F. (Thurston and Vigurs
1927); 28, by bridge over river, Egloskerry, L.J.M.; 35
above Hessenford, and in woods to Widegates, I.N.
Tideford, I.N.; 36, by bridge, Pillaton Mill, I.N.; near
Hepwell Bridge, Quethiock, I.N.; between Pillaton and

St Mellion, I.N.; 37, near Carthamartha, Rezare, I.N.; Luckett, I.N.; 46, Cotehele Woods, and valley leading to quay, I.N.; 47, by Tamar at Gunnislake, I.N.

J. foliosus Desf.

Often confused with *J. bufonius*, but a much larger plant.

*West: 87, cliff-flush near Dinas Head, Constantine Bay, 1977, L.J.M.

*East: 96, Goss Moor, L.J.M.; 97, cliff-flush, Pentire Peninsula, 1977, L.J.M.; 06, Retire Common, L.J.M.; 17, Harpurs Downs, Bodmin Moor, CNT.

J. ranarius Song. and Perr.

A species that is much like a dwarf form of *J. bufonius*. It needs to be refound in the county.

West: 61 or 71, Lizard (Suppt), not recorded since.

East: recorded without locality for v.c.2 in Cope and Stace 1978.

605/16 **J. capitatus** Weigel   Dwarf Rush

One of the Lizard rarities, not entirely confined to that area.

West: 42, Chy-an-hal Moor, near Penzance (Flora), refound 1968, J.E.Lo.; 61, now in *c* 7 stations, comm. J.H.; 71, in *c* 6 stations, comm. J.H.; 72, in three stations, comm. J.H.

Scilly: M, an old record, accepted by Lousley 1971.

605/23 **J. pygmaeus** L.C.M. Richard   Pigmy Rush

Confined to the Lizard area.

West: 61, *c* 11 stations now known, comm. J.H.; 71, *c* 5 stations, comm. J.H.; 72, in three stations, comm. J.H.

605/22 **J. kochii** F.W. Schultz

Scattered throughout the county, and probably much under-recorded.

West: 43, Carnaquidden Downs, N of Penzance, B.M.S.; 53, Upton Towans, L.J.M.; 73, Tregoniggey, Falmouth, L.J.M.; 74, Silverwell Moor, L.J.M.; 75, Ventongimps Reserve, C.J.; 85, Newlyn East Downs, L.J.M.; 87, cliff-flush, Booby Bay, L.J.M.

*East: 06, Retire Common, L.J.M.; 18, Bowithick Bodmin Moor, 1976, C.J.

605/18 J. acutiflorus x articulatus = *J. x surrejanus* Druce

x 19 West: 53, Hayle River, 1976, K.E.H., det. C.A. Stace LTR.

East: recorded for this Vice-county in Stace, 1975

LUZULA DC.

Common species: 606/8 **L. campestris** (L.) DC., Field Wood-rush, 606/9 **L. multiflora** (Retz.) Lej., subsp. **multiflora**, Heath Wood-rush, 606/3 **L. sylvatica** (Hudson) Gaudin, Great Wood-rush (absent from Scilly), and 606/1 **L. pilosa** (L.) Willd., Hairy Wood rush (absent from Scilly).

606/9+ L. multiflora subsp. **congesta** (Thuill.) Hyl.

Exact distribution unknown, but probably common West: 61 and 62, recorded without locality, post– 1950.

East: 05, Higher Stenalees, 1954, J.B.; 06, Criggan Moor, 1980, A.C.J. *et al.* Also recorded post—1950 for squares 95 and 29.

Scilly: Lousley 1971.

606/2 L. forsteri (Sm.) DC. Southern Wood-rush

Locally frequent in a few scattered localities.

West: 83, Falmouth (Flora), Swanpool, post—1950 R.H.; 85, railway bank near Newlyn East Halt, L.J.M. East: 83, E side of King Harry Ferry, B.E.M.G. Tolverne Passage, W.T. (Thurston 1930), 1969, B.E.M.G. 93, Portloe, M.E.B.; 95, Trenowth Woods, Grampound N.J.F.; 06, Lanhydrock Woods, C.J.; 97, St Minver churchyard, J.A.P.; 25, Looe (Suppt), wood at W Looe 1965, L.J.M.; Sowdens Bridge, L.J.M.; 37, Luckett Reserve, CNT.

606/2 L. forsteri x pilosa = *L. x borreri* Bromf. ex Bab.

x 1 Rather local and rare.

West: 73, hedgebank, Penjerrick, L.J.M.

East: 25, Seaton Valley (Flora), Keveral Wood, 1966 S.M.; Duloe Woods, S.M.; wood near river, W Looe L.J.M.

GRAMINEAE

ARUNDINARIA MICHX

§ **A. japonica** Siebold & Zucc. ex Steudel Bamboo
The common Bamboo of cultivation, much under-recorded as a garden throw-out, sometimes in quite wild situations.

*West: 64, Pendarves Wood, near Camborne, L.J.M.
East: 96, well-naturalised on Goss Moor, L.J.M.; 05, Carbis Moor, near Trethurgy, B.E.M.G. and L.J.M.
Scilly: Lousley 1971.

FESTUCA L.

Common species: 670/2 **F. arundinacea** Schreber (*F. elatior* L.), Tall Fescue (absent from Scilly), 670/6a **F. rubra** L., subsp. **rubra**, Red Fescue, and 670/8 **F. ovina** L., Sheep's-fescue.

[670/4 **F. altissima** All. (*F. sylvatica* Vill.), Wood Fescue. In the absence of specimens, we support Davey (Flora) in rejecting this species.]

670/3 **F. gigantea** (L.) Vill. Giant Fescue
(*Bromus giganteus* L.)
Rare, and only in a few scattered localities, except in the Lower Tamar area, where it is frequent.

West: 72, Gweek Drive, R.H.; Maenporth, R.H.; 74, Carnon Ford, Bissoe Valley, R.J.M.; 83, Feock, R.H.; 86, Carnanton Woods, Vale of Lanherne, CNT.
East: 20, Bude, J.A.P.; 21, Coombe Valley, L.J.M.; near Morwenstow Church, L.J.M.; 25, Trelawney Mill, near Polperro, 1927, Herb. Perrycoste, (TRU); 29, near Poundstock Church, L.J.M.; 35, Seaton Valley (Flora), 1966, L.J.M.; 36, between St Mellion and Pillaton, I.N.; 37, Linkinhorne, I.N.; 46, near Pentillie, I.N.; Botus-fleming (Flora), Ziggerson Wood, 1971, I.N.; Saltash (Flora), Skinham Farm, 1971, I.N.; near Cotehele Quay, I.N.; Latchley, I.N.

670/1 **F. pratensis** Hudson Meadow Fescue
Decidedly uncommon in Cornwall, and mainly in the West.

West: 53, Connor Downs (Flora), post—1950, B.M.S.; (54), Gwithian, R.H.; Godrevy, L.J.M.; 62, Helston

(Flora), Pollard Mills, R.H.; 63, Clowance, L.J.M.; 64, Portreath, L.J.M.; 72, Mawgan-in-Meneage, R.H.; 74, Cusgarne Bottoms, R.H.; 75, Penhale Sands, L.J.M. East: 97, Amble Marshes, R.W.D.; 07, abundant in Egloshayle Marsh, E.T. and F.R. (Thurston 1935); 20, Efford Down, Bude, L.J.M.; 35, S of Trematon, J.A.P. Scilly: Lousley 1971.

670/6b § **F. nigrescens** Lam., subsp. **nigrescens** Chewings Fescue
Only as an introduction in Cornwall.
*West: 74, old Council tip, Bissoe, 1976, L.J.M.
*East: 05, Par Harbour, L.T.M. (Thurston and Vigurs 1926).
Scilly: Lousley 1971.

670/6+ **F. rubra** L., subsp. **pruinosa** (Hackel) Piper
A blue-leaved Fescue, common around the coasts, especially on raised beaches. Most, if not all, of Davey's records for var. *arenaria* belong here. Cornish material is referable to the var. *pseudoarenaria* (Litardière).
West: 72, Merthen Quay, Helford River, L.J.M.; 75, Penhale Sands, L.J.M.; 83, Swanpool, Falmouth, L.J.M.
*East: 83, between Portscatho and Greeb Point, L.J.M.; 93, Camels Cove, Portloe, 1976, L.J.M.; 05, Crinnis Beach, L.J.M.; 15, Lantic Bay, R.W.D. and L.J.M.

670/ **F. rubra** L., subsp. **rubra**
6a+ var. **barbata** (Schrank) Richt.
West: 75, Penhale Sands, L.J.M.

var. **glaucescens** (Heget. & Heer) Richt.
West: 75, Penhale Sands, L.J.M.
Scilly: Lousley 1971.

F. diffusa Dumort.
Status unknown. In damp, sandy places.
*West: 53, Upton Towans, 1970, L.J.M., det. P.J.O. Trist (as *F. rubra* subsp. *multiflora* Wallr.); 87, Constantine Bay, L.J.M.
*East: 84, between Truro and Malpas, W.Bo. (Thurston 1935, as *F. rubra* var. *grandiflora* Hack.).

570/8+ **F. ovina** L.

 var. **hispidula** (Hackel) Hackel

 West: 63, old wall, Treskillard, L.J.M.; 75, St Agnes Beacon, W.Bo. (Thurston 1935).

FESTUCA X LOLIUM = X FESTULOLIUM ASCHERSON & GRAEBNER

570/1 **F. pratensis** x **L. perenne** = *x F. loliaceum* (Hudson) 671/ P. Fourn.

 *East: 97 or 07, Egloshayle Marsh, Wadebridge (B.E.C. 1931); 38, roadside verge near Launceston, comm. N.J.F.

570/2 **F. arundinacea** x **L. multiflorum**

671/*East: 83, roadside between Trewithian and Tregassa, 2 Portscatho, 1949, C.E.H., K.

FESTUCA X VULPIA = X FESTULPIA MELDERIS EX STACE & R. COTTON

570/6a **F. rubra** x **V. fasciculata** = *x Festulpia hubbardi* Stace 672/ & Cotton.

 *West: 75, Penhale Sands, 1963, L.J.M.

LOLIUM L.

671/1 **L. perenne** L., Perennial Rye-grass, and 671/2 § **L. multiflorum** Lam., Italian Rye-grass, are both common species throughout the county.

671/3 § **L. temulentum** L.   Darnel

Formerly a frequent casual, now very rare, and only on rubbish tips.

West: 64, Council tip, Tolvaddon, Redruth, L.J.M.; 74, Council tip, Bissoe, J.G.D.; 85, Council tip, Newlyn East, L.J.M.

var. **arvense** Liljebl

West: 63, old tip, Treskillard, L.J.M.; 73, waste heap, Penryn, W.T. (Thurston 1930).

East: 05, Par Harbour, L.T.M. (Thurston 1929a).

VULPIA C.C. GMELIN

672/2 **V. bromoides** (L.) S.F. Gray (*Festuca bromoides* L.), Squirrel-tail Fescue, is common and widely distributed in dry places.

672/1 **V. fasciculata** (Forskal) Samp.　　　　Dune Fescue
(*Festuca membranacea* Druce)

Limited to the sand-dunes of W Cornwall, where it sometimes appears in abundance.

*West: 53, Phillack Towans, R.O. (Thurston and Vigurs 1926), still there in 1969, G.S. and L.J.M.; (54) Gwithian Dunes, 1970, L.J.M.; 75, near the Lost Church Penhale Sands, T.L. (Thurston and Vigurs 1927), refound 1964, A.S., plentiful in other parts of Penhale Sands, 1970—80, L.J.M.; 86 (76), Crantock, 1972, R.C. 87, in old sand-quarry, Constantine Bay, 1977, L.J.M Scilly: not refound in the old station in Davey (Flora) Lousley 1971.

672/3 **V. myuros** (L.) C.C. Gmelin　　　　Rat's-tail Fescue

In waste places and by railways. Rather local.

West: 61, Lizard Town, R.J.M.; 73, railway sidings, Penryn, L.J.M.; 83, Falmouth (Flora), by railway station, 1972, L.J.M.

East: 83, Turnaware Point, Fal Estuary, B.E.M.G.; 96, Goss Moor, R.J.M.; 05, Par (Flora), 1969, L.J.M.; 06, edge of Red Moor, E.A.; 07, old railway, Slades-bridge, L.J.M.; 08, Tintagel cliffs, comm. E.A.; 15, by railway, Lostwithiel, L.J.M.; 46, Calstock, I.N.
Scilly: Lousley 1971.

DESMAZERIA DUMORT.

674/2 **D. marina** (L.) Druce (*Festuca rottboellioides* Kunth), Sea Ferngrass, and 674/1 **D. rigida** (L.) Tutin (*Festuca rigida* Kunth), Ferngrass, are both frequent and widespread species.

POA L.

Common species: 676/1 **P. annua** L., Annual Meadow-grass, 676/13 **P. trivialis** L., Rough Meadow-grass, and 676/10 **P. pratensis** L., Smooth Meadow-grass.

676/2 **P. infirma** Kunth　　　　Early Meadow-grass

A rare grass, except in Scilly, usually on coastal paths. First found in Cornwall in 1876 by William Curnow, but not recognised as this species until 1950, when it was found on the Lizard, near Padstow, and in the Isles of Scilly.

*West: 32, between Porthgwarra and Hella Point, L.J.M.; Minack Theatre, Porthcurno, D.E.C.; 33, Cape Cornwall, R.C.L.H. (*Proc. B.S.B.I.*, 4: 171); 42, cliff-path, Lamorna Cove, L.J.M.; 61, in 3 stations, comm. J.H.; 71, in 4 stations, comm. J.H.; 72, near Mawnan Church, R.G.; 97, Stepper Point, 1958—79, R.W.D.

*East: 97, Miniver Hill, New Polzeath, 1958, now gone, R.W.D.; still persisting near Pentire Farm, R.W.D.; in two places near Markham's Quay, Lundy Bay, R.W.D. Scilly: common, Lousley 1971.

676/   **P. trivialis** L. var. **laevis** Lej. and Court.
13+   (var. *glabra* Doll)

Recorded as a common variety in the Flora, but the following are the only recent records:

West: 63, lane near Bolenowe, Troon, R.J.M.; 64, Reskadinnick, Camborne, R.J.M.
Scilly: Lousley 1971.

676/12 **P. subcaerulea** Sm.   Spreading Meadow-grass

A frequent and widely distributed grass of walls, waste places, and sand-dunes.

West: 33, between Pendeen Watch and Portheras Cove, L.J.M.; 52, Perranuthnoe, L.J.M.; 53, near Clodgy Point, St Ives, R.W.D. and L.J.M.; from Lelant to (54), Godrevy, common on the dunes, L.J.M.; 63, wall, Treskillard, L.J.M.; 64, Portreath, L.J.M.; 75, Penhale Sands, A.S.; airfield, Perranporth, L.J.M.; 85, old mine-waste, Nelwyn East, CNT; 86, St Mawgan-in-Pydar, L.J.M.; (76), Porth Joke, L.J.M.; 87, Constantine Bay, L.J.M.

*East: 83, St Anthony (Flora), Place Manor, 1968, L.J.M.; Pendower Beach, L.J.M.; 97, Pentire Peninsula, L.J.M.; 08 (09), Boscastle village, L.J.M.; 15, wall-top, Fowey, L.J.M.; 20, wall of Scadghill Farm, Bude, L.J.M.; 25, The Downs, West Looe, L.J.M.; 29, wall of school-yard, Week St Mary, L.J.M.; 45, between Cremyll and Empacombe, L.J.M.
Scilly: Lousley 1971.

676/11 **P. angustifolia** L.   Narrow-leaved Meadow-grass

Davey states that this is frequent (Flora, as *P. pratensis* var. *angustifolia*), but it is doubtful if he was referring to the genuine species, as it is a plant of Eastern Britain, and is only an introduced plant here.

West: 73, garden weed, Chyvogue, Perranwell, L.J.M., det. C.E. Hubbard; 83, Penpol House, Devoran, 1974, L.J.M., det. C.E. Hubbard.

East: 05, Carvear, St Blazey, 1928, L.T.M., K.

Scilly: recorded with doubt, Lousley 1971.

676/9 **P. compressa** L.   Flattened Meadow-grass

Usually on wall-tops. Rare and local.

West: 62, Porthleven, H.B.S.; 83, path to Loe Beach, Feock, B.E.M.G.; Falmouth (Flora), wall, Lansdowne Road, L.J.M., 1975.

East: 05, Par Harbour, L.T.M. (Thurston 1928); 20, Bude, and Helebridge, J.A.P.; 25, Looe (Flora), 1969, L.J.M.; 35, Trevollard, I.N.; 37, wall, Broad Down, Downgate, I.N.; Linkinhorne churchyard, L.J.M.; 45, Saltash (Flora), near Saltash Station, and St Stephen's Church, I.N.

676/14 § **P. palustris** L.   Swamp Meadow-grass

A rare introduction in Cornwall.

East: 20, on waste ground by old railway station, Bude, 1973, L.J.M.

676/6 **P. nemoralis** L.   Wood Meadow-grass

Rare and local, except in the wooded valleys of E Cornwall, sometimes on shady walls.

West: 42, Newlyn, B.M.S.; 72, The Crag, Maenporth (Flora), post—1950, R.H.; 84, Clements Wood, Idless, L.J.M.; 96, Trewan, St Columb Major, E.T. and L.T.M. (Thurston and Vigurs 1927).

East: 97, Trelights, St Endellion, R.W.D.; 05, edge of leat, Luxulyan Valley, E.A.; 15, in two places at Golant, Fowey, L.T.M. (Thurston 1928); 17, near Dozmary Pool, E.A.; 25, in two places, W Looe Valley, L.J.M.; 28, in wood E of Lewannick, A.B.; hedgebank between Altarnun and Laneast, L.J.M.; 35, Sheviock Wood, L.J.M.; 38, near Launceston (Flora), on Town Gate, and by Polson Bridge, 1978, L.J.M.; 45, Saltash (Flora), on a wall 1974, I.N.; 46, Cotehele, L.J.M.

676/3 **P. bulbosa** L. Bulbous Meadow-grass
Rejected for Cornwall by Davey (Flora), but found
since, as below:
  *West: 53, edge of dunes near railway, Lelant, 1967,
L.J.M., K.

PUCCINELLIA PARL.

673/2 **P. distans** (L.) Parl. Reflexed Saltmarsh-grass
(*Glyceria distans* Wahlb.)
Very local and rare, as it has always been in Cornwall.
West: 86 (76), The Gannel, Newquay (Flora), still
there, 1979, K.H.
East: 84, between Pencalenick and Malpas, L.J.M.; 97,
Amble Marshes (Flora), post—1950, R.W.D.; 05, Par
Harbour, L.T.M. (Thurston and Vigurs 1926); 15,
Lerryn Creek, K.H.; 46, Cotehele Quay, I.N.

673/4 **P. fasciculata** (Torrey) E.P. Bicknell
Borrer's Saltmarsh-grass
(*Glyceria borreri* Bab.)
Still in one of its original localities.
East: 97, Wadebridge (Flora), 1951, R.W.D., det.
A. Melderis; Trevilling salt-marsh, 1972, N.J.F.; 05, Par
Harbour, L.T.M. (Thurston and Vigurs 1927).

673/1 **P. maritima** (Hudson) Parl. Common Saltmarsh-grass
(*Glyceria maritima* Mert. & Koch)
A characteristic grass of the larger areas of salt-marsh
throughout the county.
West: 53, Hayle Estuary, post—1950, various recorders;
72, Gweek, R.H.; 86, The Gannel, Newquay, C.J.
East: 84, between Malpas and Tresillian, W.Bo.
(Thurston 1935), post—1950, L.J.M.; Ardevora, near
Philleigh, K.H.; Ruan Lanihorne, D.R.; 97, Amble
Marshes (Flora), post—1950, R.W.D.; 05, Par Sands
(Suppt), 1966, J.A.P.; 35, Grove, S of Trematon, J.A.P.;
45, Yonderberry Point, Torpoint, S.M.; 46, Moditonham
Quay, L.J.M.; Cotehele (Flora), post—1950, I.N.;
Calstock, I.N.
Scilly: now extinct, Lousley 1971.

673/5 **P. rupestris** (With.) Fernald and Weatherby
Stiff Saltmarsh-grass

(*Glyceria rupestris* E.S. Marshall)

Very rare and local, but possibly overlooked to some extent.

West: 73, Penryn Quay, R.H.; 83, Mylor Bridge, R.H.

DACTYLIS L.

678/1 **D. glomerata** L., Cock's-foot, is abundant throughout the county, often forming dominant communities in old pastures and on cliff-tops.

var. **collina** Schlecht.

West: 53 (54), Godrevy Towans, 1971, R.J.M.; 64, blown sand, Porthtowan, 1977, R.J.M.

CYNOSURUS L.

679/1 **C. cristatus** L., Crested Dog's-tail, is a common and widespread grass of old and acid pastures.

679/2 § **C. echinatus** L. Rough Dog's-tail

Casual, rarely persistent.

West: 32, between Sennen and Porthcurno, E.B. (Thurston and Vigurs 1926); 43, Penzance (Flora), 1962, G.L.; Little London, Zennor, E.A.R. (Thurston 1935); between Marazion and Penzance, B.M.S.; 53, between Copperhouse and Phillack, E.A.R.; Carnsew, Hayle, P.J.R.; Upton Towans, L.J.M.; 61, Poldhu, S.K. (Thurston 1935); one plant, Kynance, R.O. (Thurston and Vigurs 1926); 71, Housel Bay (Thurston 1929); 73, ashfield, Falmouth, W.T. (Thurston 1930); 83, by, railway, Falmouth (Thurston 1929a); between Trefusis and Flushing, W.T. (Thurston 1935).

East: 84, near Boscawen Park, Truro, 1923, W.Bo. (B.E.C. 1924); 05, between Polkerris and Par, W.T. (Thurston and Vigurs 1926); Par Harbour, 1926, W.Wi., Herb. Wise, (LAUS).

Scilly: Lousley 1971.

CATABROSA BEAUV.

677/1 **C. aquatica** (L.) Beauv. Whorl-grass

Extremely local. Not refound in any of the old stations.

East: 97, in small marsh between Polzeath and Pentire,

1946, R.W.D.; by stream below Pentire Farm, 1979, R.W.D.; 07, below Little Trevisquite, below St Tudy and St Mabyn, 1962, E.A.; 46, by Tamar, Calstock, I.N.

BRIZA L.

680/1 **B. media L.**   Quaking-grass
In a few scattered localities throughout the county, rarely in quantity.

West: 53, Carbis Bay (Flora), 1971, B.M.S.; Loggans Moor, Hayle, B.M.S.; 75, Rose, near Perranporth, B.M.S.; Gear Sands, Penhale, L.J.M.

East: 20, Bude (Flora), Efford Down, 1970, L.J.M.; Moreton Mill, near Kilkhampton, C.C.; 21, Greena Moor (Flora), near Greenamoor Bridge, 1977, C.C.

680/3 § **B. maxima L.**   Great Quaking-grass
A frequent garden escape, rarely persisting for more than a year or two.

West: 42, Newlyn, G.B.M.; Penzance (Flora), 1970, G.B.M.; 53, Phillack, B.M.S.; Upton Towans, R.J.M.; 61, Lizard (Flora), 1971, LFC; 64, Portreath, K.E.H.; 73, Union Corner, Falmouth, L.J.M.; 74, Bissoe, L.J.M.; 75, Perranporth, L.J.M.; 83, Swanpool (Flora), 1961, L.J.M.; Falmouth Docks, L.J.M.

East: 83, St Mawes, L.J.M.; 05, St Austell, B.G.; 15, Fowey, L.J.M.; 25, Looe, G.B.M.; Plaidy, near Looe, L.J.M.; 27, Rillaton, N.J.F.; 35, near Seaton, and Downderry, various recorders; 38, between Launceston and Dutson, L.J.M.; 45, by railway, Wearde, E.G.; in two places at Torpoint, S.M.
Scilly: Lousley 1971.

680/2 **B. minor L.**   Lesser Quaking-grass
Formerly a frequent weed of cultivation, now much decreased.

West: 42, plentiful in field, Mousehole, B.M.S.; 43, Gulval (Flora), still there 1962, B.M.S.; 63, Godolphin, R.H.; Townshend, R.H.; 72, Gweek, R.H.; 75, greenhouse weed, Zelah Nurseries, L.J.M.; 83, Feock, R.H.; Falmouth (Flora), 1972, L.J.M.

East: 83, weed in garden, St Mawes, L.J.M.; 84, Fentongollan, near St Michael Penkevil, B.E.M.G.; 94, St Ewe, R.W.D.; 96, in abundance near Winnards Perch,

J.G.; Rosenannon, BRC; field border N of Withiel, R.W.D.

Scilly: common, Lousley 1971.

SESLERIA SCOP.

[682/1 **S. albicans** Kit. ex Schultes (*S. caerulea* auct.), Blue Moor Grass, was recorded in error for Scilly (Flora), see Lousley 1971.]

MELICA L.

[681/2 **M. nutans** L.   Mountain Melick
(*M. montana* Huds.)

Davey's specimen from 94, St Ewe, in Herb. Davey, (TRU), is correctly named, but the plant could hardly have been more than a casual there. It has not been refound, and must be presumed extinct.]

681/1   **M. uniflora** Retz.   Wood Melick
Rare and local. Mainly in the wooded valleys of Central and E Cornwall.

West: 63, Penponds Viaduct, near Camborne, W.E.B. (Thurston and Vigurs 1923), still there, 1967, L.J.M.; 73, near Ponsanooth Viaduct (Flora), 1972, L.J.M.; 84, Bishops Wood, Idless, J.B.

East: 84, Tresillian, W.H.F. (Thurston and Vigurs 1926), one plant, Pencalenick, 1966, L.J.M.; 06, Polbrock, near Grogley, L.J.M.; 07, Pencarrow, St Mabyn, E.A.; railway S of Hellandbridge, K.H.J.; 08, Hustyn Wood (Flora), 1966, J.A.P.; 16, woods between Doublebois and Bodmin Road Station, S.M.; Restormel Road, Lostwithiel (Suppt), still there, 1978, E.A.; 25, between Sandplace and Looe (Flora), at both places, 1966, J.A.P.; St Martin Wood, Looe, S.M.; 35, between Hessenford and Seaton (Flora), Bake Wood, 1966, J.A.P.; 37, Greenscombe Wood, Luckett, S.M.; by the Tamar at Luckett, I.N.; near Carthamartha Wood, I.N.; 46, Cotehele (Flora), post—1950, I.N.

GLYCERIA R.BR.

669/3 **G. declinata** Bréb., Small Sweet-grass, and 669/1 **G. fluitans** (L.) R.Br., Floating Sweet-grass, are common in streams, ditches, and ponds.

669/4 **G. maxima** (Hartman) Holmberg   Reed Sweet-grass
(*G. aquatica* Wahlb.)

Extremely rare, and probably now extinct in its original station at Marazion (Flora).

*East: 37, abundant on site of dried-up lake, Inny Foot, Tamar Valley, 1970, L.J.M.

669/3 **G. declinata x fluitans**
x 1   West: recorded for v.c.1. in Stace 1975.

669/2 **G. plicata** (Fries) Fries   Plicate Sweet-grass

Very rare in Cornwall, with no recent localised records, but probably still in its original stations.

West: 62, and 71, recorded without localities for these squares, (Perring and Walters 1962).

East: 05, Par Harbour, L.T.M. (Thurston 1929a); 45, abundant at Salt Mill Creek, Saltash, 1923, W.B. (Thurston and Vigurs 1924).

Scilly: not refound, Lousley 1971.

669/1 **G. fluitans x plicata** = *G. x pedicellata* Townsend
x 2   No recent localised records.

East: 45, Salt Mill Creek, Saltash, 1923, E.T., det. C.E. Hubbard. K.

BROMUS L.

683/5 **B. sterilis** L., Barren Brome, and   683/10 **B. hordeaceus** L., subsp. **hordeaceus,** Soft-brome, are common and widespread, in a variety of habitats.

683/7   § **B. diandrus** Roth   Great Brome

A rare casual, not found for many years on the mainland, but common in the Isles of Scilly.

East: 04, Mevagissey, W.T. (Thurston 1935).

Scilly: common, Lousley 1971.

683/4   § **B. inermis** Leysser   Hungarian Brome
*East: 20, well-established on waste ground, Bude, 1973, L.J.M.

683/2 **B. ramosus** Hudson   Hairy-brome

Rather rare and local, except in the wooded lanes of the East.

West: 73, Penryn waste-heap, W.T. (Thurston 1935).

East: 84, Lamorran Wood, W.Bo. (Thurston 1936); 05, Tregorrick, St Austell, W.T. (Thurston 1935); 15, St Winnow, near Lostwithiel, L.T.M. (Thurston 1930); frequent in squares 35—39, 46, and 47.

683/1 **B. erectus** Hudson   Upright Brome
Very rare, and only on dunes or blown sand.
West: 71, Kennack Sands, 1969, D.E.C.; 75, scattered over Penhale Sands, 1966, L.J.M.
East: 20, edge of golf-course, Bude, 1978, L.J.M.

var. **villosus** Leight.
West: 75, Rose, near Perranporth, 1965, L.J.M.

683/18 **B. secalinus** L.   Rye Brome
Formerly an infrequent weed of cultivation, this grass seems to have now gone from the county. Some of the old records may, however, refer to the recently described *B. pseudosecalinus* P.M.Sm. A specimen in Herb. Perrycoste, (TRU), collected at 25, Polperro, in 1895, is almost certainly the latter.
West: 71, wheat-field, Erisey, The Lizard, E.J.P. (Thurston and Vigurs 1926).
East: 84, near Boscawen Park, Truro, 1922, W.Bo. (Thurston and Vigurs 1923); 05, Duporth, W.T. (Thurston and Vigurs 1926); 15, around Lanreath, F.R. (Thurston and Vigurs 1925).

683/15 **B. commutatus** Schrader   Meadow Brome
Much confused with forms of *B. hordeaceus*, and probably not as widespread as implied in the Flora. It is, however, almost certainly under-recorded.
West: 71, roadside, Crousa Downs, L.J.M.; 75, near Perran Dunes Holiday Camp, Perranporth, L.J.M.
East: 05, Par Moor, L.T.M. (Thurston and Vigurs 1927); Par Harbour, 1923, L.T.M. (Thurston and Vigurs 1924).

var. **pubens** Wats.
East: 83, near Towan Beach, St Anthony, L.J.M.; 05, in old orchard, Tregrehan, St Austell, 1922, L.T.M. (Thurston and Vigurs 1923).

683/14 **B. racemosus** L. Smooth Brome

A rare grass, almost confined to the East of the county, but possibly under-recorded.

*West: 75, Budnick Hill, Perranporth, E.T. (Thurston and Vigurs 1925).

East: 05, Par Harbour, L.T.M. (Thurston and Vigurs 1926); 37, in wood at Linkinhorne, I.N.; 46, in hedges, Botusfleming, I.N.; Ziggerson Wood, Botusfleming, I.N.; Pentillie Wood, Halton Quay, I.N.

Scilly: casual only, Lousley 1971.

B. hordeaceus agg.

This group of Brome-grasses is complex and critical. Dwarf plants of all the segregates occur on cliffs, and are then extremely difficult to separate.

683/ 10+ subsp. **hordeaceus** var. **leiostachys** Hartm. (var. *glabratus* Hartm.)

West: 97, near the sea, Padstow, 1972, L.J.M.

var. **leptostachys** (Pers.) Beck

East: 84, between Truro and Malpas, E.S.T. (Thurston and Vigurs 1925); 05, school garden, Biscovey, L.T.M. (Thurston and Vigurs 1927); Par Harbour, 1923, L.T.M. (Thurston and Vigurs 1923).

Scilly: Lousley 1971.

683/ 10+ subsp. **molliformis** (Lloyd) Maire and Weiller

Stated (Martin and Fraser 1939) to be present in Cornwall, but Davey's 'var. *lloydianus*' (Flora) may refer to other taxa, probably the dwarf forms mentioned above. The Scilly record also requires confirmation.

683/11 subsp. **ferronii** (Mabille) P.M.Sm. Least Soft-brome

A dwarf Brome, very characteristic of the Lizard cliffs, but easily confused with dwarfed Bromes of other species, and possibly over-recorded as a result.

*West: 32, Gwennap Head, Porthgwarra, R.G.; 53, The Island, St Ives, L.B. and P.J.R.; 61, in numerous stations, comm. J.H.; 62, Loe Bar, R.G.; Porthleven, H.B.S.; in numerous stations on the Lizard, comm. J.H.; 71, numerous stations, comm. J.H.; 72, Porth Kerris Cove, J.H.; Porthoustock, R.H.

*East: 20, and 35, recorded without locality (Perring 1968), and requiring confirmation.

683/12 subsp. **thominii** (Hard.) Maire and Weiller

> Another dwarf Brome that is a characteristic grass of fixed dunes.

> *West: 53, Phillack Towans, L.J.M.; 71, Ruan Minor, 1937, N.Y.S.; 75, Penhale Sands, L.J.M.

> *East: 05, Par Moor, 1926, L.T.M., **K**; 20, Bude, 1933, N.D.S.; 35, near Antony, T.A.B., **BM**.

> Scilly: rare, Lousley 1971.

683/10 **B. hordeaceus** subsp. **hordeaceus** x **lepidus** = *B. x*
x 13 *pseudothominii* P.M.Sm.

> Probably now frequent throughout the county, but much overlooked because of its close resemblance to one or other of its parents.

> *West: 53, Phillack Towans, CRNHS; 62, Nancemerrin, Culdrose, CNT; 64, Portreath, K.E.H.; 75, Trevellas Combe, St Agnes, 1969, L.J.M.; Penhale Sands, L.J.M.

> var. **hirsutus** (Holmb.)

> West: 43, Eastern Green, B.M.S.; 74, old tip, Bissoe, L.J.M.; 75, Penhale Sands, L.J.M.

683/13 **B. lepidus** Holmberg   Slender Soft-brome

> Another overlooked species, certainly more frequent than these few records indicate.

> *West: 64, Portreath, L.J.M.; 72, Merthen, Helford River, L.J.M.; 75, Carnkief, 1963, B.M.S. and L.J.M.; Ellenglaze, Penhale Sands, L.J.M.; 87, on wall, Constantine Bay, L.J.M.

> *East: 97, Trevilling, Wadebridge, WFS; 05, Par Harbour, 1922, L.T.M., K (Thurston 1936); 35, road-side near Antony, T.G.Tu.

> Scilly: one record, Lousley 1971.

683/20 § **B. willdenowii** Kunth   Rescue Brome
        (*B. unioloides* Kunth)

> A sporadic grass, now very rare, except in Scilly.

> West: 43, Penzance (Flora), one plant, Heamoor, comm. B.M.S.; 62, near station, Helston, W.T. (Thurston 1930); 83, Falmouth (Flora), W.T. (Thurston 1935).

> East: 05, Tregorrick, St Austell, W.T. (Thurston and Vigurs 1927); 20, Bude, R.O. (Thurston and Vigurs 1925).

> Scilly: frequent, Lousley 1971.

BRACHYPODIUM BEAUV.

684/1 **B. sylvaticum** (Hudson) Beauv.   False Brome

A very common grass in Cornwall, usually in shady places, but also in open habitats, including cliff-tops.

684/2 **B. pinnatum** (L.) Beauv.   Tor-grass

A fairly recent arrival in the county, now spreading rapidly on dunes.

*West: 53, hedgebanks at Gwealavellan, Red River Valley, R.J.M. and L.J.M.; on the crest of Godrevy Towans, L.J.M.; Upton Towans, G.B.M.; Gear Sands, Penhale, L.J.M., 1966.

*East: 83, cliff-path near St Mawes Castle, B.E.M.G.; 05, hedge of Grove field, Charlestown, W.T. (Thurston and Vigurs 1925); ballast-heap, Charlestown, W.T. (Thurston 1928).

LEYMUS HOCHST. (ELYMUS L.)

686/1 **L. arenarius** (L.) Hochst.   Lyme-grass
(*Elymus arenarius* L.)

Very local and rare.

West: 53, Phillack Towans, 1967, S.M.

East: 97, St Minver (Flora) = Daymer Bay, R.W.D.

ELYMUS L. (AGROPYRON GAERTN.)

Common species: 685/4 **E. pycnanthus** (Godron) Melderis (*Agropyron pungens* auct), Sea Couch (rejected for Scilly, Lousley 1971), 685/3 **E. repens** (L.) Gould (*A. repens* Beauv.), Common Couch, and 685/5 **E. farctus** (Viv.) Runemark ex Melderis, subsp. **boreali-atlanticus** (Simonet & Guinochet) Melderis (*A. junceum* auct.), Sand Couch.

685/1 **E. caninus** (L.) L.   Bearded Couch
(*Agropyron caninum* Beauv.)

Very local, but no doubt overlooked, to some extent.

West: 53, Marazion Marsh, A.B.; 71, Kennack Wood, R.M.P.

East: 97, small patch by cliff-path, Greenaway Beach, Pentire Peninsula, R.W.D.; 15, creek-side at Lerryn, L.J.M.

685/4 **E. pycnanthus x repens** = *Agropyron x oliveri* Druce
x 3 East: 45, St Johns, Torpoint, 1976, comm. R.P.

685/3+ **E. repens** var. **aristatum** Baunmg.
West: 53, Gwealavellan, Red River Valley, R.J.M.
and L.J.M.; 62, Halsferran Cliff, Gunwalloe, LFC and
CNT; 64, Reskadinnick, Camborne, R.J.M.
East: 97, Pentire Peninsula, L.J.M.; 05, Par Moor,
L.T.M. (Thurston and Vigurs 1925).

685/5 **E. farctus** subsp. **boreali-atlanticus x pycnanthus**
x 4 = *A. x obtusiusculum* Lange
Some of Davey's records of *A. junceum x repens* (Flora)
belong here.
East: 97, N end of dunes, Daymer Bay, 1979, R.W.D.;
05, Par Harbour, L.T.M. (Thurston and Vigurs 1927).

HORDEUM L.

687/2 **H. murinum** L. Wall Barley
Rather local in Cornwall, and mainly near the sea.
West: 61, Lizard Town, R.J.M.; 63, Four Lanes, near
Redruth, L.J.M.; 64, Camborne, J.S.R.; 72, Porthallow,
J.A.P.; 75, Perranporth, C.J.; 83, Falmouth (Flora),
1977, J.S.R.; 86, Newquay (Flora), 1977, J.S.R.; 87,
Trevone, J.A.P.; Constantine Bay, L.J.M.; 97, Hawkers
Cove, Padstow, J.S.R.
East: 83, Pendower Beach, B.E.M.G.; 94, Portholland,
J.S.R.; 20, Bude (Flora), 1966, J.A.P.; Helenbridge,
near Bude, J.A.P.; 21, Morwenstow, K.H.; 25, Polperro,
L.J.M.; 35, Downderry, and Freathy, S.M.; 45, Saltash,
and Torpoint (Flora), still in both places, S.M.
Scilly: Lousley 1971. 1971.

687/1 **H. secalinum** Schreber Meadow Barley
(*H. nodosum* L.)
Local and rare, as it has always been.
West: 73, waste-heap, Penryn, W.T. (Thurston 1935).
East: 84, between Truro and Malpas (Flora), still
there *c* 1930, W.Bo. (Thurston 1935); 97, Amble
Marshes, 1954, R.W.D.
Scilly: still in one station, Lousley 1971.

AVENA L.

692/3 § **A. strigosa** Schreber   Bristle Oat
Once frequent as a casual, now rarely found.
East: 05, Par, L.T.M. (Thurston and Vigurs 1925 and 1926; and Thurston 1929a).

692/1 § **A. fatua** L.   Wild-oat
Only as a casual.
West: 53, Carbis Bay, B.M.S.; 63, waste ground, Porkellis Moor, L.J.M.; 64, Reskadinnick, R.J.M.; 74, old tip, Bissoe, L.J.M.; 75, Bolingey Marshes, C.J.; 85, old tip, Newlyn East, L.J.M.
East: 96, roadside, Goss Moor, L.J.M.; 05, Par Sands, L.T.M. (Thurston and Vigurs 1927).
Scilly: Lousley 1971.

AVENULA (DUMORT.) DUMORT. (HELICTOTRICHON)

693/2 **A. pubescens** (Hudson) Dumort.   Downy Oat-grass
(*Avena pubescens* Huds.)

A characteristic grass of the larger dune areas. Certainly more common than in Davey's day.
West: 53, Phillack Towans, L.J.M.; Copperhouse, Hayle, R.J.M. and L.J.M.; 74, St Agnes (Flora), on wall, Goonbell, 1963, L.J.M.; 75, Penhale Sands, L.J.M.; 87, Constantine Bay, L.J.M.
East: 97, Rock dunes, E.A.; in small quantity W of Miniver Hill, New Polzeath, L.J.M.; 20, Bude (Flora), on golf-course, and on Efford Down, L.J.M.

ARRHENATHERUM BEAUV.

694/1 **A. elatius** (L.) Beauv. ex J. & C. Presl, subsp. **elatius**, False Oat-grass, and subsp. **bulbosum** (Willd.) Schubler and Martens (var. *bulbosum* Presl), Onion Couch, are both common and widespread.

KOELERIA PERS.

689/1 **K. macrantha** (Ledeb.) Schultes   Crested Hair-grass
(*K. gracilis* Pers.)

This account includes several taxa which were once maintained as separate species: *K. brittanica* (Domin) Druce, *K. arenaria* Dumort., and *K. albescens* DC., all of which have been recorded for Cornwall.   Frequent around the coast of W Cornwall in sandy soils, but very rare in the East.

West: 53, near Marazion Marsh, L.J.M.; Upton Towans, L.J.M.; (54), The Island, St Ives, P.J.R.; Godrevy, near the car-park, L.J.M.; Gwithian, R.H.; 61, Kynance (Flora), 1966, J.A.P.; Mullion Cliff, J.A.P.; heath N of Penhale, The Lizard, J.A.P.; Goonhilly Reserve, D.E.C. *et al.*; 62, Gunwalloe, R.H.; by Loe Pool, K.H.; 64, Portreath (Flora), post—1950, L.J.M.; Porthtowan (Flora), 1977, CRNHS; 71, The Lizard, L.A.B.; Downas Valley, CNT; 75, near St Agnes, L.J.M.; 86 (76), Porth Joke, K.H.; Cubert Common, L.J.M.

East: 83, St Anthony-in-Roseland (Flora), 1968, L.J.M.; 97, Pentire Peninsula, R.W.D.; (98), Doyden, K.H.

Scilly: Lousley 1971.

TRISETUM PERS.

691/1 **T. flavescens** (L.) Beauv.   Yellow Oat-grass

Very local in W Cornwall, becoming more frequent in dune areas, and on the less acid soils of the Lower Tamar area.

West: 53, Upton Towans, J.A.P. and A.B.; 75, Perranporth (Flora), Penhale Sands, 1965, L.J.M.; 87, Constantine Bay, L.J.M.; 97, between Padstow and Harbour Cove, R.W.D.

East: 97, Wadebridge (Flora), 1979, B.E.M.G. and L.J.M.; Com Head, Pentire Peninsula, L.J.M.; (98), Doyden, Port Quin, K.H.; 05, Charlestown, W.T. (Thurston 1929); Par Harbour, L.T.M. (Thurston 1935); 35, Wivelscombe, I.N.; 45, near Wearde Quay, I.N.; (44), frequent on the Rame Peninsula, L.J.M.

Scilly: rare, Lousley 1971.

DESCHAMPSIA BEAUV.

696/1 **D. cespitosa** (L.) Beauv., Tufted Hair-grass, is frequent and widespread in damp places (doubtfully in Scilly).

696/3 **D. flexuosa** (L.) Trin.   Wavy Hair-grass

A rare grass of acid soils, except on the higher moors, where it sometimes occurs in quantity.

West: 63, a few plants on hedgebank, Treskillard, Redruth, L.J.M.

East: 95, abundant at Nanpean, E.T. (Thurston and Vigurs 1925); between St Stephen and Gonnabarn, L.J.M.; Roche Rock, E.T. and L.T.M. (Thurston 1930); 17, 18, and 27, frequent on Bodmin Moor.

AIRA L.

697/1 A. praecox L., Early Hair-grass, and 697/2 A. caryophyllea L., subsp. caryophyllea, Silver Hair-grass, are both common and widespread in dry places.

697/3 A. caryophyllea L.
subsp. multiculmis (Dumort.) Bonnier & Layens
*West: 84, old railway track, Newham, Truro, 1976, J.M.M. and R.P.
Scilly: frequent, Lousley 1971.

A. armoricana Albers (*Willdenowia*, 9 (1979): 283—284) This new species was described by Dr Albers from material collected in Cornwall and NW France. It may well be a Lusitanian species. Further work is required to distinguish this taxon from *A. caryophyllea* and its subsp. *multiculmis*.
*West: 64, cliff-top between Portreath and Porthcadjack Cove, 1976, L.J.M., BM and KIEL.

ANTHOXANTHUM L.

712/1 A. odoratum L., Sweet Vernal-grass, is very common and widespread in Cornwall.

HOLCUS L.

695/1 H. lanatus L., Yorkshire Fog, and 695/2 H. mollis L., Creeping Soft-grass (absent from Scilly), are very common grasses throughout the county.

AGROSTIS L.

Common species: 701/2a A. canina L., Velvet Bent, 701/1 A. curtisii Kerguelen (*A. setacea* Curt.), Bristle Bent (absent from Scilly), 701/3 A. capillaris L. (*A. tenuis* Sibth.), Common Bent, and 701/5 A. stolonifera L. (*A. alba* L.), Creeping Bent.

701/2b A. vinealis Schreber   Brown Bent
= A. canina L., subsp. montana (Hartman) Hartman
Distribution not fully known through confusion with A. canina, but probably less common.

*West: 64, near Navax Point, N Cliffs, 1976, L.J.M.; cliff-heath W of Portreath, L.J.M.; 84, Clements Wood, Truro, L.J.M.

701/2b **A. vinealis x stolonifera**
x 5   West: 84, Truro, 1932 (Stace 1975).

701/4   **A. gigantea** Roth   Black Bent
        (*A. nigra* With.)

Apparently local and rare, though no doubt overlooked to some extent.

West: 33, garden weed, St Just, M.C.;   42 or 43, Penzance, B.M.S.; 53 (54), edge of marsh, Gwealavellan, Red River Valley, R.J.M. and L.J.M.; 63, mine-waste, Condurrow, Camborne, R.J.M.; 64, waste ground, Reskadinnick, 1953—78, R.J.M.; 72, Gweek, R.H.

East: 83, Treworthal, near Philleigh, B.E.M.G.; 96, Winnards Perch, R.J.M. and L.J.M.; 37, Stare Bridge, Linkinhorne, I.N.; 47, Latchley, I.N.

Scilly: Lousley 1971; M, derelict field, Old Town, 1975, F.W.S.

§ **A. castellana** Boiss. & Reuter
var. **mixta** Hackel

*West: 73, in quantity in arable field, Chyvogue, Perranwell, 1976, L.J.M.

GASTRIDIUM BEAUV.

705/1   **G. ventricosum** (Gouan) Schinz & Thell.   Nit-grass

Once frequent as a colonist of newly-disturbed land, this species has, in the last 60 years, suffered a severe decline that is difficult to account for.   There are 36 stations listed in the Flora and Suppt.

West: 84, on a wall, Trelissick Gardens, King Harry, 1973, B.E.M.G.

East: 05, near St Austell railway station, W.T. (Thurston 1929a).

Scilly: no recent records, (Lousley 1971).

POLYPOGON DESF.

703/1   **P. monspeliensis** (L.) Desf.   Annual Beard-grass

Mainly as a rare casual.

West: 61, garden weed, Mullion, 1923, E.J.P.

(Thurston and Vigurs 1924); 63, old tip, Treskillard, Redruth, 1969, L.J.M.; 83, Falmouth Docks, 1972, L.J.M.

East: 05, Par, 1929, Herb. Perrycoste, (TRU).

701/8 § **P. viridis** (Gouan) Breistr. Water Bent
(Suppt as *Agrostis verticillata* Vill.)
A rare but persistent introduction.

West: 53, waste ground, Long Rock, 1979, B.M.S.; (54), St Ives, E.A.R. (Thurston and Vigurs 1927); 83, Falmouth Docks (Suppt), still plentiful, 1972, L.J.M.

East: 05, abundant, Par Harbour, 1921, L.T.M. (Thurston and Vigurs 1923), still there, 1971, comm. B.E.M.G.; 07, 40 plants on clay-tip, Poleys Bridge, St Breward, 1962, E.A.

AMMOPHILA HOST

699/1 **A. arenaria** (L.) Link, Marram, is locally abundant in the dune areas of the mainland and the Isles of Scilly.

CALAMAGROSTIS ADANSON

700/1 **C. epigejos** (L.) Roth Wood Small-reed
Unaccountably local and rare in Cornwall, except in Scilly, where it occurs on four of the Isles.

West: 71, on cliff between Chynalls Point, Coverack, and Ebber Rocks, 1979, J.H.

East: not refound in any of its old stations.

Scilly: Lousley 1971; M, *c* one acre N of Bants Carn, 1973, L.A.H.; T, East side of Back Porth, 1972, J.P.B.

PHLEUM L.

707/2 **P. pratense** L., subsp. **pratense**, Timothy, and 707/1 subsp. **bertolonii** (DC.) Bornm. (var. *nodosum* L.), Smaller Cat's-tail (absent from Scilly), are common and widespread in the county.

707/5 **P. arenarium** L. Sand Cat's-tail
Local, but very persistent. Still in most of the old stations on the dunes.

West: 53, Phillack Towans, B.M.S.; Upton Towans, G.L.; (54), Gwithian (Flora), 1978, J.S.R.; Godrevy, K.H.; 75, Penhale Sands (Flora), 1966—80, L.J.M.; 87, Constantine Bay, L.J.M.; Harlyn Bay, L.T.M. (Thurston and Vigurs 1925).

East: 97, St Minver, and Polzeath (Flora), Rock dunes, 1966, J.A.P., 1980, R.W.D.; 20, Bude (Flora), 1970, J.A.P.

ALOPECURUS L.

708/3   **A. geniculatus** L., Marsh Foxtail, is frequent and widely distributed in marshes and damp fields.

708/2   **A. pratensis** L.   Meadow Foxtail
Frequent throughout the county as a roadside intro-duction.   As a native of old pastures it is very local. The following appear to be native occurrences:

West: 42, Paul, near Penzance, B.M.S.; 73, and 83, Falmouth (Flora), in both squares, post—1950, L.J.M.; 61, Lizard area, J.S.R.; 64, Camborne (Flora), Tehidy, 1977, J.S.R.; 72, near Helford Passage, J.S.R.; 84, Truro (Flora), 1977, J.S.R.

East: 83, Philleigh, B.E.M.G.; 97, Pentire Peninsula, R.W.D.; 05, between Polkerris and Par, W.T. (Thurston and Vigurs 1926); 15, Restormel Road, Lostwithiel, E.T. (Thurston 1935); 20, Marhamchurch, R.W.D. and L.J.M.; canal towing-path, Bude, L.J.M.; 25, near W Looe, L.J.M.; 38, near Launceston (Flora), water-meadow near Polson Bridge, 1978, L.J.M.
Scilly: only as an introduction, Lousley 1971.

708/5   **A. bulbosus** Gouan   Bulbous Foxtail
A very rare and local grass.   It should be looked for in its two other old stations.
East: 05, ballast-heap, Charlestown, 1923, W.T. (Thurston and Vigurs 1924); 46, salt-marsh near Cotehele (Flora), still there, and also near the quay, post—1950, I.N.

708/1   **A. myosuroides** Hudson   Black-grass
Never a common grass in Cornwall, this weed of cultivation has become exceptionally rare in recent years.
West: 62, near Helston station, W.T. (Thurston 1930); 84, Calenick, S of Truro, W.Bo. (Thurston 1935).
East: 05, Charlestown (Suppt), in the churchyard, W.T. (Thurston and Vigurs 1926); Par (Flora), Crinnis, W.T. (Thurston 1929a).

PARAPHOLIS C.E. HUBBARD

[714/2 **P. incurva** (L.) C.E. Hubbard   Curved Hard-grass
(*Lepturus filiformis* Trin. var. *incurvatus* (Trin.)

This species has been recorded for Cornwall (Flora),
but the records refer to a closely related taxon, as
follows.]

P. sp.

This is the plant mentioned above. It is similar to
that species, but differs in its culms curving downwards
rather than upwards. Further investigation is required,
as it might be worthy of a specific name.

West: 53, dry ground, Copperhouse, Hayle, 1963,
L.J.M.; 72, Gweek, L.J.M.

East: 97, Trevilling salt-marsh, Wadebridge (Flora),
Herb. Davey, (TRU); 05, Par, 1914, Herb. Perrycoste,
(TRU); 35, Wivelscombe, Tamar Estuary, post—1950,
I.N. Tellam's specimens, on two sheets in Davey's
Herbarium, display the characters of this taxon well.

714/1   **P. strigosa** (Dumort.) C.E. Hubbard   Hard-grass
(*Lepturus filiformis* Trin.)

Rather local, but present in the larger stretches of salt-
marsh throughout the county.

West: 53, Hayle (Flora), still there, 1970, B.M.S.; 86,
Newquay (Flora), The Gannel, post—1950, R.L.G.L.;
97, Padstow (Flora), Harbour Cove, 1964, R.W.D.

East: 84, between Tresillian and Malpas, L.J.M.; 97,
Amble Marshes, R.W.D.; Porthilly Cove, E.A.; 05, Par,
1928, Herb. Perrycoste (TRU); 07, Egloshayle Marsh,
R.W.D.; 25, between Sandplace and Looe, J.A.P.; 46,
Cargreen, Tamar Estuary, I.N.

PHALARIS L.

713/1   **P. arundinacea** L.   Reed Canary-grass

Rather rare in the West, becoming more frequent in
the East.

West: 42, Lamorna Valley, E.A.R. (Thurston and
Vigurs 1926), post—1950, B.M.S.; 43, Gulval, B.M.S.;
53 (54), Gwealavellan Marsh, Red River, R.J.M. and
L.J.M.; 61, Cadgwith, NCS; 62, Loe Pool, NCS; Gunwalloe (Flora), post—1950, B.M.S.; 85, Trevemper

Mill (Flora), 1976, L.J.M.; 75, Holywell Valley, A.B.; 86 (76), Porth Joke Valley, L.J.M.

East: 83, N of Pendower Beach, B.E.M.G.; Willow-bed, St Mawes, W.T. (Thurston 1935); 05, Charlestown, W.T. (Thurston 1928); 17, De Lank River, near St Breward, R.W.D.; 20, Bude, L.J.M.; 21, Tamar Lake, J.G.D.; Wrasford Moor, R.W.D.; 25, Polperro (Flora), post—1950, S.M.; 28, Inny Valley, E of Lewannick, J.A.P.; 29, SE of Canworthy Water, J.A.P.; 35, Port-wrinkle, S.M.; 36, S of Newbridge, J.A.P.; 37, above Horsebridge, R Tamar, J.A.P.; 39, NE of Boyton, J.A.P., 45, 46, and 47, frequent in the Lower Tamar area.

§ var. **picta** L.   Ribbon Grass

The well-known variegated garden plant.

West: 63, naturalised near Porkellis Moor, 1965, L.J.M.; 64, near Carn Brea Station, L.J.M.

East: 95, by roadside, Fraddon, 1965, now gone, L.J.M.

713/2 § **P. canariensis** L.   Canary-grass

A frequent bird-seed alien, very frequent on rubbish-tips and in waste places.

West: 42 and 43, Penzance (Flora), 1978, G.B.M.; 62, Porthleven, H.B.S.; Helston tip, L.J.M.; 64, Council tip, Tolvaddon, Redruth, L.J.M.; opposite Camborne School, R.J.M.; 73, council tip, Falmouth, L.J.M.; 74, Council tip, Bissoe, L.J.M.; 75, Higher Bal, St Agnes (Thurston 1929).

East: 05, St Austell (Flora), 1960, B.Sh.; 20, Bude (Flora), 1973, L.J.M.; 45, between Torpoint and St Johns (Flora), at both places, 1963, S.M.

Scilly: Lousley 1971.

713/3 § **P. minor** Retz.   Lesser Canary-grass

A rare casual, except in the Isles, where it is locally plentiful.

*West: 53, Hayle, 1926, E.A.R.; 72, Gweek Quay, R.O. (Thurston and Vigurs 1926).

*East: 84, near Truro School, 1962—3, A.S.

Scilly: Lousley 1971.

MILIUM L.

709/1 **M. effusum L.** Wood Millet

A rather rare woodland grass, becoming more frequent in the deep wooded valleys of the East.

West: 73, Kennall Wood, Ponsanooth (Flora), 1972, L.J.M.

East: 95, Trenowth Wood, near Grampound, CNT; 05, clay-works, St Blazey, L.T.M. (Thurston 1928); Pelyn Wood, E.A.; Luxulyan Valley (Flora), 1979, E.A. and E.W.M.; Prideaux Wood, L.J.M.; 06, Dunmere Forest, E.A.; 07, wood between Sladesbridge and Washaway (Flora), 1948—60, R.W.D.; 16, Draw Wood, Fowey Valley, L.J.M.; 19, Dizzard Wood, CNT; Valency Valley (B.E.C. 1939—40), 1967, J.A.P.; wood in Millook Valley, L.J.M.; 21, Coombe Valley, H.H.H. (Thurston and Vigurs 1926), 1979, K.H.; 27, Trebartha Park, C.B., R.J.M. and L.J.M.; 35, Sheviock Wood (Flora), 1970, L.J.M.; 36, wood above R Lynher at Newton Ferrers, 1923, H.H.H. (Thurston and Vigurs 1924).

PHRAGMITES ADANSON

665/1 **P. australis** (Cav.) Trin. ex Steudel (*P. communis* Trin.), Common Reed, is frequent in a variety of habitats, especially heads of creeks and on low cliffs. Sometimes forming vast reed-beds in sub-maritime marshes.

CORTADERIA STAPF

666/1 § **C. selloana** (Schultes & Schultes fil.) Ascherson & Graebner Pampas Grass

This familiar garden plant is occasionally found growing amongst native vegetation some way from houses.

*West: 32, several clumps naturalised at Porthcurno, L.J.M.; 42, one clump near Mousehole, R.W.D. and L.J.M.; 62, Porthleven, H.B.S.; 73, several clumps near reedswamp, Devoran, 1965, L.J.M.; 83, one clump on railway embankment, Falmouth, L.J.M.

*East: 15, Fowey, 1970, L.J.M.

Scilly: Lousley 1971.

DANTHONIA DC. (SIEGLINGIA BERNH.)

668/1 **D. decumbens** (L.) DC. (*Sieglingia decumbens* Bernh.), Heath Grass, is common and widely distributed throughout Cornwall.

MOLINIA SCHRANK

667/1 **M. caerulea** (L.) Moench, Purple Moor-grass, is common and widespread in undisturbed moorland and on heaths throughout the county.

NARDUS L.

715/1 **N. stricta** L., Mat-grass, is a frequent moorland grass of upland grassland, though absent from parts of the Lower Tamar area, and from Scilly (rejected, Lousley 1971).

CYNODON L.C.M. RICHARD

717/1 **C. dactylon** (L.) Pers.   Bermuda-grass

Probably originally introduced, but known from Marazion since John Ray found it there in 1688. Along Mounts Bay it seems to be resistant to tourist damage. West: 43, lawn of house, Lannoweth Terrace, Penzance, G.B.M.; higher part of Lariggan stream, Penzance, B.M.S.; 43 — 53, between Penzance and Marazion (Flora), still plentiful in various places between the two, 1950 onwards, various recorders; 53, patch near the lifeboat house, Hayle, E.A.R. (Thurston 1928); 64, abundant on bank of Red River, Portreath, 1922, W.E.B. (Thurston and Vigurs 1923), still plentiful, 1968—80, L.J.M. (but note that the stream here is not the Red River); small patch on Portreath Beach, 1966, L.J.M.

Scilly: one colony on Tresco, Lousley 1971.

SPARTINA SCHREBER

716+ **S. anglica** C.E. Hubbard   Common Cord-grass

Previously recorded as *S. x townsendii* H. & J. Groves, but distinct from that species in its ability to produce fertile seed. All Cornish records belong here. Unknown in the county until 1940, since when it has spread rapidly in tidal mud.

*West: 53, Copperhouse, Hayle, 1959, P.J.G., now spreading, R.J.M. and L.J.M.; 72, Gweek Creek, post—

1950, various recorders; edge of creek, Merthen, Helford River, J.F.A.

*East: 97, Porthilly Beach, Rock, E.A.; 05, Par Sands, J.A.P.; 35, 45, and 46, abundant in the creeks of the Tamar Estuary from 35, St Germans, S.M., to 45, Millbrook, S.M., amd Saltash (B.E.C. 1939—40), up as far as 46, Cotehele, I.N.

DIGITARIA HALLER

719/2 § **D. sanguinalis** (L.) Scop. Hairy Finger-grass
(*Panicum sanguinale* L.)

A fairly frequent bird-seed alien.

West: 43, Penzance (Flora), 1971, comm. G.B.M.; a further station, B.M.S.; 53 (54), St Ives, L.B.; Windsor Hill, St Ives, G.B.M.; 71, Erisey, Ruan Major (Thurston 1935); 73, garden, Chyvogue, Perranwell, L.J.M.; 97, several plants in pavement, Padstow, L.J.M.

Scilly: Lousley 1971; M, garden path, Porthloo, E.A.; in bulbfield, Porthloo, G.F.

PASPALUM L.

§ **P. paspalodes** (Michx) Scribner

*West: 42, inner harbour, Mousehole, a patch well-established for several years, 1971—79, L.J.M.

SETARIA BEAUV.

720/1 § **S. viridis** (L.) Beauv. Green Bristle-grass

Casual, and hardly permanent anywhere.

West: 42, Mousehole, B.M.S.; 73, Council tip, Falmouth, L.J.M.; Old Hill, Falmouth, W.T. (Thurston 1935); 74, Council tip, Bissoe, L.J.M.; 83, Falmouth Docks (Flora), 1972, L.J.M.; 84, old tip, Newham, Truro, L.J.M.

East: 05, Tregorrick, and St Austell by-pass, W.T. (Thurston 1928 and 1929).

ARACEAE

LYSICHITON SCHOTT

648/1 § **L. americanus** Hultén & St John Skunk Cabbage

A popular swamp plant on the larger estates, now becoming established from seed in nearby locations.

*West: 43, near Tremethick Cross, Trengwainton,

B.M.S.; in mill dam, and in nearby stream, Rosehill, Penzance, G.B.M.; in stream at Gulval, B.M.S.; 72, by roadside 3 miles W of St Keverne, R.B.G.; 75, by stream near Chyverton House, Zelah, N.H.

ZANTEDESCHIA SPRENGEL

§ **Z. aethiopica** (L.) Sprengel   Arum Lily

This well-known white florists' 'Lily' is well-established in Scilly.

*West: 42, inner harbour, Mousehole, 1971, L.J.M.

*East: 94, three clumps by stream, Portholland, 1979, L.J.M.

Scilly: Lousley 1971; M, between Buzza Hill and Peninning, J.P.B.; B, 1975, F.W.S.; MN, Higher Town, 1973—5, F.W.S.

ARUM L.

649/1 **A. maculatum** L., Lords-and-Ladies, is a common plant of hedges and woods, becoming rare in W Penwith (absent from Scilly).

649/2 **A. italicum** Miller   Italian Lords-and-Ladies
       subsp. **italicum**

This subspecies, with strongly cream-veined leaves, is almost certainly an introduction that has increased rapidly in W Cornwall in recent years.

West: 43, Penlee Park, Penzance, G.B.M.; weed in Trengwainton Gardens, L.J.M.; 53, Hayle Estuary, L.J.M.; 63, Trevarno (Flora), L.J.M.; several patches by roadside, Treskillard, Redruth, L.J.M.; Camborne garden, J.S.R.; Killivose Lane, Camborne, R.J.M.; Horsedowns, J.S.R.; Praze-an-Beeble, J.B.; 64, Wheal Uny, Redruth, W.D.W. (Thurston 1928); near Reskadinnick, Camborne, R.J.M.; Trewirgie, Redruth, L.J.M.; 71, Cadgwith, L.A.B.; 72, Mawgan village, R.H.; 74, Chapel Coombe, near St Agnes, B.B.; between Bissoe and Gwennap, L.J.M.; 85, near Legonna, SE of Newquay, B.B.; 86, St Mawgan-in-Pydar, L.G.

East: 84, between Truro and St Clements, M.Ca.; 96, near St Wenn church, B.B.; 06, near Respryn Bridge, B.B.

subsp. **neglectum** (Townsend) Prime 'Late Cuckoo Pint'

A rare native of sheltered hedges not usually far from the sea. The only Arum in Scilly. Perhaps over-recorded in mistake for the preceding subsp.

West: 42, between Newlyn and Penzance, B.M.S.; Love Lane, Penzance (Flora), 1962, G.B.M.; 42, and 43, Penlee Park, Penzance, G.B.M.; 53, Carbis Bay (Flora), 1969, L.J.M.; Lelant (Flora), near the Station, 1972, CRNHS; N side of Copperhouse Creek, Hayle, J.A.P.; 61, Porth Mellin, D.E.C.; 62, Helston, B.Sh.; Porthleven, H.B.S.; 63, Chynhale, near Sithney, F.G.F.; 71, St Keverne, C.T.P. and O.B.; 87, Constantine Bay, W.G.

East: 84, Lamorran, L.J.M.; 25, in a wild garden, Looe, J.L.; W of Polperro (Suppt), M.M.P. (Thurston and Vigurs 1924)

Scilly: common, Lousley 1971.

649/2 **A. italicum** subsp. **neglectum** x **maculatum**
x 1 *West: 53, several plants in lane near Lelant Station, 1972, CRNHS.

DRACUNCULUS MILLER

§ **D. vulgaris** Schott   Dragon Arum

A garden throw-out, becoming established in a few places.

West: 53, six plants on slope behind Municipal Gardens, Hayle, CRNHS; 63, near Carleen, Breage, comm. G.B.M.; 75, Perranporth, 1969, A.Bi., comm. C.W.

*East: 83, Portscatho cliffs, 1978, B.E.M.G.; 20, Bude (Thurston 1928); 28, opposite Tresmeer Church, L.J.M.

Scilly: Lousley 1971.

LEMNACEAE

LEMNA L.

650/3 **L. minor** L., Common Duckweed, is common and widespread in freshwater habitats.

650/2 **L. trisulca** L.   Ivy-leaved Duckweed
Exceptionally rare in Cornwall.

West: 53, Marazion Marsh, 1979, L.J.M.; pool S of

St Erth, 1976, L.J.M.; 62, in stream, Gunwalloe Cove, post—1950, various recorders.

*East: 26, Moorswater, Liskeard, 1966, J.A.P.

SPARGANIACEAE
SPARGANIUM L.

652/1 **S. erectum** L.   Branched Bur-reed
(*S. ramosum* Huds.)

Frequent and widespread in freshwater pools and marshes.

1b   subsp. **neglectum** (Beeby) Schinz & Thell.

West: 53, pool S of St Erth, L.J.M.; (54), Gwithian marsh and stream, L.J.M.; 63, Penhale Moor, near Carnhell Green, L.J.M.; 72, near Durgan, L.J.M.

East: 06, Polbrock, near Grogley, E.A.; Red Moor, L.J.M.; 20, Bude Canal, E.A.; 36, Heskyn Mill, near Tideford, S.M.

652/2 **S. emersum** Rehmann   Unbranched Bur-reed
(*S. simplex* Huds.)

Local and rare, but still present in many of its old stations.

West: 63, Porkellis Moor (Flora), still there, various recorders; 73, pond near Lanner, L.J.M.; Stithians (Flora), in the reservoir, 1978, L.J.M.; 75, Carnkief Pond, 1921, W.T. (Thurston and Vigurs 1924).

East: 05, Par (Flora), 1970, J.A.P.; 06, Criggan Moor, A.C.J. *et. al.*; Red Moor (Flora), 1978, L.J.M.; 21, Tamar Lake, J.G.D.; 'common in the Upper Tamar Valley' (Flora), by the Tamar near Kilkhampton, post—1950, D.H.

TYPHACEAE
TYPHA L.

653/1 **T. latifolia** L., Bulrush or Reedmace, listed by Davey (Flora) as 'very local', is now frequent throughout much of the county, but apparently very rare in the Lower Tamar area, where it is largely replaced by the next species.

653/2 **T. angustifolia** L.   Lesser Bulrush or Reedmace
Local and rare.
West: 62, Loe Pool, 1969, NCS, probably originally planted.
East: 04, in a marsh by the bridge at Pentewan, 1966, S.M.; 35, Tideford (Flora), still there, 1966, I.N.; Wacker Mill Creek, 1966, S.M.; 45, New Inn Marsh, Wilcove, 1966, S.M.

CYPERACEAE

SCIRPUS L.

Common species: 655/3 S. **maritimus** L., Sea Club-rush, 655/10 S. **setaceus** L., Bristle Club-rush, 655/11 S. **cernuus** Vahl (*S. filiformis* Savi), Slender Club-rush, and 655/12 S. **fluitans** L., Floating Club-rush (probably extinct in Scilly).

655/4 **S. sylvaticus** L.   Wood Club-rush
Only in the extreme NE of the county, mainly by the Tamar and its tributaries.
East: 19, SE of Canworthy Water, J.A.P.; near Bridgerule Station, R.O. (Thurston and Vigurs 1926); 20, Helebridge, near Bude, R.O., by the canal, 1960, B.Sh.; 28, banks of the Inny at Trelaske, Lewannick, S.M.; 37, by the Inny near Trecarrel Bridge, J.A.P.; 38, near Launceston (Flora), Polson Bridge, 1978, L.J.M.; 39, Tamar Valley, N of Boyton, J.A.P.; by the Tamar near N Tamerton, L.J.M.

655/8 **S. lacustris** L.   Common Club-rush
subsp. **lacustris**
Only in three very scattered stations in the county.
*West: 75, a large stand in freshwater pool, Penhale Sands, 1979, R.J.M., E.W.M., and L.J.M., **CGE**.
East: 05, Par (Flora), near Par Station, 1954, J.B.; 20, Bude (Flora), 1921, H.H.H., K.

655/9 subsp. **tabernaemontani** (C.C. Gmelin) Syme
                                                  Grey Club-rush
Locally frequent in suitable habitats.
West: 53, Long Rock, B.M.S.; Marazion (Flora), still there, 1950 onwards, various recorders; (54), Gwithian Marsh, L.J.M.; 61, Kynance, L.A.B.; 75, Perranporth

(Flora), Penhale Sands, 1976, C.J.; 84, Calenick, S of Truro,· W.H.F. (Thurston and Vigurs 1923), still there, 1966, L.J.M.

East: 84, Lamorran, D.R.; 97, Amble Marshes, R.W.D.; 05, Par (Flora), Par Sands, 1966, L.A.B.; 15, Lostwithiel (Flora), 1966, L.J.M.; 20, Bude (Flora), 1971, L.J.M.; 21, Tamar Lake, L.J.M.; 46, Calstock (Flora), post—1950, I.N.

Scilly: not seen recently, Lousley 1971.

655/8   S. lacustris x triqueter = *S. x carinatus* Sm.
x 6   East: 46, between Calstock and Morwellham (Flora), still there, post—1950, I.N.

This record is possibly more correctly named as *S. tabernaemontani x triqueter* = *S. x kuekenthalianus* Junge.   Stace (1975), lists both hybrids for v.c.2. Davey's specimen, in Herb. Davey, (TRU), has glabrous glumes, however, and is no doubt *S. x carinatus.*

655/6   S. triqueter L.   Triangular Club-rush
Only from one short stretch of the Tamar.
East: 46, Calstock (Flora), still there in 1958, I.N.
The plant is more plentiful on the Devon bank.

655/2b S. cespitosus L.   Deergrass
subsp. germanicus (Palla) Broddeson
Listed by Davey (Flora) as very rare, but it is widespread on Bodmin Moor, and in a few other scattered localities.
West: 61, Lizard (Flora), Kynance, recorder unknown; 63, Polgear, Carnmenellis, L.J.M.; 74, E of Carharrack, J.A.P.
East: 96, Goss Moor, A.B.; Tregoss Moor, L.J.M.; 06, Withiel (Flora), Retire Common, 1977, L.J.M.; 16, Cardinham Downs, L.J.M.; 17, Redhill Marsh, R.Go. and L.J.M.; near Brown Willy, L.J.M.; Emblance Downs, St Breward, E.A.; near Bowaters' works, RNHS; 18, near Rough Tor, E.A.; Crowdy Marsh, R.Go. and L.J.M.; Otterham, L.J.M.; 27, Smallacombe, R.Go. and L.J.M.; under Hawks Tor, C.B., R.J.M. and L.J.M.; 28, Laneast Moor, L.J.M.; Badgall Downs, L.J.M.; 36, Viverdon Down (Flora), post—1950, D.B.

BLYSMUS PANZER

657/1   **B. compressus** (L.) Panzer ex Link   Flat-sedge
(*Scirpus compressus* Pers.)

Extremely local, but still present in great quantity in its main locality.

West: 75, Ponsmere Marsh, Perranporth (Flora), still there in small quantity, 1966, L.J.M.; marsh near the Lost Church, Penhale Sands, 1966, L.J.M.; Ellenglaze Valley, Penhale Sands (Flora), still abundant, 1961—80, L.J.M.

ERIOPHORUM L.

654/1   **E. angustifolium** Honckeny, Common Cottongrass, is frequent and widespread in marshes and on wet heaths throughout most of the county, but is absent from the Lower Tamar area.

var. **elatius** Koch

West: 74, Allet Bog, G.A. and L.J.M.

East: 37, valley near Haye, Callington, E.A., E.W.M. and L.J.M.

654/4   **E. vaginatum** L.   Hare's-tail Cottongrass
Almost confined to Bodmin Moor, where it is locally common.

West: no recent records.

East: 06, Helmentor Moor (Flora), 1967, J.A.P.; 17, Menacrin Downs, near Temple, E.A.; Brockabarrow Common, both sides of the A 30, E.A.; Harpurs Downs, E.A.; marsh SW of Brown Willy (Flora), 1961, L.J.M.; Dozmary Pool, NCS; 27, Lower Langdon Farm, Fowey Valley, S.M.T. *et al*,; Carkeet, Fowey Valley, J.B.; Twelve Men's Moor, above Northill, J.A.P.

ELEOCHARIS R.BR.

656/5a **E. palustris** (L.) Roemer and Schultes, subsp. **vulgaris** Walters, Common Spike-rush, and   656/4 **E. multicaulis** (Sm.) Desv., Many-stalked Spike-rush, are both frequent and widespread in suitable places.

656/3   **E. quinqueflora** (F.X. Hartmann) O. Schwartz
                 Few-flowered Spike-rush
(*Scirpus pauciflorus* Lightf.)

Very rare and local, though possibly overlooked.

West: 53 (54), Gwithian Marsh, W.R.H.; near Godrevy, R.J.M.; 61, Kynance (Flora), still there, 1966, J.A.P.; 75, Trebisken Moor, Penhale Sands (Suppt), still there, 1968—79, L.J.M.

Scilly: rejected, Lousley 1971.

656/2 **E. acicularis** (L.) Roemer and Schultes Needle Spike-rush
Local and rare, in undisturbed pools.

West: 43, near Gurnards Head, Zennor, 1948, J.B.; 53, Marazion Marsh (Flora), 1948, J.B.; 61, near Ruan Pool, J.S.R.;62, Municipal Lake, Helston, L.J.M.; Loe Pool (Flora), plentiful, 1968, T.M. and L.J.M.

*East: 17, near Temple, Bodmin Moor, 1960, B.Sh.

656/6 **E. uniglumis** (Link) Schultes Slender Spike-rush
*West: 72, Chygarkye Quarry, Goonhilly Downs, post— 1950, R.H.

*East: 20, Bude, 1933, N.D.S.

Scilly: (Flora), 'not typical', Lousley 1971.

CYPERUS L.

685/1 **C. longus** L. Galingale

Always local, this is now a decreasing species.

West: 61, Predannack Wollas (Thurston 1929); 62, Gunwalloe (Flora), post—1950, R.H.; border of Gunwalloe Marsh, 1968, CNT; 71, Landewednack, E.A.R.; Kennack Cove (Flora), still there, 1950 on-wards, various recorders; in Kennack Wood, 1976, S.M.T. *et al.*; 75, Treago, Crantock (Flora), still there, 1970, L.G.; 86, Watergate Bay, 1954, R.W.D.; 97, Lellizzick, near Padstow (Flora), still there (Harbour Cove), 1964, R.W.D.

East: 97, Polzeath (Flora), until *c* 1970, now gone, R.W.D.; S of lane to Trenain Farm, St Enodoc, 1979, R.W.D.; 25, meadow at Talland, M.M.P. (Thurston and Vigurs 1925).

§ **C. eragrostis** Lam.

A fairly recent introduction.

*West: 33, St Just, by roadside, E.L.W., comm. C.A.S. (*Proc. B.S.B.I.*, 7 (1967): 32, as *C. vegetus* Willd.); 42, by boating-pool, Lariggan, Penzance, 1980, B.M.S.; 53, five plants on waste ground by Model Village, Lelant, 1976, L.J.M.

CLADIUM BROWNE

661/1 **C. mariscus** (L.) Pohl   Great Fen-sedge
Very local, and not now known outside The Lizard.
West: 61, Kynance (Flora), still there, 1950 onwards,
various recorders; 71, Erisey, Ruan Major (Flora),
still there, post—1950, R.H.; Downas Valley, comm.
J.H.; near Trevothen, Coverack, 1959—77, J.Fo.; 72,
Main Dale, 1950 onwards, various recorders.

RHYNCHOSPORA VAHL

660/1 **R. alba** (L.) Vahl   White Beak-sedge
Not recently recorded much outside Bodmin Moor,
but possibly overlooked.
West: no recent localised records.
East: 96, Retire Common, R.W.D.; 06, E side of
Retire, L.J.M.; 17, Dozmary Pool (Flora), post—1950,
R.W.D.; near Temple Bridge, L.J.M.; Redhill Marsh,
J.A.P.; Menacrin Downs, J.A.P.; 18, Crowdy Marsh,
R.Go. and L.J.M.; Bowithick Marsh, J.A.P.; Stannon
Clay-works, near Rough Tor, E.A.; 27, near Smallacombe,
R.Go. and L.J.M.; bog below Fox Tor, E.W.M. and
L.J.M.
Scilly: rejected, Lousley 1971.

[660/2 **R. fusca** (L.) Aiton fil., Brown Beak-sedge, was another
of Pascoe's records, rightly rejected, in our opinion, by
Davey (Flora). An earlier record of Ray's must similarly
have been an error.]

SCHOENUS L.

659/1 **S. nigricans** L.   Black Bog-rush
Common on wet heaths and in cliff-flushes in W
Cornwall, but rare in the East, and completely absent
E and N of Lostwithiel, and from Scilly.
West: frequent and widespread.
East: 96 or 06, Retire Common, near Withiel, post—
1950, R.W.D., 1977, L.J.M.

CAREX L.

Common species: 663/54 **C. paniculata** L., Greater
Tussock-sedge, 663/57 **C. otrubae** Podp. (*C. vulpina*
auct. non L.), False Fox-sedge, 663/61 **C. arenaria**
L., Sand Sedge, 663/71 **C. remota** L., Remote Sedge.

(absent from Scilly), 663/74 **C. ovalis** Good. (*C* *leporina* auct. non L.), Oval Sedge (absent from Scilly) 663/70 **C. echinata** Murr., Star Sedge, 663/22 **C** **pendula** L., Pendulous Sedge, 663/12 **C. sylvatica** Huds., Wood-sedge, 663/31 **C. flacca** Schreb., Glaucous Sedge, 663/26 **C. panicea** L., Carnation Sedge, 663/5 **C. binervis** Sm., Green-ribbed Sedge, 663/8 **C. demissa** Hornem. (*C. flava* auct. non L.), Common Yellow sedge, 663/36 **C. caryophyllea** Latourr., Spring-sedge (absent from Scilly), 663/34 **C. pilulifera** L., Pill Sedge 663/50 **C. nigra** (L.) Reichard (*C. goodenowii* Gay) Common Sedge.

663/54 **C. paniculata** L. x **C. remota** L. = *C. x boenninghausiana* x 71   Weihe

West: 53, Nanpusker valley, Angarrack, Hayle, A.B
*East: 20, Bude Canal, R.O. (Thurston and Vigur 1927).

663/57 **C. otrubae** Podp. x **C. remota** L. = *C. x pseudaxillaris* x 71   Richter

*East: 07, Camel Valley near Sladesbridge, R.W.D.; 20 Marhamchurch (B.E.C. 1939—40).

[663/   **C. spicata** Huds. (*C. contigua* Hoppe), Spiked Sedge 67   Flora records many localities for *C. contigua*, but every herbarium specimen examined has proved to be *C* *muricata* subsp. *lamprocarpa*, and it is unlikely that *C. spicata*, an eastern taxon, ever occurred in Cornwall although there is a single plant at Braunton, N Devon and herbarium specimens from three other Devon localities.]

663/   **C. muricata** L., subsp. **lamprocarpa** Čelak. (*C. pairae* 68+   F.W. Schultz), Prickly Sedge, is widespread, becoming common in the West, so that detailed localities are unnecessary. It has one station in Scilly: T, 1975 D.E.A.

663/65 **C. divulsa** Stokes, subsp. **divulsa**   Grey Sedge Plentiful, as Flora says, round Millbrook and Rame in the East, but scarce elsewhere, and not recently seen in the other stations quoted except West: 62, Penrose R.W.D., and East: 25, East Looe, R.W.D. Additional localities are:

West: 62, Gunwalloe, J.H.; 72, Trelowarren, R.H.; 83, Mylor Church woods, R.H.

East: 05, Charlestown, W.T. (Thurston 1935); Par, B.G.; 25, West Looe, L.J.M.; 38, Launceston, L.J.M.; 46, Halton Quay, N.J.F.; Cotehele Quay, J.A.P.

Scilly: Lousley 1971.

663/66 **C. divulsa** Stokes, subsp. **leersii** (Kneucker) W. Koch
= *C. polyphylla* Kar. & Kir.

The presence of this northern and eastern taxon in West: 62, Penrose (Suppt), is confirmed, R.W.D.

663/60 **C. disticha** Huds. Brown Sedge

Additonal records are:

West: 61, Ogo Down, Mullion, A.L.S. (Thurston 1935); Poldhu, R.O. (Thurston and Vigurs 1926), confirmed 1978, L.J.M.; 75, Penhale, J.F.F., J.H.H. and J.F.A.

East: 97, Polzeath (Suppt), seen post—1950, R.W.D., but since destroyed.

663/62 **C. divisa** Huds. Divided Sedge

The stations in Flora and Suppt have been destroyed, as has that in West: 53, Hayle, R.O. (Thurston and Vigurs 1927), but the sedge still occurs in West: 87, Harlyn Bay, L.J.M.

663/81 **C. dioica** L. Dioecious Sedge

No recent record.

663/72 **C. curta** Good. White Sedge
(*C. canescens* auct.)

Local and scarce. Not refound in the localities given in Flora and Suppt, but seen in:

West: 73, Budock, L.J.M.

East: 06, Red Moor, CNT; Criggan Moor, A.C.J. *et al.*; 17, De Lank River, R.W.D.

663/32 **C. hirta** L. Hairy Sedge

Additional records are:

West: 32, Whitesand Bay, R.W.D.; 53, Loggans Moor, and Marazion, B.M.S.; (54), Gwithian, R.H.; Gwealavellan marsh, L.J.M.; 64, Porthtowan, L.J.M.; 75, Cligga Head, C.J.; Penhale Sands and Holywell Bay,

L.J.M.; Cubert, L.J.M.; 85, marsh near Rosecliston, R.W.D.; Constantine Bay, L.J.M.

East: 97, St Endellion, B.E.M.G. and L.J.M.; 18, Camelford, L.J.M.; 20, Mere, Bude, L.J.M.; Widemouth Bay, (B.E.C. 1939—40).

663/21 **C. acutiformis** Ehrh.   Lesser Pond-sedge

Very rare. Of the records in Flora and Suppt, only Vigurs' from Tregear Moor, **BM**, is genuine *C. acutiformis;* all the others refer to *C. riparia* Curt. The colony reported from West: 62, Poldhu, A.L.S. (Thurston 1935), is, however, the true plant, R.W.D. and L.J.M.

663/20 **C. riparia** Curt.   Greater Pond-sedge

Additional records are:

West: 54, Gwithian, R.H.; 64, Tehidy Woods, L.J.M.; 71, Kennack, R.H.; 75, Ellenglaze valley, Perranporth, L.J.M.

East: 94, Porthluney, L.J.M.; 05, Par Beach, L.J.M.; 06, Polbrock, E.A.; 15, Ethy Wood, CNT; Lerryn, K.H.; 46, Danescombe, Calstock, I.N.

Scilly: Lousley 1971.

663/15 **C. pseudocyperus** L.   Cyperus Sedge

*West: 71, Crousa Downs, J.H.

*East: 04, Pentewan, W.T. (Thurston 1928), confirmed 1980, L.J.M.

663/16 **C. rostrata** Stokes   Bottle Sedge
(*C. inflata* Huds.)

Surprisingly local, though locally abundant. Additional records are:

East: 84, Tresillian, J.A.P.; 05, Lanlivery, L.J.M.; 17, Blisland, D.S.D.; De Lank River, R.W.D.; Bowithick, Bray Down, L.J.M.; 27, Siblyback Lake, R.W.D.; Rushyford Gate, G.L.K.; and I.N.; Smallacombe, R.Go. and L.J.M.; 21, Kilkhampton, D.H.

663/17 **C. vesicaria** L.   Bladder-sedge

Just extends into East Cornwall, but not recently seen in any of the localities listed in Flora. E.S. Marshall's record for 62, Gunwalloe (Flora) is an error: the specimen in **BM** is depauperate *C. riparia* Curt.

335

[663/   C. strigosa Huds., Thin-spiked Wood-sedge. A specimen
23   from East: 07, St Tudy (Thurston and Vigurs 1925),
        now in K, was determined by Arthur Bennett as this
        species, but has long-beaked utricles and can only be an
        aberrant form of C. sylvatica Huds., with which it was
        reported to be growing.]

663/1   C. laevigata Sm.   Smooth-stalked Sedge
        (C. helodes Link)
        Widespread in marshy copses and wet meadows,
        especially in the East. The following records appear to
        be additional to those in Flora and Suppt:
        West: 43, Trendrine, L.J.M.; Trevean Cliffs, K.H.; 63,
        Bolenowe valley, L.J.M.; Clowance Lake, W.T. (Thurston
        1928), post—1950, L.J.M.; 64, Tehidy Woods, L.J.M.;
        Portreath, R.W.D.; 73, Budock Bottom, CNT; Penryn
        reservoir, W.T. (Thurston 1929); 84, Bishops Wood,
        G.A. and L.J.M.
        East: 95, Trenowth Woods, CNT; St Mewan, W.T.
        (Thurston 1928); 05, Pelyn Wood, L.J.M.; 06, Dunmere
        Wood, E.A.; 07, St Teath Mill, R.W.D.; 15, Lostwithiel,
        R.W.D.; Lerryn Creek, K.H.; 17, De Lank River, E.A.;
        18, Slaughterbridge, R.W.D.; 25, St Martins Wood, E
        Looe, S.M.; 27, Upper Fowey valley, S.M.; Notter, and
        Trebartha, R.W.D.; marsh near Caradon Town, R.W.D.
        and L.J.M.; 28, Treneglos, R.W.D. and L.J.M.; old rail-
        way, Egloskerry, L.J.M.; 29, Trefrowe, Week St Mary
        (B.E.C. 1939—40); 35, Polbathic, S.M.; 36, Cadsonbury,
        E.G.; 37, Luckett Reserve, CNT; 21, Coombe Valley,
        L.J.M.
        Scilly: Lousley 1971.

663/2   C. distans L.   Distant Sedge
        Locally plentiful on wet cliffs and in salt-marshes all
        round the coast. The following localities appear to be
        additional to Flora and Suppt:
        West: 32, Nanjizal, B.M.S.; 42, Lamorna, B.M.S.;
        Kemyel Point, R.W.D. and L.J.M.; 53, Hayle Cause-
        way, B.M.S.; Phillack Towans, L.J.M.; (54), Gwithian,
        and Godrevy, L.J.M.; 64, Chapel Porth, L.J.M.; 73, near
        Maenporth, L.J.M.; 75, Penhale Sands, L.J.M.; (82),
        Godrevy Cove, St Keverne, J.H. and L.J.M.; 83, between
        Pencarrow and Trefusis Points, S.M.T.; 84, Calenick,

L.J.M.; 87, Porthcothan, and Constantine Bay, L.J.M.; Mother Ivey Bay, R.W.D.; 97, Harbour Cove, Padstow, R.W.D.

East: 83, St Mawes Castle, L.J.M.; St Just-in-Roseland, L.J.M.; between Portscatho and Greeb Point, L.J.M.; 93, Camels Cove, Portloe, R.W.D. and L.J.M.; 94, Pendower, Porthluney, and Hemmick, R.W.D.; 97, Daymer Bay, and Lundy Bay, R.W.D.; (98), Pentire, and Port Quin, R.W.D.; 05, Duporth, B.M.S.; 15, Gribbin Head, and Lansallos, R.W.D.; 36, St Mellion, D.B.; (44), Rame Head, R.W.D.; Penlee Point, L.J.M.

Scilly: apparently not present, though this is surprising.

663/2 **C. distans** L. x **C. extensa** Good. = *C. x tornabenii*
x 11 Chiov.

A specimen from West: 97, Harbour Cove, Padstow (where both parents grow together), 1964, R.W.D., was confirmed as this hybrid by A.C. Jermy, but there is now some doubt as to whether the determination was correct, and the plant has disappeared.

663/3 **C. punctata** Gaud. Dotted Sedge
Very local indeed.

*West: 42, Kemyel Crease, B.M.S., confirmed and found in quantity, R.W.D. and L.J.M.; (61, the record from Caerthillian, 1948, K and OXF, was an error for *C. distans*).

East: 93, Camels Cove, Portloe, L.J.M.; 04, Polstreath, R.W.D., confirming Miss Todd's 1935 record, OXF.; 05, persists in some quantity at Charlestown, R.W.D.; 15, Lantivet Bay, R.W.D. and L.J.M.; not yet refound at Freshwater, Polperro (Suppt), though the Perrycostes' specimens in TRU are correctly determined; (44), not refound at Rame Head (specimen, 1878, in BIRM).

663/11 **C. extensa** Good. Long-bracted Sedge
Coastal, frequent. Stations added to those in Flora and Suppt are:

West: 42, Kemyel Crease, G.L.; 53, Hayle, L.J.M.; Copperhouse, J.B.; Phillack, B.M.S.; 72, Gweek, R.H.; 73, Newporth Head, L.J.M.; 83, Falmouth, L.J.M.; Maylor Church, R.H.; 87, Dinas Head, L.J.M.; 97, Harbour Cove, Padstow, R.W.D.

East: 83, Portscatho, L.J.M.; Froe Lake, B.E.M.G.; 84, between Tresillian and Malpas, L.J.M.; 93, Pendower, and Portloe, R.W.D.; 35, Yonderberry Point, and Clift Quay, S.M.; (44) Penlee Point, L.J.M.; 45, Antony Passage, J.A.P.

663/4 **C. hostiana** DC.   Tawny Sedge
(*C. fulva* Host)

Widespread in the extreme East of the county, as Flora reports, scarce elsewhere. Additional records are: West: 61, Hayle Kimbro Pool, M.C.H., T.M. and L.J.M.; 71, Crousa Downs, L.J.M.; Goonhilly N.N. Reserve, D.E.C.; Downas Valley, CNT; 73, Halvossa Moor, Mabe, D.S.D.; (97, the record (Suppt) from Mother Ivey's Bay is almost certainly an error for C. distans).

East: 19, Tresparrett, and Newham, R.W.D.

663/8 **C. demissa** Hornem. x **C. hostiana** DC.
x 4   This, one of the commoner *Carex* hybrids in Britain, is likely to occur wherever the parents grow together.
West: 71, Crousa Downs, R.W.D.; 75, Ventongimps, P.Tu., B.E.M.G., E.W.M. and L.J.M.
  *East: 19, Tresparrett, R.W.D.

663/10 **C. serotina** Mérat   Small-fruited Yellow-sedge
(*C. oederi* Retz)

All the records in Flora, as Davey himself suggests, and in Suppt, almost certainly refer to small forms of *C. demissa* Hornem., which is also the '*C. flava*' and 'var. *lepidocarpa*' of those works. True *C. serotina* does, however, occur in West: 64, Chapel Porth, L.J.M., and 75, Penhale Sands, J.F.F., J.H.H., and J.F.A. In both places it is the subspecies *serotina*, although subspecies *pulchella* (Lönnr.) Van Ooststr. (= *C. scandinavica* E.W. Davies) is at Braunton in North Devon and might well turn up in Cornwall.

663/24 **C. pallescens** L.   Pale Sedge
Uncommon. Persists in East: 06, Hustyn Wood, R.W.D., and has also been found in:
West: 84, Calenick Moor, W.Bo. (Thurston 1935).
East: 06, Fletchers Bridge, L.J.M.; 29, Week St Mary,

R.O. (Thurston and Vigurs 1925); 37, Carthamartha, L.J.M.

Scilly: M, Porth Hellick, 1974, V.G., though uncon firmed, unlikely to be an error.

663/37 **C. montana** L. Hill Sedge

*West: 53, Carbis Bay, J.E.Lo. (Thurston 1936); 75 Cross Coombe, L.J.M.

East: 97, or 06, Hustyn Wood (Flora); the specimen is in **BM** and is correctly determined; but the wood has been extensively replanted and the sedge has not been refound.

[663/ 46 **C. elata** All., Tufted-sedge. It is most unlikely that the two records in the Flora are correct or that this plant occurs in Cornwall. The nearest certain record is from North Somerset. The errors were probably due to a confusion (a common one) with the tussock form of *C. nigra* (L.) Reichard.]

[663/ 47 **C. acuta** L. (*C. gracilis* Curt.), Slender Tufted-sedge Davey's rejection (Flora) of the Cornish record must be accepted as correct. Again, the nearest known station is in North Somerset.]

663/80 **C. pulicaris** L. Flea Sedge

Not now as common as Flora suggests, but sufficiently widespread to make details of localities unnecessary (absent from Scilly).

ORCHIDACEAE

EPIPACTIS ZINN

625/1 **E. palustris** (L.) Crantz Marsh Helleborine (*Helleborine longifolia* Rendle & Britten

Very local and rare.

West: 32, Brewgate Moor, Sennen (Flora), regularly seen until *c* 1971, B.M.S.; the site has since been drained, and the colony has gone.; 75, Penhale Sands, 1965, NCS, since when it has spread into several colonies, one of which is extensive.

East: 08, St Teath, 1977, C.C., two plants, 1979, E.W.M.

625/2 **E. helleborine** (L.) Crantz   Broad-leaved Helleborine
(*Helleborine latifolia* Druce)

Only in the far North and East of the county.

East: 19, near Millook, R.D.; 21, hillside near Stowe
Barton, Coombe, T.D.; wood NW of Kilkhampton,
T.D.; near Tamar Lake, R.D.; 35, Wacker Wood (Flora),
1967, S.M.; 36, Cadsonbury (Thurston and Vigurs
1926), 1970, B.E.M.G. and J.A.P.; Clapper Bridge
(Flora), 1966, I.N., 1980, BSBI; 37, Old Mill, Stoke
Climsland, I.N.; near Carthamartha, I.N.; 46, Broadmoor
Wood, Carkeel, E.G.; near railway crossing, Harewood,
E.G.

625/3 **E. purpurata** Sm. (*Helleborine violacea* Druce), Violet
Helleborine, was recorded in the Addenda to the Suppt,
and there are subsequent records for 38, near
Launceston, and 39, North Tamerton (Thurston 1935);
but, in the absence of confirmatory specimens, we have
considerable doubt as to their authenticity. They were
probably forms of the preceding species.]

NEOTTIA LUDWIG

629/1 **N. nidus-avis** (L.) L.C.M. Richard   Bird's-nest Orchid

Extremely local, occurring mainly as single specimens.

West: 83, Trelissick, 1972, J.N.; The only recent
record for v.c.1.

East: 06, Lanhydrock (Thurston 1935); 06 or 07, N
of Dunmere, K.H.J.; 15, Readymoney, Fowey, two
plants, H.P.; 19, Millook, L.J.M.; 21, Coombe Valley
(Thurston and Vigurs 1924 and 1925); 25, near the
canning factory, W. Looe, comm. H.P.; Polvellan Wood,
W Looe (Flora), 1969, L.J.M.; 37, Luckett Reserve,
R.Go.

LISTERA R.BR.

628/1 **L. ovata** (L.) R.Br., Common Twayblade, is scattered
throughout the county in numerous localities, but is
absent from West Penwith and from Scilly.

SPIRANTHES L.C.M. RICHARD

627/1 **S. spiralis** (L.) Chevall., Autumn Lady's-tresses, is
frequent and widespread, more especially in coastal
habitats. There are 28 additional records subsequent
to the Flora and Suppt.

PLATANTHERA L.C.M. RICHARD

638/2 P. bifolia (L.) L.C.M. Richard   Lesser Butterfly-orchid
(*Habenaria bifolia* Br.)

Still widespread on heathland in the county, though decidedly local.

West: 43, Nancledra, G.L.; 63, Crowan, J.B.; 71 Main Dale, J.F.A.; Crousa Downs, J.Fo.; 72, Goonhilly Downs (Suppt), near Traboe various recorders; 74 Allet Common, G.A. and L.J.M.; 75, Ventongimps Moor (Flora), still there, various recorders.

East: 95, near Roche (Flora), still there, R.H.; 96 near Tremayne Farm, St Columb, C.W.; Tregonetha Downs, T.H.A.; 05, Bugle, J.B.; 06, Breney Common J.B.; Retire Common, J.A.P.; 16, St Neot, C.W.; 26 Redgate, J.L.; St Cleer, J.L.; 28, Laneast Downs, G.L.K. 29, Greena Moor (Flora), near Greenamoor Bridge 1977, C.C.; 36, Cadsonbury, I.N.; Herod Down, S.M. 37, plentiful in valley N of Haye, Callington, E.G. Luckett, I.N.; 46, Halton Quay, E.G.

638/1 P. chlorantha (Custer) Reichenb.

Greater Butterfly-orchid
(*Habenaria virescens* Druce)

Rare, and now confined to East Cornwall.

East: 96, Goss Moor (Thurston and Vigurs 1927) 1958, J.G.T.; 06, a large colony by railway bridge near Bodmin, E.A.; Breney Common, J.B.; 16, between St Neot and Pantersbridge, E.A.; 17, W of Temple, J.A.P. two colonies near De Lank Quarry, E.A.; 18, near Davidstow Moor, C.J.B.; 27, Dwellamill Wood, near Caradon Town, E.G.; 28, Polyphant (Thurston and Vigurs 1923); Inny Valley E of Lewannick, reported independently by S.M. and J.A.P.; 36, wood below Viverdon Down (Flora), still there, D.B.; 37, plentiful in valley N of Haye, Callington, E.G.; Luckett Reserve A.B.

GYMNADENIA R.BR.

636/1a G. conopsea (L.) R.Br.   Fragrant Orchid
(*Habenaria conopsea* Benth.)

Scattered throughout the county, but rather local except on parts of the Lizard, where it is often in quantity.

West: 53, Hawks Point, near St Ives (Flora), 1949, J.B.; 61, 71, and 72, frequent on the Lizard heaths; 72, Gweek, R.H.; Polwheveral, near Helford River, L.J.M.

East: 96, St Breock Downs (Suppt), still there, various recorders; 16, Cardinham (Flora), c 1950, K.H.J.; 37, Luckett Reserve, S.M.; below Hingston Down, E.G.

*Scilly: MN, W end of Great Bay, 1974, L.A.H. *et al.*

36/1b var. **densiflora** (Wahlenb.) Lindl. Marsh Fragrant Orchid
West: 75, Penhale Sands, in marsh, 1967, G.A., R.Go. and L.J.M., plentiful 1980, L.J.M.

COELOGLOSSUM HARTMAN

35/1 **C. viride** (L.) Hartman   Frog Orchid
(*Habenaria viridis* Br.)

Always extremely rare, this species has not been re-found in its old locality at 19, Otterham (Flora). The following is the only post-Flora record:

East: 38, one plant, near South Petherwin, A.V. (Thurston and Vigurs 1927).

DACTYLORHIZA NECKER EX NEVSKI

Common species: 643/2b **D. maculata** (L.) Soó, subsp. **ericetorum** (E.F. Linton) P.F. Hunt & Summerhayes, Heath Spotted-orchid (absent from Scilly, and 643/4 **D. majalis** (Reichenb.) P.F. Hunt & Summerhayes, subsp. **praetermissa** (Druce) D. Moresby Moore & Soó (*Orchis latifolia* auct.), Southern Marsh-orchid (a recent arrival in Scilly, now in 4 places).

643/3a **D. incarnata** (L.) Soó, subsp. **incarnata**
        Early Marsh-orchid

Rather rare and local, except on parts of the Lizard, but often overlooked.

West: 32, Sennen (Flora), 1932, T.S.S. (Thurston 1935); 53, Loggans Moor, Hayle, 1932, T.S.S. (Thurston 1935), still there, post—1950, B.M.S.; Marazion Marsh, J.R.P.; (54), Gwithian Marsh, R.M. and L.J.M.; 61, marsh N of Erisey, J.H.; Ponsonjoppa, J.H.; 61 and 71, Goonhilly N.N. Reserve, comm. J.H.; 71, Crousa Downs, J.A.P.; 72, Traboe Cross, J.H.; 75, Penhale Sands, NCS; 87, Constantine Bay, W.G.

East: 94, Caerhayes, J.S.R.

3c   subsp. **coccinea** (Pugsley) Soó

At present this dune-slack species is known only from
the following station:

*West: 53 (54), Gwithian Marsh, L.J.M., 1967—78

3b   subsp. **pulchella** (Druce) Soó

This very distinct subspecies occurs only on wet heaths.
It has only recently been recognised in the county
and may well be more frequent than these records show.

*West: 72, near Traboe Cross, 1978, J.H. and L.J.M.
*East: 06, Retire Common, in quantity, 1977, L.J.M.

D. majalis (Reichenb.) P.F. Hunt & Summerhayes
subsp. **pardalina** (Pugsley) Nelson Leopard Marsh-orchid
Frequent, and often in quantity, in dune-slacks.

*West: 53 (54), Gwithian Marsh, L.J.M.; Upton
Towans, L.J.M.; 75, Penhale Sands, 1968, L.J.M.
*East: 35, pool at Sheviock (B.E.C. 1943). *Bude Golf Course*

643/2b **D. maculata** subsp. **ericetorum** x **majalis** subsp.
x 4   **praetermissa** = *D. x hallii* (Druce) Soó

An overlooked hybrid, often frequent where the parents
grow together.

West: 61, Hayle Kimbro, R.M.P.; 63, Bolenowe Moor,
Troon, L.J.M.; 71, Crousa Downs, B.E.M.G.; Goonhilly
N.N. Reserve, J.H. and L.J.M.; 72, Main Dale, LFC; 73,
Budock Bottom, CNT; 74, Trevince Moor, Gwennap,
L.J.M.; 75, railway near Shepherds Halt, L.J.M.
*East: 06, Red Moor, 1979, E.A.

643/1a **D. fuchsii** (Druce) Soó, subsp. **fuchsii**

Common Spotted-orchid
Extremely rare and local in Cornwall.

*West: 53, Hawks Point, near Carbis Bay, date of first
record unknown, still there, 1976—80; Phillack, one
plant, L.J.M.; 73, one plant, Devoran, L.J.M.; 87, old
airfield, St Ervan, T.H.A.

subsp. **hebridensis** (Wilmott) Soó   Hebridean Orchid
*West: 53, Lelant, K, refound 1974, CNT.
*East: 08, Lye Cove, Bossiney, K, refound 1975,
L.J.M.

643/1a D. fuchsii subsp. fuchsii x majalis subsp. praetermissa
x 4   = *D. x grandis* (Druce) P.F. Hunt
    *West: 53, St Ives, 1968, L.M.L.; (54), Gwithian Marsh, L.J.M.

DACTYLORHIZA X GYMNADENIA

643/2b D. maculata subsp. ericetorum x G. conopsea
x 636/   = *Dactylogymnadenia legrandiana* (Camus) Soó
1a   *West: 71, Crousa Downs, 1973, B.E.M.G.; 72, near Countybridge Quarry, J.H.; opposite the Earth Station, Goonhilly, one plant, W.R.H.

ORCHIS L.

642/7   **O. mascula** (L.) L., Early-purple Orchid, is common and widespread, mainly on hedgebanks, but also on hillsides, woodland, and cliff-tops (absent from Scilly).

642/5   **O. morio** L.   Green-winged Orchid
Always rare in Cornwall, this species has further declined in the last fifty years, though it still occurs in most of its old localities on the Lizard.
West: 61, Kynance (Flora), W of Kynance Gate, 1974, R.M.P.; plentiful near Kynance Farm, 1974, D.E.C.; Gew Graze, comm. J.H.; Predannack Downs (Suppt), S of Predannack Wollas, J.A.P., 1979, L.C.F., M.M., and J.H.; Mullion (Flora), Mullion Cove, 1955, J.B., 1978, J.S.R.; Mullion Cliff, one plant, D.E.C.; 71, Cadgwith (Suppt), Kilndown Point, 1959—77, J.Fo.; Chynalls Point, Coverack, comm. J.H.; 72, Rosemullion Head, L.J.M.; Trelowarren, J.H.
East: 20, Bude Golf Links, R.O. (Thurston and Vigurs 1925).

ANACAMPTIS L.C.M. RICHARD

645/1   **A. pyramidalis** (L.) L.C.M. Richard   Pyramidal Orchid
This species has been steadily increasing on the sandhills since Davey's day.
West: 53, Marazion to Long Rock, L.J.M.; between St Ives and Clodgy Point, L.B.; Carbis Bay (Flora), still there, post—1950, J.B.; common all the way from Lelant Dunes to (54) Godrevy, various recorders; 75, Penhale Sands, L.J.M.; 86 (76), Crantock, and Cubert, K.H.; 87, Constantine Bay (Flora), abundant 1977, L.J.M.; Trevose, J.L.

East: 97, St Enodoc golf-links, G.T.P. (Thurstoi 1935), still there, and at Rock, various recorders; 19 Dizzard, and Chapmans Point, R.D.

OPHRYS L.

640/3 **O. sphegodes** Miller   Early Spider-orchi<

A single occurrence, not reported since.

*West: 53, Upton Towans, 1961, J.R.

640/1 **O. apifera** Hudson   Bee Orchi<

Always extremely rare in Cornwall, and mainly a single occurrences.

West: 53, Lelant, one plant, post—1950, B.M.S. Upton Towans, one plant, c 1965, B.E.M.G.

East: 45 (44), between Rame Head and Cawsanc Bay, in quantity (Thurston 1930), Penlee Point, c 1930 T.W., and apparently seen again in 1977 or 1978 comm. E.G.

HAMMARBYA O. KUNTZE

631/1 **H. paludosa** (L.) O. Kuntze   Bog Orchic
(*Malaxis paludosa* Sw.)

Extremely local and rare, sometimes not appearing fo: several years. It has not been refound in its origina station at 27, Cheesewring (Suppt).

East: 18, Crowdy Marsh, 1967, R.Go.; Bowithick. 1967, R.Go. and J.A.P.

SUPPLEMENTARY LIST OF RARE GARDEN ESCAPES AND CASUALS, AND DOUBTFUL RECORDS.

Doubtful records are placed in round brackets.

DICKSONIACEAE

Dicksonia antarctica Labill, Tree-fern. *West: 73, naturalised on roadbank, Penjerrick, Falmouth, 1961—78, L.J.M. Self-sown inside gardens at 43, Trengwainton, and 72, Glendurgan, 1978, L.J.M.

ASPIDIACEAE

23/1 **Polystichum falcatum** (L. fil.) Diels (*Cyrtomium falcatum* (L. fil.) C. Presl.), House Holly Fern. *West: 42, Penzance, 1977, G.B.M.; 43, near Albert Pier, Penzance, 1971, J.R.P. Scilly: Lousley 1971; M, in two places, P.M.

22/2 **P. x bicknellii** (Christ) Hahne. West: 75, Chyverton
x 1 Wood, 1912, W.T. Herb. Druce (OXF), and E.T., K, have both been checked by Dr A. Sleep. The specimens may have come from the same plant, which could have been an introduction.

BLECHNACEAE

Blechnum chilense (Kaulf.) Mett. *West: 85, railway bank, Shepherds, near Goonhavern, 1965, L.J.M. *East: 84, Pencalenick, 1975, L.J.M. Scilly: Lousley 1971; M, near Rose Hill, 1972, L.A.H.; Salakee Farm, B.E.M.G. and S.C.H.

PINACEAE

Abies alba Miller, Silver Fir. *East: 27, seedlings at Trebartha Park, C.B., R.J.M. and L.J.M.

31/1 **Picea abies** (L.) Karsten, Norway Spruce. *East: 27, seedlings frequent in Trebartha Park, C.B., R.J.M. and L.J.M.

33/2 **Pinus pinaster** Aiton, Maritime Pine. West: 84, self-sown saplings, Carrine Common, L.J.M.

P. nigra Arnold, subsp. **nigra,** Austrian Pine. *West: 84, self-sown, Carrine Common, L.J.M.

ARAUCARIACEAE

Araucaria araucana (Molina) C. Koch, Monkey Puzzle.
*East: 06 or 07, Pencarrow Woods, Bodmin, E.A.

SALICACEAE

343/1 **Salix pentandra** L., Bay Willow. *East: 18, several
bushes by R. Inny near Davidstow, J.E.L. (B.E.C. 1924).

343/7 **S. daphnoides** Vill., Violet Willow. *West: 43, near
Tremethick Moor, M.Bo. (Thurston and Vigurs 1926).

342/4+ **Populus nigra** L., cv. italica, Lombardy Poplar. *East:
26, by river at Factory, Menheniot, S.M.

BETULACEAE

Alnus cordata (Loisel.) Loisel. *East: 05, Par Harbour,
L.T.M. (Thurston 1935).

ULMACEAE

Ulmus x sarniensis (Loud.) Melville, Jersey Elm. West
and East. Recorded for both vice-counties in Stace,
1975.

MORACEAE

331/1 **Ficus carica** L., Fig. *West: 33, Bosorne, St Just, M.C.;
63, old tip, Treskillard, L.J.M. *East: 08 (09), Boscastle,
B.E.M.G. Scilly: M, Holy Vale, P.G.

CANNABACEAE

Cannabis sativa L., Hemp. West: 42 and 43, Penzance,
G.B.M. East: 83, old tip, Gerrans, B.E.M.G.

SANTALACEAE

(264/1 **Thesium humifusum** DC., Bastard Toadflax. Early
records were treated by Davey (Flora) with suspicion.
This species is hardly likely to have occurred).

ARISTOLOCHIACEAE

316/1 **Asarum europaeum** L., Asarabacca. *West: 61, Mullion,
M.Re.

POLYGONACEAE

(320/ **P. minus** Hudson, Small Water-pepper, and 320/13
14 **P. mite** Schrank, Tasteless Water-pepper, were both
recorded in the Flora. In the absence of authentic

specimens, these records should be regarded with caution.)

325/3 **Rumex scutatus** L., French Sorrel. *West: 63, grounds of Godolphin House (B.E.C. 1927).

R. dentatus L. *East: 05, Par Harbour, L.T.M. (Thurston and Vigurs 1927).

(325/ **R. palustris** Sm., Marsh Dock, and 325/18 **R. maritimus** 17 L., Golden Dock (Flora), should be regarded as doubtful, pending further evidence.)

CHENOPODIACEAE

155/1+ **Beta vulgaris** L., subsp. **vulgaris**, Beetroot. *West: 74, Council tip, Bissoe, L.J.M.

Chenopodium detestans J. Kirk. *East: 05, Charlestown, W.T. (Thurston 1929b).

154/10 **C. pratericola** Rydb. East: 05, Par, as *C. leptophyllum* (Flora), G.C.D. (Thurston 1935).

154/6 **C. berlandieri** Moq., subsp. **zschackei** (J. Murr) Zobel. East: 05, Par (b.E.C. 1929).

C. ambrosioides L. *East: 05, Charlestown, W.T. (B.E.C. 1926).

154/ **C. rubrum** L., var. **pseudobotryoides** Wats. West: 53, 14+ Phillack, 1932, E.A.R.

154/12 **C. urbicum** L., Upright Goosefoot. West: 73, Penryn, 1933, E.S.T. (Thurston 1935).

(154/7 **C. opulifolium** Schrad. ex Koch & Ziz, Grey Goosefoot. Scilly: MN, E.S.T. (Thurston 1935). The specimen in Herb. E.S. Todd (SDN), was later seen by J.E. Lousley, and re-determined as *C. murale*, Lousley 1971.)

154/4 **C. album x berlandieri** = *C. x variabile* Aellen. *East: x 6 05, Par, G.C.D. (Thurston 1935).

156/7 **Atriplex halimus** L., Tree Purslane. West: 42, one bush between Mousehole and Kemyel Crease, R.W.D. and L.J.M.

Axyris amaranthoides L. Russian Pigweed. *East: 05, waste heap, St Austell, W.T. (B.E.C. 1926); Par, (B.E.C. 1927).

(**Salicornia procumbens** Sm. (Flora). It is not clear what species Davey means by this, as there is no specimen in his herbarium. At present, this is best excluded from the Flora).

AMARANTHACEAE

153/1 **Amaranthus retroflexus** L., Common Amaranth.
West: 61, Mullion, E.J.P. (Thurston and Vigurs 1926); 73, fallow field, Tresamble, Perranwell, R.A.G. Scilly: Lousley 1971.

153/3 **A. albus** L.   East: 05, Par Harbour, E.S.T. (B.E.C. 1923).

154/4 **A. lividus** L.   East: 05, Par Harbour, L.T.M. (B.E.C. 1926).

NYCTAGINACEAE

Mirabilis jalapa L., Marvel of Peru.   *West: old tip, St Erth, L.J.M.

PHYTOLACCACEAE

Phytolacca acinosa Roxb. agg., Indian Poke.   *East: 84, garden weed, Pencalenick, CNT.

AIZOACEAE

Drosanthemum floribundum (Haw.) Schwant.   *West: 52, Rinsey Head, near garden, L.J.M.; 62, between Porthleven and Loe Bar, C.P.; 71, Cadgwith, L.J.M. Scilly: Lousley 1971.   *Mesembryanthemum candens* Harv., West: 86, Newquay (B.E.C. 1925, p. 771) may belong here.

Oscularia deltoides (Mill.) Schwant.   Scilly: Lousley 1971.

Aptenia cordifolia (L. fil.) N.E.Br. Scilly: Lousley 1971.

Lampranthus falciformis (Haw.) N.E.Br. Scilly: Lousley 1971.

L. roseus (Willd.) Schwantes. West: 61, Lizard; Poldhu, both C.P.

Ruschia caroli (L. Bol.) Schwant. Scilly: Lousley 1971.

Erepsia heteropetala (Haw.) Schwant. Scilly: Lousley 1971.

TETRAGONIACEAE

Tetragonia tetragonoides (Pallas) O. Kuntze. West: 52, Praa Sands, H.H. (Thurston 1935).

PORTULACACEAE

151/1 **Portulaca oleracea** L., subsp. **oleracea. Scilly: Lousley** 1971.

CARYOPHYLLACEAE

(133/6 **Stellaria palustris** Retz., Marsh Stitchwort. There is no positive evidence that this species has ever been found in the county. The collections of Davey and Perrycoste in TRU contain no correctly-named specimens, and the material in K, from Lostwithiel, A.B. Jackson, 1927, is **S. graminea.** The latter species often grows in marshes in Cornwall, and this could be the source of the records and mistakes. It is better to exclude this plant in the absence of confirmatory material.)

Cerastium biebersteinii DC., Snow Plant. *West: 74, old railway, S of St Agnes, P.D.S.

132/1 **Myosoton aquaticum** (L.) Moench (*Stellaria aquatica* Scop.), Water Chickweed, occurs purely as a casual. West: 75, weed in nursery, Zelah, L.J.M. East: 05, Par Harbour, 1923, L.T.M., K.

146/3 **Herniaria hirsuta** L. West: 83, Penpol House, as tan-bark alien, L.J.M.

Lychnis coronaria (L.) Desr., Rose Campion. *West: 63, 18 plants on reclaimed land, Treskillard, Redruth, L.J.M.; 73, a few on steep bank, Ponsharden, Penryn, L.J.M. East: 05, Par, 1925, L.T.M.

Silene coeli-rosa (L.) Godron. *Scilly: M, garden in St Mary's, 1973, L.A.H.

S. nocturna L., var. **pauciflora** Otth. *East: 05, Par Harbour, L.T.M. (Thurston 1929a).

Gypsophila pilosa Hudson (Suppt as *G. porrigens* Boiss.). East: 05, Par Harbour, L.T.M. (B.E.C. 1927).

128/1 **Vaccaria pyramidata** Medicus (*Saponaria vaccaria* L.), Cow Basil. West: 63, Lanner, R.L.S. and W.D.W. (Thurston and Vigurs 1925); 73, waste ground, Penryn,

W.T. (Thurston 1930); 85, old tip, Newlyn East, L.J.M. East: 05, Par (Flora), still there in 1926, W.T. (Thurston 1928); 45, one plant in garden, Saltash, I.N.

NYMPHAEACEAE

Nymphaea sp. *West: 71, one clump of a deep pink water-lily, Coft Pascoe Pool, L.J.M.

RANUNCULACEAE

Nigella damascena L., Love-in-a-Mist. West: 84, old mine-ground, Newbridge, Truro, L.J.M. Often on Council tips.

Caltha polypetala Hochst. ex Lorent. *West: 53, Marazion Marsh, originally planted here, and found by E.A.R. in 1934, still there, post—1950, B.M.S.

Anemone japonica (Thunb.) Sieb. & Zucc. *West: 63, old mine, Wheal Grenville, Troon, L.J.M.; old spoil-heaps, Tolvaddon, R.J.M. and L.J.M.

Clematis tangutica Korsh. *West: 53, Marazion, 1973, J.Ro., comm. B.M.S.

45/2 **C. flammula** L., Virgins Bower. *West: 53, Marazion, 1973, J.Ro., comm. B.M.S.

(46/20 **Ranunculus circinatus** Sibth., Fan-leaved Water-crowfoot. We have found no specimen to substantiate the record in the Flora, to which, in our opinion, some doubt attaches).

(46/ **R. aquatilis x tripartitus.** Listed for v.c.1. in Stace
22a x 1975.
18

(46/ **R. aquatilis x baudotii.** Similarly recorded for v.c.1. in
22a x Stace 1975.
23

50/1 **Thalictrum flavum** L., Common Meadow-rue. *East: edge of car-park, in small stream, no doubt introduced, 1965, L.J.M.

BERBERIDACEAE

Berberis darwinii Hooker. *West: 62, one plant in scrub, Poldhu Cove, L.J.M.; 64, one plant in gorse scrub near Porthtowan, 1967, L.J.M.

LAURACEAE

Laurus nobilis L., Bay. *West: 74, one bush on mine waste, United Mines, Gwennap, 1977, L.J.M.

PAPAVERACEAE

Papaver arenarium Bieb. *Scilly: MN, Middle Town, 1975, J.E.Lo.

58/8   **P. atlanticum** (Ball) Cosson, Atlas Poppy. *East: 08, on wall, Trevalga, Tintagel, 1971, M.Wa.

P. orientale L., Oriental Poppy. *East: 97, on grassy slope near Ship Inn, Wadebridge, 1977, L.J.M.

Glaucium corniculatum (L.) J.H. Rudolph, Red Horned-poppy. East: 05, Par Harbour, 1961, B.Sh.

63/1   **Eschscholzia californica** Cham., Californian Poppy. *West: 62, waste ground, Helston, L.J.M.; 64, Camborne, B.Sh.; 74, old tip, Bissoe, L.J.M.

Dicentra eximia Torr. (Suppt as *Diclytra eximia* DC.). *East: 15, wood at Menabilly, Fowey, as *Capnorchis* (B.E.C. 1933).

(66/6a   **Fumaria muralis** Sonder ex Koch, subsp. **muralis**. We have seen no completely reliable specimen, most, if not all, of the records referring to forms of subsp. **boraei**).

66/7   **F. densiflora** DC., Dense-flowered Fumitory (Flora). Only ever casual. There are no recent records.

66/10 **F. parviflora** Lam, Fine-leaved Fumitory (Flora). A rare casual, not seen since.

CRUCIFERAE

Sisymbrium polyceratium L. *West: 43, Gulval, 1882 (Thurston 1930).

111/1 **Descurainia sophia** (L.) Webb ex Prantl, (*Sisymbrium sophia* L.), Flixweed. West: 84, County Hall, Truro, W.Bo. (Thurston and Vigurs 1925).

90/2   **Bunias orientalis** L., Warty Cabbage. *East: 84, between Truro and Malpas, 1932, E.S.T. (B.E.C. 1933).

Malcolmia maritima (L.) R.Br., Virginia Stock. East: 94, weed in Demosntration Garden, Probus, L.J.M.

Matthiola longipetala (Vent.) DC., subsp. **bicornis** (Sibth. & Sm.) P.W. Ball, Night-scented Stock. *West: 53, Phillack Towans, E.S.T. (B.E.C. 1923, p. 26); 64, hundreds of plants in sandy lane near Connor Downs, L.J.M.

98/2   **Barbarea stricta** Andrz., Small-flowered Winter-cress. *West: 53, one plant, Hayle Causeway, E.A.R. (Thurston and Vigurs 1927).

102/5 **Rorippa amphibia** (L.) Besser, Great Yellow-cress. *West: 53, Trevethoe, Lelant, one plant, T.J.P. (Thurston 1935). Scilly: rejected, Lousley 1971.

100/3 **Arabis caucasica** Schlect., Garden Arabis. *East: 15, ten plants on high wall, Fowey, L.J.M.; 26, Liskeard, post—1950, D.B.; 36, St Mellion, post—1950, D.B.; 38, hedgebank along Dutson road, Launceston, L.J.M.

Aubrieta deltoidea (L.) DC., Aubretia. *West: 84, several plants self-sown on wall by stream, Truro, 1978, L.J.M.

93/1   **Berteroa incana** (L.) DC. (*Alyssum incanum* L.), Hoary Alison. East: 84, between Truro and Malpas, E.S.T. (Thurston 1935).

Neslia paniculata (L.) Desv. (*Vogelia sagittata* Medicus). East: 15, Fowey (B.E.C. 1925).

Ionopsidium acaule (Desf.) Reichenb. Scilly: Lousley 1971.

83/1   **Iberis amara** L., Wild Candytuft (Flora). East: 20, Bude sand-dunes, R.O. (Thurston and Vigurs 1925). Purely casual here. Most of the old records probably refer to garden cultivars.

Lepidium ramosissimum A. Nelson. *East: 05, Charlestown, W.T. (B.E.C. 1924); Par Harbour, L.T.M. (Thurston 1928).

79/1   **L. sativum** L., Garden Cress. West: 61, Mullion, E.J.P. (Thurston and Vigurs 1927); 74, old tip, Bissoe, L.J.M.; 85, Council tip, Newlyn East, L.J.M.

L. bonariense L. *East: 84, near Boscawen Park, Truro, W.Bo. (B.E.C. 1924)

L. **densiflorum** Schrader, American Pepperwort. West: 73, Penryn, W.T. (Thurston 1928); 84, County Hall, Truro, 1924, W.Bo. (Thurston and Vigurs 1926). East: 84, near Boscawen Park, Truro, 1922, W.Bo. (Thurston and Vigurs 1923); 05, Par (Suppt), Par Harbour, L.T.M. (Thurston and Vigurs 1927).

79/5   L. **neglectum** Thell., Least Pepperwort. East: 15, Fowey (B.E.C. 1925); 36, garden weed, St Mellion, W.Ch. (Thurston and Vigurs 1924).

78/1   **Conringia orientalis** (L.) Dumort. (*Erysimum orientale* Mill.), Hare's-ear Mustard. Only a casual here. West: 53, Copperhouse, Hayle, R.O. (Thurston and Vigurs 1925); 61, roadside bank, Mullion, E.J.P. (Thurston and Vigurs 1925); 71, Poldhu (B.E.C. 1924); 74, garden weed, Trevarth, Lanner, W.D.W. (Thurston 1928). East: 83, half-way between Gerrans and St Anthony, A.J.S.; 84, garden, Tresillian, C.N. (Thurston 1935); 05, Par Sands, L.T.M. (Thurston and Vigurs 1925); 25, Polperro (Suppt), (Thurston 1928).

Brassica juncea (L.) Czern., Chinese Mustard. East: 84, between Truro and Malpas (B.E.C. 1923); 20, Bude, E.T. (B.E.C. 1925).

73/1   **Eruca vesicaria** (L.) Cav., subsp. **sativa** (Miller) Thell., Garden Rocket. East: 84, between Truro and Malpas, W.Bo. (Thurston 1935).

69/1   **Rhynchosinapis monensis** (L.) Dandy ex Clapham (*Brassica monensis* Hudson), Isle of Man Cabbage, an introduction at East: 05, Par (Flora), refound 1971, N.J.F.

71/1   **Hirshfeldia incana** (L.) Lagrèze-Fossat (*Brassica adpressa* Boiss.), Hoary Mustard. East: 05, Par (Flora), still there, 1933 (B.E.C. 1933).

76/2   **Rapistrum rugosum** (L.) All., Bastard Cabbage. West: 53, Hayle (Suppt), still there, 1971, B.M.S.; 74, old tip, Bissoe, B.E.M.G.

CRASSULACEAE

Crassula helmsii (T. Kirk) Cockayne. *East: 20, Moreton Pound Farm, near Bude, 1979, L.P., comm. B.E.M.G.

C. decumbens Thunb. Scilly: Lousley 1971.

236/1 **Sempervivum tectorum** L., House-leek. East: 06, Tregawne, near Withiel, H.F.D. (Thurston 1928); 27, roof of barn, Northill, W.H.F. (Thurston and Vigurs 1926); 45, on old buildings at Torpoint, post—1950, now gone, S.M. Scilly: Lousley 1971.

Sedum confusum Hensley. *West: 42, Newlyn Harbour, 1976, L.J.M.; 83, side of quarry car-park, Falmouth, L.J.M.

235/3 **S. spurium** Bieb., Caucasian Stonecrop. *West: 73, Mabe, 1963, L.J.M.; 83, wall near Swanpool, L.J.M. East: 93, Gwendra, near Pendower Beach, L.J.M.; 19, Crackington Haven, T.N.S.P. (Thurston 1930); 20, churchyard wall, Bude, L.J.M.

SAXIFRAGACEAE

239/7 **Saxifraga cymbalaria** L., Celandine Saxifrage. *West: 43, weed in greenhouse, Penlee Park, 1977, B.M.S.; on china-clay dump near Nancledra, B.M.S. *East: 84, weed in Trehane Gardens, 1977, B.E.M.G.

239/9 **S. granulata** L., Meadow Saxifrage. Not native in Cornwall. *West: 73, weed in Penjerrick Gardens, near Falmouth, 1980, CNT (flore pleno). *East: 97, Trevine, St Endellion, B.E.M.G.; 05, Charlestown, W.T. (B.E.C. 1936).

240/1 **Tellima grandiflora** (Pursh) Douglas ex Lindley, Fringe-cups. East: 27, hedgebank at Rillaton, N.J.F.; 37, one clump by roadside near Kit Hill, Callington, I.N.

GROSSULARIACEAE

246/4 **Ribes sanguineum** Pursh, Flowering Currant. *West: 63, Carwynnen, near Camborne, 1963, L.J.M. *East: 07, Allen Valley, 1971, C.H.W.; 15, waste ground at Fowey, N.J.F.

PITTOSPORACEAE

116/1 **Pittosporum crassifolium** Putterl., Karo. *West: 53 (54), one bush, The Island, St Ives, 1972, S.M.T. *et al.*, Scilly: Lousley 1971.

ROSACEAE

Spiraea x billiardii Herincq. *East: 26, South Caradon, BSBI, det. A.Si.

211/10 **Rubus loganobaccus** L.H. Bailey. *West: 74, Wheal Rose, Scorrier, 1980, L.J.M.

211/11 **R. iricus** Rogers West: 75, Chyverton (Flora), two /105 sheets in Herb. Davey (TRU), collected by W.T., have been confirmed as correct by E.S. Edees. We have included it in this section as it may have been intro- duced. There are no recent records.

225/3 **Rosa multiflora** Thunb., Bramble-flowered Rose. *West: 72, Porthallow, 1979, J.H.; Treleague, St Keverne, J.H. Scilly: Lousley 1971.

225/2 **R. sempervirens** L. Garden cultivars, partly descended from this species, occur in hedges and on waste ground, but more work is required before more exact names can be given to them.

(225/ **R. arvensis x stylosa** = *R. x bibracteoides* W.-Dod. 1 x 7 Listed for both vice-counties in Stace, 1975.

212/8 **Potentilla norvegica** L., Ternate-leaved Cinquefoil. East: 05, Par (Flora), still there, 1923, L.T.M. (Thurston and Vigurs 1925).

212/9 **P. intermedia** L., Russian Cinquefoil. *East: 05, Tre- gorrick, St Austell, W.T. (Thurston 1929a).

226/3 **Prunus cerasifera** Ehrh., Cherry Plum. *West: 75, Perrancombe, Perranporth, 1975, C.J. *East: 37, in a thicket in a garden, Linkinhorne, N.J.F.; 45, at two places in Saltash, E.G.

226/6 **P. padus** L., Bird Cherry. East: 84, near Ruan Lanihorne, J.F.A.; 19, Marshgate, R.W.D. and L.J.M.

226/8 **P. lusitanica** L., Portugal Laurel. *West: 86, Carnanton Wood, Mawgan, CNT.

LEGUMINOSAE

(187/ **Ulex europaeus x gallii.** Listed in Stace, 1975. 1 x 2

186/1 **Spartium junceum** L., Spanish Broom. East: 05, Par Harbour (Suppt), still there, 1961, B.Sh.

Lupinus polyphyllus Lindley, Lupin. *East: 35, Seaton, 1967, S.M.

198/1 **Robinia pseudacacia** L., Acacia. *East: 16, one tree near Bodmin Road Station, 1977, E.G.

200/4 **Astragalus boeticus** L. *East: 05, Par Harbour, L.T.M. (Thurston and Vigurs 1927a).

206/5 **Vicia tenuifolia** Roth, Fine-leaved Vetch (Suppt). There are no subsequent records.

206/6 **V. villosa** Roth, Fodder Vetch. West: 42 or 43, Penzance (Flora), 1952, S.B.

206/3 **V. tenuissima** (Bieb.) Schinz and Thell. (*V. gracilis* Lois.), Slender Tare. East: 15, Bodinnick Hill, near Fowey, H.H.M. (Thurston 1930), Tredudwell, near Bodinnick, F.H.P. (B.E.C. 1926), but his specimen, in Herb. Perrycoste, (TRU), is *V. tetrasperma*.

V. pannonica Crantz. *West: 42 or 43, council tip, Penzance, 1952, S.B.

206/16 **V. lathyroides** L., Spring Vetch. Rejected by Davey (Flora), but since found in Scilly: T, Apple-tree Banks, 1971, J.E.R., Lousley 1971. It may, however, be a chance introduction.

Lathyrus inconspicuus L. *West: 72, garden, Helford Passage, L.J.M.; 83, Penpol House, Devoran, L.J.M., 1973. Tan-bark aliens here.

L. cicera L. *West: in field, Carnon Downs, 1958, R.H. The record could have been in any of the squares 73, 74, 83, or 84. Tan-bark alien.

L. annuus L. *West: 43, one plant in garden, Penzance, B.M.S.; 64, one plant on edge of garden, Tolvaddon, 1977, R.Sm. *Scilly: in garden at Macfarlanes Down, 1972, L.A.H.

207/3 **L. hirsutus** L., Hairy Vetchling. *West: 42 or 43, Council tip, Penzance, S.B.

Trigonella procumbens (Besser) Reichenb. East: 84, between Truro and Malpas, E.S.T. (B.E.C. 1923).

190/4 **Medicago minima** (L.) Bartal., Bur Medick. Rejected by Davey, but included in the Suppt as an introduction. *West: 83, as tan-bark alien at Penpol House, Devoran, 1973, L.J.M.

Trifolium retusum L. West: 73, Council tip, Falmouth, L.J.M.

192/20 **T. resupinatum** L., Reversed Clover. West: tan-bark alien, in field, Carnon Downs, 1958, R.H., in one of the squares 73, 74, 83, or 84. East: 05, Par, 1924, Herb. Perrycoste, (TRU).

T. tomentosum L., Wool Clover. *West: 72, tan-bark alien in garden, Helford Passage, 1973, L.J.M.

T. speciosum Will. *West: 83, tan-bark alien, Penpol House, Devoran, 1973, L.J.M.

192/22 **T. aureum** Poll (*T. agrarium* auct.), Large Hop Trefoil (Flora). There are no subsequent records.

T. affine C. Presl. *West: 83, tan-bark alien, Penpol House, Devoran, 1973, L.J.M.

T. angustifolium L., Narrow Clover. Tan-bark alien at *West: 72, garden, Helford Passage, L.J.M.; 83, Penpol House, Devoran. 1973, L.J.M. *East: 94, Manor Tannery, Grampound, 1973, L.J.M.

T. constantinopolitanum Ser. *West: 83, Falmouth (B.E.C. 1924).

Securigera securidaca (L.) Degen and Dorfler. *West: tan-bark alien, in field, Carnon Downs, 1958, R.H. (Either 73, 74, 83, or 84).

(193/ **Anthyllis vulneraria** L., subsp. **maritima** (Schweigger)
1+ Corb. West: 53, (54), St Ives, E.D. (Thurston 1929a). This is an unlikely subspecies for Britain).

Ornithopus sativus Brot., subsp. **sativus** *East: 05, Carbis Moor, N of St Austell, 1978, B.E.M.G. and L.J.M. Sown on china-clay waste, and possibly elsewhere in the area.

Coronilla scorpioides (L.) Koch. Found as both a birdseed alien and as a tan-bark introduction. *West: 83, Penpol House, Devoran, 1973, L.J.M. *East: 94, one plant, Demonstration Garden, Probus, N.D.W.; 05, Par Harbour, L.T.M. (Thurston and Vigurs 1927).

Scorpiurus muricatus L., another bird-seed alien. *West: 72, garden, Porth Navas, 1975, B.M.K. *East: 83, garden, Philleigh, 1973, B.E.M.G.

OXALIDACEAE

Oxalis rosea Jacq. *West: 86, waste ground near Newquay, G.C.D. (B.E.C. 1931, p. 554).

O. semiloba Sond. *East: 97, Polzeath, J.D.G. (B.E.C. 1933, p. 468).

170/7 **O. corymbosa** DC., Small Pink Oxalis. *West: 83, weed in Trelissick Gardens, B.E.M.G. *East: 04, Gorranhaven, 1966, L.J.M.

LIMNANTHACEAE

Limnanthes douglasii R.Br. *West: 74, Council tip, Bissoe, 1976, L.J.M.

GERANIACEAE

Geranium x magnificum Hyl. *West: 33, roadside near Bojewyan, Morvah, 1972, L.J.M.; 63, near Four Lanes, R.M. *East: 25, Polvellan, Looe, 1978, L.J.M.; 36, N of Trematon, and near Hatt, D.B.

TROPAEOLACEAE

Tropaeolum majus L., Nasturtium. West: 63, waste-heap, Porkellis Moor, L.J.M. East: 08, Rocky Valley, B.G. A frequent garden escape on rubbish tips.

EUPHORBIACEAE

319/7 **Euphorbia platyphyllos** L., Broad-leaved Spurge. *West: 84, one plant in nursery, Truro, 1975, B.E.M.G. East: 45, between Trevol and St John, Herb. Marl. Coll., comm. E.W.M. (Thurston 1928).

319/15 **E. esula** L., Leafy Spurge. West: 84, deserted garden, Truro, W.Bo. (Thurston 1935).

319/16 **E. cyparissias** L., Cypress Spurge. *West: 74, waste ground, Bissoe, post—1950, L.J.M. *East: 21, Coombe Valley, 1925, W.Wi., Herb. W. Wise (LAUS).

ANACARDIACEAE

Rhus typhina L., Stag's-horn Sumach. *East: 05, Carlyon Bay, 1980, L.J.M.

ACERACEAE

173/2 **Acer platanoides** L., Norway Maple. *West: 64, several large trees in Nance Wood, 1976, L.J.M.

BALSAMINACEAE

171/3 **Impatiens parviflora** DC., Small Balsam (Flora). Not refound in Davey's locality (Ponsanooth).

CELASTRACEAE

Euonymus japonicus L. fil. *West: 32, Sennen Cove, 1980, L.J.M. *East: 15, cliff-face between Fowey and Readymoney Beach, 1980, L.J.M. Scilly: frequent, Lousley 1971.

VITACEAE

181/1 **Vitis vinifera** L., Grape Vine, appears rarely from thrown-out pips. *West: 64, mine-waste, Gilbert's Coombe, near Redruth, L.J.M.; 74, near Chacewater Station, 1965, L.J.M. *East: 05, mine-waste E of St Blazey, 1970, J.A.P.

TILIACEAE

162/1 **Tilia platyphyllos** Scop., Large-leaved Lime. West: 73, near Penmere, Falmouth (Flora), still there, post—1950, L.J.M. *East: 94, wood near Porthluney Beach, 1965, L.J.M.

162/2 **T. cordata** Miller, Small-leaved Lime (Flora). If correct, only as a planted tree. Not refound.

MALVACEAE

Malope malacoides L. West: 53, near the explosives factory, Phillack, R.O. (Thurston and Vigurs 1925).

M. trifida Cav. *West: 64, two plants in garden, Kieve Mills, near Camborne, 1977, comm. S.M.T.

163/3 **Malva nicaeensis** All. Mainly as a tan-bark alien. *West: 83, Penpol House, Devoran, 1973, L.J.M. *East: 84, near Boscawen Park, Truro, W.Bo. (Thurston and Vigurs 1926); 94, Demonstration Garden, Probus, L.J.M.;

360

Manor Tannery, Grampound, L.J.M.; 15, Fowey (B.E.C. 1926).

163/6 **M. parviflora** L., Least Mallow. *West: 53, Phillack, E.S.T. (Thurston 1935). *East: 05, Par Harbour, 1924, L.T.M. (Thurston and Vigurs 1926); 15, Fowey (B.E.C. 1925); 38, Launceston, T.N.S.P. (B.E.C. 1928).

Lavatera olbia L. *West: 74, roadside, Bissoe, L.J.M.; 84, old tip, Newham, Truro, 1976, L.J.M.

L. punctata All. *East: 84, between Truro and Malpas (B.E.C. 1922).

L. trimestris L. *West: 73, Council tip, Falmouth, L.J.M.; 61 or 71, garden, The Lizard, comm. B.E.M.G. (*B.S.B.I. News*, 23).

165/2 **Althaea hirsuta** L., Rough Marsh-mallow (Flora). There have been no recent records.

Hibiscus trionum L. West: 73, Council tip, Falmouth, L.J.M.

GUTTIFERAE

115/2 **Hypericum inodorum** Miller (*H. elatum* Aiton), Tall Tutsan. West: 62, near Breage Church, H.B.S.; 84, two bushes by leat, Truro, L.J.M.

VIOLACEAE

113/2a **Viola hirta** L. subsp. **hirta x odorata** = *V. x permixta* x 1 Jordan (Flora and Suppt). There have been no subsequent records.

113/9b **V. palustris** L. subsp. **juressi** (Neves) P. Fourn. x subsp. x 9a **palustris**. East: 28, Egloskerry Marsh, 1923, T.N.S.P., det. E.S. Gregory (Thurston and Vigurs 1924); 36, below Newbridge, Callington, 1923, H.H.H. (Thurston and Vigurs 1924).

It is probable that these records referred to the glabrous form of subsp. *juressi*. There is no definite evidence that subsp. *palustris* occurs in Cornwall.

113/10 **V. cornuta** L. *West: 43, naturalised at Georgia, near Nancledra, B.M.S.

FRANKENIACEAE

(121/1 **Frankenia laevis** L., Sea Heath. *East: 93, Pendower Beach, post—1950, comm. BRC. This record should be accepted only with caution, in the absence of confirmatory material).

CUCURBITACEAE

315/1 **Bryonia cretica** L., subsp. **dioica** (Jacq.) Tutin, White Bryony, only as an introduction, has been recorded, without locality, for East: 94, 36, and 47.

Cucurbita pepo L., Marrow. *West: 74, Council tip, Bissoe, 1975, L.J.M.

Sicyos angulatus L., Chocho Vine. *West: 63, Coswinsawsen Farm, Baripper, Camborne, 1968, L.J.M.

LYTHRACEAE

Lythrum junceum Banks and Solander (*L. graefferri* Ten.). West: 74, Council tip, Bissoe, B.E.M.G. *East: 05, waste tip, Par Sands, B.E.M.G.

L. hyssopifolia L., Grass Poly (Flora, extinct). The inclusion of this plant appears to be based on a single finding. It has not been refound.

ONAGRACEAE

Oenothera cambrica Rost, Small-flowered Evening-primrose. *West: 42 or 43, Penzance. *East: 97, Rock, 1940. Both records from D.Mc. (*Watsonia*, **12** (1978): 164—5). The record of *O. ammophila* Focke, from West: 53, Phillack Towans, 1970, B.M.S., probably belongs here.

O. laciniata Hill. *East: 05, Par Harbour, L.T.M. (B.E.C. 1927).

O. rosea L'Hér. ex Aiton. *East: 45, Wearde Quay, 1975, A.C.L. (*B.S.B.I. News*, 18).

(254/3 **Epilobium montanum x roseum** = *E. x mutabile* Boiss. x 5 & Reut. Listed for v.c.1. in Stace 1975.

E. komarovianum Lévéille. *West: 74, near Coombe, Gwennap, 1976, B.B.

HALORAGACEAE

Myriophyllum brasiliense Camb. A tender aquarists' throw-out, sometimes surviving for a few years. *West: 42, outlet of Lariggan Stream, Penzance, 1972, L.J.M.; 71, Croft Pascoe Pool, E.Ch.

HIPPURIDACEAE

(261/1 **Hippurus vulgaris** L., Mare's-tail. The two records in the Flora do not bear the stamp of authenticity, and, in the absence of herbarium material, we think it better to remove this species provisionally from the Cornish list.)

CORNACEAE

Cornus sericea L. (Suppt as *C. stolonifera* Michx). No recent records.

UMBELLIFERAE

274/3 **Anthriscus cerefolium** (L.) Hoffm., Garden Chervil (Suppt). Not found since outside gardens.

279/1 **Coriandrum sativum** L., Coriander. West: 53, old tip, St Erth, 1962, L.J.M.; 62, tip, Helston, R.O. (Thurston 1928); 63, Council tip, Treskillard, Redruth, L.J.M.; 73, Penryn, W.T. (Thurston 1935); Council tip, Falmouth, L.J.M.

Anethum graveolens L., Dill. *West: 53, Council tip, Newlyn East, 1969, L.J.M.

289/1 **Ammi majus** L., Bullwort. *West: 63, old tip, Treskillard, Redruth, 1969, L.J.M. East: 45, one plant in nursery, Saltash, E.G.

307/2 **Angelica archangelica** L. (*Archangelica officinalis* (Hoffm.), Garden Angelica (Flora). There are no subsequent records.

277/2 **Torilis arvensis** (Hudson) Link (*Caucalis arvensis* Huds.), Spreading Hedge-parsley (Flora and Suppt, two doubtful records). *West: 74, recorded for this square, without locality, post—1950, comm. BRC.

278/2 **Turgenia latifolia** (L.) Hoffm, (*Caucalis latifolia* L.), Greater Bur-parsley (Flora and Suppt). No subsequent records.

ERICACEAE

349/1 **Daboecia cantabrica** (Hudson) C. Koch, St Dabeoc's Heath. *East: 16, a large patch in valley near W Taphouse, J.L.F. (Thurston and Vigurs 1927).

353/1 **Arbutus unedo** L., Strawberry-tree. Garden escape. *West: one bush, between Perranzabuloe Church and Callestick, 1974, E.S.E. and L.J.M. *East: 35, one bush, Freathy valley below farm, 1971, S.M.

352/1 **Pernettya mucronata** (L. fil.) Gaud-Beaupré ex Sprengel, Prickly Heath, *West: 62, plentiful along railway track, Truthall Halt, near Helston, 1966, L.J.M. *East: 05, St Austell, B.Sh.

PRIMULACEAE

Primula japonica L. *West: 63, by rivulet, Clowance Wood, 1966, L.J.M.; 73, Enys Woods, L.J.M.

368/1 **Hottonia palustris** L., Water-violet. *West: in pool, Enys Woods, originally planted, L.J.M.

Cyclamen repandum Sibth, and Sm. *West: 64, several plants in Tehidy Woods, Camborne, 1978, L.J.H.

RUBIACEAE

Crucianella angustifolia L. *West: 84, garden path, Truro, 1976, B.E.M.G.

(483/2 **Asperula cynanchica** L., Squinancywort, was rejected by Davey (Flora), and, although there has been a subsequent record from West: 72, Mudgeon, near St Keverne, R.B.G., this is also most unlikely, and is best disregarded).

A. arvensis L. West: 61, one plant, Mullion (Thurston 1935); 62, Council tip, Helston, R.W.D.

(485/9 **Galium debile** Desv. Slender Marsh-bedstraw, is mentioned in Martin and Fraser (1939), as occurring in W Cornwall. There are no further details, but the reference may be to a distinct form of *G. palustre* with pinkish flowers and narrow leaves. This taxon was found recently in West: 53, St Erth, 1980, R.Ge., and seems to differ from true *G. debile* only in its spreading fruit).

485/13 G. spurium L. (*G. vaillantii* DC.), False Cleavers, was rejected by Davey (Flora), but the two specimens from West: 32, Sennen, in Herb. Marl. Coll., comm. E.W.M., were thought by Druce to be correct.

Coprosma repens A. Rich. Scilly: Lousley 1971, A, abundant on a carn near St Warna's Well, 1972.

POLEMONIACEAE

388/1 Polemonium caeruleum L., Jacob's-ladder. Introduced, in Cornwall. West: 64, mine waste, Penhallick, near Redruth, L.J.M.; 83, well-established at Loe Beach, Feock, B.E.M.G.

CONVOLVULACEAE

Cuscuta suaveolens Ser. (Suppt). A rare introduction, not found subsequently.

BORAGINACEAE

Echium sp., Tree Echium. Several species occur as escapes on Scilly: Lousley 1971.

399/2 Pulmonaria officinalis L., Lungwort. A garden throw-out at West: 33, wild garden, Pendeen, D.D.

392/2 Symphytum asperum Lepechin (*S. asperrimum* Donn.), Rough Comfrey (Flora). There are no recent records.

392/4 S. caucasicum Bieb., Caucasian Comfrey (Suppt). No recent records.

394/1 Trachystemon orientalis (L.) G. Don fil., Abraham-Isaac-Jacob. *West: 43, near Trevarrick, Gulval, 1970, B.M.S. *East: 84, amongst ruins at Trehane, near Truro, 1977, B.E.M.G.

Amsinckia lycopsoides (Lehm.) Lehm., and A. calycina (Moris) Chater (*A. angustifolia* Lehm.) were recorded as casuals in the Flora, but have not reappeared.

A. intermedia Fischer & C.A. Meyer, Fiddleneck. West: 61, Parc Venton, Mullion, W.B. (Thurston 1935).

A. menziesii (Lehm.) A. Nelson & MacBride. *East: 04, Gorranhaven, E.T. and L.T.M. (B.E.C. 1924).

391/1 Asperugo procumbens L., Madwort. *East: 05, Par Harbour, L.T.M. (Thurston and Vigurs 1927).

Myosotis sp., Forget-me-not. Garden forms, mainly hybrids of complex origin, are frequent and widespread throughout the county. Records for *M. sylvatica* Hoffm. belong here.

Lappula squarrosa (Retz) Dumort., subsp. **squarrosa** (*Echinospermum lappula* Lehm.), Bur Forget-me-not. West: 61, Parc Venton, Mullion (B.E.C. 1930); 74, garden weed, Threemilestone, near Truro, V.S., comm. S.M.T. East: 26, Liskeard Station, C.P.F. (Thurston and Vigurs 1927).

CALLITRICHACEAE

(262/5 **Callitriche hermaphroditica** L. (*C. autumnalis* L.), Autumnal Water-starwort, was thought by Davey (Flora) to be most unlikely for Cornwall; we share this doubt, and accordingly reject this plant.)

(**C. palustris** L. (Flora and Suppt). As this species was not seen by Davey, and as there are no specimens to support the records, we prefer to remove this plant, which is only doubtfully British, from the Cornish list. No doubt many of the records refer to *C. platycarpa*).

LABIATAE

464/1 **Phlomis fruticosa** L., Jerusalem Sage. *West: 73, one large bush, Maen Valley, near Falmouth, L.J.M.

(459/4 **Stachys germanica** L., Downy Woundwort (Flora). Davey thought the plants recorded as such could have been garden outcasts, but it is much more likely that a different species was involved.)

S. byzantina C. Koch = *S. lanata* Jacq. *East: 25, escape at Hannafore, Looe, 1970, J.L.

Thymus vulgaris L., Garden Thyme *East: 20, steep road-bank, Stratton, L.J.M.

(445/4 **Mentha aquatica** L. x **longifolia** (L.) Hudson = *M. x*
x 6 *dumetorum* Schultes. Plants referred to this taxon are doubtfully the true hybrid, but probably hairy forms of *M. x piperita*).

Salvia reflexa Hornem. *West: 73, Council tip, Falmouth, 1973, L.J.M. *East: 20, Council tip, Bude, 1973, L.J.M.

S. aethiopis L. *West: 75, St Agnes, K.M.S. (Thurston 1935).

SOLANACEAE

Physalis fendleri Gray *West: 53, Upton Towans, F.Ha. (Thurston and Vigurs 1924).

413/4 **Solanum sarrachoides** Sendtner. *West: 74, Council tip, Bissoe, B.E.M.G. Scilly: Lousley 1971.

413/5 **S. triflorum** Nutt. *East: 05, Par (B.E.C. 1929).

S. tuberosum L., Potato, is frequent and widespread on rubbish heaps and waste ground near farms and gardens.

S. laciniatum Aiton (Suppt as *S. aviculare* auct.), Kangaroo Apple, is an increasing casual in W Cornwall. *West: 53 (54), greenhouse weed, St Ives, comm. J.B.B.; 73, Council tip, Falmouth, L.J.M.; 75, weed in Model Village, St Agnes, 1976, L.J.M. *East: 83, waste ground, St Mawes, L.J.M. Scilly: Lousley 1971.

S. cornutum Lam. (*S. rostratum* Dunal). East: 46, near Harrowbarrow, S.R.

Lycopersicum esculentum Miller, Tomato, is frequent and widespread as a casual on council tips and waste ground. Not recorded for Scilly.

Nicotiana rustica L., was recorded as a casual in the Flora, but there are no recent records.

N. alata Link & Otto, Sweet-scented Tobacco. *West: 73, Council tip, Falmouth, 1970, L.J.M.

BUDDLEJACEAE

Buddleja x weyeriana Weyer. *East: one bush in scrub, Tolverne, King Harry, B.E.M.G.

SCROPHULARIACEAE

Verbascum creticum (L.) Cav. (*Celsia cretica* L.) West: 73 or 74, waste-heap, Redruth, R.L.S. and W.D.W. (Thurston and Vigurs 1925).

V. sinuatum L. *West: 53, Hayle, 1929 (B.E.C. 1929).

416/4 **V. lychnitis** L., White Mullein. West: 53, Hayle (B.E.C. 1931). Scilly: Lousley 1971.

416/4 **V. lychnitis x nigrum** = *V. x schiedeanum* Koch. Listed
x 7 for v.c.2 in Stace 1975.

416/5 **V. pulverulentum** Vill. Hoary Mullein, 416/7 x 5 **V. nigrum x pulverulentum** = *V. x wirtgenii* Franch., and **V. phoeniceum** L. were all recorded as casuals in the Suppt, but there have been no further records.

418/1 **Antirrhinum majus** L., Snapdragon. West: 53, Halamanning, St Hilary, 1975—7, K.P.; 64, waste ground, Tuckingmill, Camborne, L.J.M. East: 35, roadside hedges between Antony and Wacker, S.M.; 45, hedges between Torpoint and Antony, S.M. Also regularly found on council tips.

Calceolaria chelidonioides H.B. and K. *East: 16, in a mowhay, Lostwithiel (Thurston 1935).

Misopates calycinum Rothm. *East: 83, weed in garden, Philleigh, 1979, B.E.M.G.

Veronica spuria L. Garden escape. *East: 94, Hemmick Beach, 1961, B.Sh.

Hebe spp. Various garden cultivars seed themselves from time to time on cliffs and waste ground, and particularly on walls, but rarely persist.

439/2 **Lathraea clandestina** L., Purple Toothwort. *East: 47, near Gunnislake Bridge, 1980, J.Fo.

OROBANCHACEAE

440/7 **Orobanche reticulata** Wallr., Thistle Broomrape. Casual, in Suppt. Not found since.

PLANTAGINACEAE

Plantago lagopus L. Scilly: Lousley 1971.

472/6 **P. arenaria** Waldst. & Kit. East: 05, Par (Flora), Par Harbour, L.T.M. (B.E.C. 1924); 25, on low wall near E Looe River, near Sandplace, F.R. (Thurston 1935).

CAPRIFOLIACEAE

491/1 **Lonicera xylosteum** L., Fly Honeysuckle. *East: 05, one plant, edge of field, Charlestown, 1923, W.T. (Thurston and Vigurs 1924).

491/4 **L. caprifolium** L., Perfoliate Honeysuckle. Scilly: Lousley 1971.

VALERIANACEAE

495/2 **Valeriana pyrenaica** L., Pyrenean Valerian. *East: 94, recorded for this square, 1951, P.T.B.

(495/3 **V. dioica** L., Marsh Valerian (Flora). This has not been refound in the county, and in the absence of a voucher specimen, we prefer to exclude it at present).

DIPSACACEAE

Cephalaria gigantea (Ledeb.) Bobrov. = *C. tartarica* auct. *West: 53, one plant by railway, Angarrack, Hayle, 1970, B.E.M.G.

CAMPANULACEAE

475/5 **Campanula persicifolia** L., Peach-leaved Bellflower. *East: 25, hedge near Sclerder, Polperro, now gone, H.H.P. (Thurston and Vigurs 1927).

475/11 **C. medium** L., Canterbury-bells. *West: 73, railway bank between Falmouth and Perranwell, L.J.M. *East: 05, Par Harbour, 1961, B.Sh.

C. portenschlagiana Schultes, Adria Bellflower. *West: 42, walls, Penzance, 1979, L.J.M.

C. poscharskyana Degen, Trailing Bellflower, *West: 42, wall, Penzance, 1979, L.J.M. *East: 36, Cadsonbury, 1980, BSBI.

478/2 **Phyteuma spicatum** L., Spiked Rampion. Purely a casual in shrubbery at *West: 72, one plant, Lanarth, St Keverne, (Thurston and Vigurs 1927).

COMPOSITAE

Erigeron philadelphicus L., Robin's Plantain. *West: 42, Penzance, 1978, B.M.S.

Chrysocoma coma-aurea L. *Scilly: MN, Porth Seal, 1972, J.E.Lo.; T, Pentle Bay, 1974, R.D.E.

515/6 **Gnaphalium undulatum** L. *East: 05, Par Harbour, L.T.M. (B.E.C. 1927).

Guizotia abyssinica (L. fil.) Cass., Niger. *West: 73, Council tip, Falmouth, L.J.M.; 74, Council tip, Bissoe, 1970, B.E.M.G. *East: 84, garden weed, Nansgwithick, Tresillian, C.N. (Thurston 1930).

504/1 **Ambrosia artemisiifolia** L., Ragweed. West: 74, Council tip, Bissoe, L.J.M.

A. trifida L. East: 20, waste ground, Bude, E.T. (Thurston and Vigurs 1926).

Xanthium orientale L. East: 05, Par (Suppt), 1925, L.T.M. (Thurston and Vigurs 1926).

Cladanthus arabicus (L.) Cass. *East: 05, Par Harbour, L.T.M. (B.E.C. 1927).

Anacyclus clavatus (Desf.) Pers. *East: 05, Par Harbour, L.T.M. (B.E.C. 1927).

534/1 **Cotula coronopifolia** L. *West: 86, garden weed, Newquay, 1977, C.W.

535/3 **Artemisia biennis** Willd., Lesser Mugwort. East: 05, garden weed, Charlestown, W.T. (Thurston 1929a).

A. dracunculus L., Tarragon. *East: 05, Par, Herb. Perrycoste, (TRU).

A. scoparia Waldst. & Kit. West: 85, Council tip, Newlyn East, 1970, L.J.M.

511/1 **Calendula officinalis** L., Marigold. West: 64, waste ground, Tuckingmill, Camborne, L.J.M. East: 35, Downderry, N.J.F. Scilly: Lousley 1971. In addition, this is a common plant of rubbish tips throughout the county.

511/2 **C. arvensis** L., Field Marigold. Scilly: Lousley 1971; M, abundant in two fields, Rocky Hill Farm, 1972, C.H.

Brachyglottis repanda J.R. & G. Forst. Scilly: Lousley 1971.

Gazania rigens (L.) Gaertner, Treasure-flower. *West: 32, Sennen cliffs, E.B.W. (B.E.C. 1925, p. 997). *East:

83, walls of St Mawes Castle, 1968, L.J.M. Scilly: Lousley 1971.

539/2 **Carduus pycnocephalus** L., Plymouth Thistle. *West: 83, Falmouth, 1927, K, (Thurston 1936).

Centaurea diluta Aiton, Lesser Star-thistle. *West: 63, old tip, Treskillard, Redruth, L.J.M.; 73, Council tip, Falmouth, L.J.M.; 74, Council tip, Bissoe, 1968, J.G.D.; 85, Council tip, Newlyn East, L.J.M. *East: 83, roadside, Philleigh, 1969, B.E.M.G.

Carthamus tinctorius L., Safflower. *West: 97, Dennis, Padstow, G.C.D. (B.E.C. 1927). East: 05, Charlestown (B.E.C. 1930).

Cicerbita plumieri (L.) Kirschleger, Blue Sow-thistle. *East: 45, Saltash, *c* 1975, E.G.

559/7 **Crepis nicaeensis** Balbis. Once found in Cornwall (Flora), but not since.

ALISMATACEAE

565/1 **Sagittaria sagittifolia** L., Arrowhead, was added to the Cornish List in 1918 on the discovery of a single plant growing in a most atypical situation, East: 15, Lansallos, F.R. (Suppt). This was surely a purely casual occurrence, and the plant has not been refound.

565/3 **S. rigida** Pursh, Canadian Arrowhead. *West: 63, Clowance Lake, near Camborne, 1965, H.B.S., originally planted there.

(563/2 **Alisma lanceolatum** With., Narrow-leaved Water-plantain (Flora and Suppt). We have not been able to trace a voucher specimen in any of the herbaria we have searched, and we feel a narrow-leaved form of *A. plantago-aquatica* is the basis of all the Cornish records).

(564/1 **Damasonium alisma** Miller, Starfruit, was rejected by Davey (Flora) as an obvious error. If it ever occurred on Gulval Marsh, it could only have been a garden throwout, but there is no real evidence to retain it, even as an introduction).

BUTOMACEAE

566/1 **Butomus umbellatus** L., Flowering Rush. We agree with Davey (Flora) in rejecting this species as a native plant, but it has been much planted in the past in the pools of the larger estates, and as such it has been recorded, post—1950, for *West: 42 and 83, and more recently for *East: 20, Bude, comm. R.D.

LILIACEAE

Asphodelus fistulosus L., Hollow-stemmed Asphodel. *East: 05, Par Harbour, L.T.M. (Thurston and Vigurs 1927); 15, Fowey (B.E.C. 1926).

586/1 **Hemerocallis fulva** (L.) L., Orange Day Lily. *East: 95, on edge of Goss Moor, L.J.M.

Phormium colensoi Hooker fil., Lesser New Zealand Flax. Scilly: Lousley 1971.

(594/1 **Fritillaria meleagris** L., Fritillary, was another of Pascoe's records that was rejected by Davey (Flora). If correct, it could only have been a garden throw-out, but it is best to disregard the record).

Scilla peruviana L., Peruvian Squill. *West: 53, Phillack Towans, B.M.S.; 87, one mile S of St Merryn, W.W. (Thurston 1935).

610/1 **Agapanthus praecox** Willd., subsp. **orientalis** (F.M. Leighton) F.M. Leighton, African Lily. Scilly: well-established, Lousley 1971; MN, old dunes, Great Bay, 1975, F.W.S.

Allium neapolitanum Cyr., White Garlic. West: 42 or 43, near Penzance, F.N.S. (B.E.C. 1922). Scilly: Lousley 1971.

A. subhirsutum L. *East: 20, steep road-bank, Stratton, L.J.M.

607/11 **A. paradoxum** (Bieb.) G. Don, Few-flowered Leek. *East: 84, weed in Trehane Gardens 1977, B.E.M.G.

(607/6 **A. oleraceum** L., Field Garlic. *West: 63, in shrubbery and hedge, Praze-an-Beeble, W.T. (Thurston 1935). This record should be accepted only with caution, in view of the possibility of confusion with some of the introduced species).

607/7 **A. carinatum** L., Keeled Garlic. *West: 42, Love Lane, Penzance, 1963, G.B.M.; 64, roadside near Old Merrose Farm, near Camborne, 1976, R.Sm.

608/1 **Nothoscordum inodorum** (Aiton) Nicholson. Scilly: Lousley 1971.

609/1 **Ipheion uniflorum** (R.G. Graham) Rafin., Spring Starflower. *West: 53, between Long Rock and Marazion, 1971, E.G. and S.M., comm. B.M.S. Scilly: Lousley 1971.

(603/1 **Paris quadrifolia** L., Herb-Paris. *West: 72, Merthen Wood, 'many years ago', comm. 1963, R.B.G. If correct, this would undoubtedly be a casual occurrence).

Kniphofia praecox Baker, Red-hot Poker. *West: 53, banks by Marazion Station, L.J.M.; 63, old mine-waste, Troon, 1963, L.J.M. *East: 97, around New Polzeath, R.W.D.; 08 (09), Boscastle Harbour, L.J.M.

AGAVACEAE

Cordyline australis Hooker fil., Dracaena Palm. *West: 64, several seedlings near Redruth Station, 1965, L.J.M.; 83, 19 seedlings near Falmouth Station, L.J.M. Scilly: Lousley 1971. This well-known 'Palm' of the SW often produces seedlings in gardens.

AMARYLLIDACEAE

Amaryllis bella-donna L., Belladonna Lily. *Scilly: M, in grass by the shore, 1974, R.D.E.; T, NE of Great Pool, 1974, R.D.E.

IRIDACEAE

Libertia chilensis (Molina) Gunck. *West: two clumps near the sea, 'the Towans', 1966, M.M.W., E (*B.S.B.I. News:* 19). Probably square 53.

615/1 **Sisyrinchium bermudiana** L. (Suppt as *S. angustifolium* Mill.), Blue-eyed-grass. *West: 72, Carwinnion valley, near Mawnan, 1965, R.B.G. East: 20, near Bude (Suppt), one plant W of Bude, 1932, R.R.B. (Thurston 1935).

615/2 **S. californicum** (Ker-Gawler) Aiton fil., Yellow-eyed-grass. Scilly: Lousley 1971; T, W of Abbey Pool, 1967, J.A.P.

S. striatum Smith. Scilly: Lousley 1971.

618/2 **Crocus vernus** (L.) Hill, subsp. **vernus**, Spring Crocus. *West: 74, old tip, Bissoe, L.J.M. East: 20, Summerleaze, Bude, R.O. (Thurston and Vigurs 1925).

JUNCACEAE

(605/ **Juncus subnodulosus** Schrank, Blunt-flowered Rush, 17 was recorded from four stations in W Cornwall (Flora), but not subsequently. In the absence of specimens, we can only cast some doubt on these records).

606/4 **Luzula luzuloides** (Lam.) Dandy & Wilmott (Suppt as *L. albida* DC.), White Wood-rush. East: 05, yard of Wesleyan Chapel, St Blazey Gate, 1923, L.T.M. (B.E.C. 1924), var. **rubella** (Hoppe).

BROMELIACEAE

Fascicularia pitcairniifolia (Verlot) Mez. *West: 32, one large mass by slipway, Porthgwarra, L.J.M.; 62, cliff-slope N of Gunwalloe, L.J.M. Scilly: Lousley 1971.

GRAMINEAE

Sasa palmata (Burbidge) E.G. Camus, Broad-leaved Bamboo. *West: 72, naturalised and in flower, Gweek valley, 1966, L.J.M.

Arundinaria anceps Mitf. *East: 15, waste ground, Fowey, 1980, L.J.M.

(670/9 **Festuca tenuifolia** Sibth., Fine-leaved Sheep's-fescue. We have no definite records, but it may be in the county, and needs searching for. Davey's *F. ovina* var. *capillata* Hackel may refer to this species, but there are no specimens in his herbarium).

670/2 **Festuca arundinacea** Schreb. x **Lolium perenne** L. = *x* x 671/ *Festulolium holmbergii* (Dorfler) P. Fourn. *East: 94, 1 probably this, Porthluney Beach, Caerhayes, 1963, L.J.M.

670/6a **Festuca rubra** L. x **Lolium perenne** L. = *x Festulolium* x 671/ *fredericii* Cugnac & A. Camus *West: 53 (54), 1 probably this, Upton Towans, 1969, L.J.M.

Vulpia ligustica (All.) Link *West: 72, Gweek Quay, 1926, R.O. (B.E.C. 1926).

V. muralis (Kunth) Nees. *Scilly: A, bulbfield weed, Lower Town, 1957, as *V. broteri* Boiss. & Reut., det. C.A. Stace, 1973.

676/15 **Poa chaixii** Vill., Broad-leaved Meadow-grass. West: 96, Trewan, near St Columb Major, E.T. and L.T.M. (Thurston and Vigurs 1927).

(**Puccinellia festuciformis** (Host) Parl. (Suppt as *Atropis festuciformis* Richt.). The 1918 record from Egloshayle Marsh, Wadebridge, should be accepted only with caution).

702/1 **Apera spica-venti** (L.) Beauv., Loose Silky-bent. East: 84, waste ground near Boscawen Park, Truro, E.B. (Thurston and Vigurs 1925). Scilly: rejected, Lousley 1971.

704/1 **Mibora minima** (L.) Desv., Early Sand-grass, was recorded once (Suppt) as a casual at East: 05, Par. It has not been seen since, but its very small size makes it easily overlooked.

683/8 **Bromus rigidus** Roth (*B. maximus* Desf.). *Scilly: B, top of wall, All Saints, 1973, P.J.T.; MN, in two places, 1973, P.J.T.

683/9 **B. tectorum** L., Drooping Brome. West: 62, wall-top, Rinsey Croft, 1978, R.G. *East: 05, Par, L.T.M. (Thurston and Vigurs 1925).

683/6 **B. madritensis** L., Compact Brome. Scilly: Lousley 1971; A, bulbfield weed near Troy Town Church, 1973, J.B. The record for Par (Flora and Suppt) is *B. tectorum* (Thurston and Vigurs 1924).

683/17 **B. arvensis** L., Field Brome (Flora). There are no later records.

B. japonicus Thunb. (*B. patulus* Mert. & Koch.). *East: 05, Par Harbour, 1923, L.T.M. (Thurston and Vigurs 1924).

B. squarrosus L. *East: 05, Par Harbour, L.T.M. (Thurston 1928).

B. ligusticus All. *West: 72, Gweek Quay, R.O. (Thurston and Vigurs 1926).

Brachypodium distachyum (L.) Beauv. *East: 05, Par Harbour, L.T.M. (Thurston and Vigurs 1926).

685/3
x 687/
1
Elymus repens (L.) Gould x **Hordeum secalinum** Schreb. = x *Agrohordeum langei* (K. Richter) Camus. *Scilly: B, on wall outside cottage, The Town, probably this, C.E. Hubbard.

Aegilops cylindrica Host (*Triticum cylindricum* (Host) C.P. & G. East: 05, Par (Flora), refound at Par Harbour, L.T.M. (Thurston 1927).

Secale cereale L., Rye. West: 62, waste-heap, Helston, W.T. (Thurston 1935).

Hordeum distichon L., Two-rowed Barley. West: 74, Council tip, Bissoe, L.J.M.; 86, waste ground, Newquay, 1922, E.T. (Thurston and Vigurs 1923).

687/3
H. marinum Hudson, Sea Barley. Not native in Cornwall. East: 05, Par Harbour, 1923, L.T.M. (Thurston and Vigurs 1924). Scilly: rejected, Lousley 1971.

687/4
H. hystrix Roth, Mediterranean Barley. *West: 63, old tip, Treskillard, Redruth, 1969, L.J.M.

H. jubatum L., Foxtail Barley. *West: 61, fowl-run, Mullion, E.J.P. (Thurston 1935). East: 84, near Boscawen Park, Truro (Suppt), still there 1934, W.Bo. (Thurston 1935); 05, Par Harbour, L.T.M. (Thurston and Vigurs 1927); fowl-run, Biscovey, L.T.M. (Thurston 1930).

Lophochola cristata (L.) Hyl. (*Koeleria phleoides* Pers.). Scilly: Lousley 1971.

Avena sativa L., Common Oat. West: 63, opposite Camborne School, 1977—8, R.J.M.; 64, Reskadinnick, Camborne, 1977—8, R.J.M. East: 05, Par Sands, L.T.M. (Thurston and Vigurs 1927).

A. sterilis L., Animated Oat. *East: 05, Par Harbour and Sands, L.T.M. (Thurston 1928).

690/1
Gaudinia fragilis (L.) Beauv., French Oat. East: 84, refuse heaps, Truro, W.Bo., K; 05, Charlestown, W.T. 1914.

706/1 **Lagurus ovatus** L., Hare's-tail. Scilly: Lousley 1971; M, post—1950, B.M.S. No recent record for the mainland.

712/2 **Anthoxanthum aristatum** Boiss. Annual Vernal-grass (Flora). There are no subsequent records.

Triplachne nitens (Guss.) Link. *East: 05, Par Harbour, L.T.M. (Thurston and Vigurs 1927).

713/4 **Phalaris paradoxa** L., Awned Canary-grass. West: 72, Gweek Quay, R.O. (Thurston and Vigurs 1926); 73, waste heap, Penryn, W.T. (Thurston 1930); 84, County Hall, Truro, W.Bo. (Thurston and Vigurs 1925). East: 05, Par (Suppt), Par Harbour and Sands, L.T.M. (Thurston and Vigurs 1925); between Polkerris and Par, W.T. (Thurston and Vigurs 1927).

P. angusta Nees. *East: 05, Par Harbour, L.T.M. (Thurston 1928).

710/1 **Piptatherum miliaceum** (L.) Cosson. West: 73, waste ground, Penryn, W.T. (Thurston 1935).

Panicum miliaceum L., Common Millet. West: 63, old tip at Treskillard and Piece, Carnkie, Redruth, L.J.M.; 64, Council tip, Tolvaddon, Camborne, L.J.M.; 73, Council tip, Falmouth, L.J.M.; 74, Council tip, Bissoe, L.J.M.; 85, Council tip, Newlyn East, L.J.M. East: 84, near Boscawen Park, Truro, 1922, W.Bo. (Thurston and Vigurs 1923).

718/1 **Echinochloa crus-gallii** (L.) Beauv., Cockspur. West: 43, nursery, Gulval, B.M.S.; 73, Council tip, Falmouth, L.J.M. East: 05, garden, Charlestown, W.T. (Thurston and Vigurs 1927).

E. frumentacea Link. *West: 63, old tips at Treskillard, and Piece, Carnkie, Redruth, 1966, L.J.M.; 64, Council tip, Tolvaddon, Camborne, L.J.M.; 73, Council tip, Falmouth, L.J.M.; 74, Council tip, Bissoe, B.E.M.G.; 85, Council tip, Newlyn East, L.J.M.

719/1 **Digitaria ischaemum** (Schreber) Muhl., Smooth Fingergrass. *East: 83, garden, Philleigh, 1975, B.E.M.G.

720/3 **Setaria pumila** (Poiret) Schultes (*Setaria glauca* Beauv.), Yellow Bristle-grass. West: 74, Council tip, Bissoe, L.J.M.

720/2 **S. verticillata** (L.) Beauv., Rough Bristle-grass. West: 85, near Newlyn East tip, B.E.M.G. Scilly: Lousley 1971.

S. italica (L.) Beauv., Italian Millet. *West: 73, Council tip, Falmouth, 1970, L.J.M.; 85, council tip, Newlyn East, L.J.M.

LEMNACEAE

651/1 **Wolffia arrhiza** (L.) Horkel ex Wimmer, Rootless Duckweed. *East: 45, Mount Edgcumbe Country Park, in pool, probably planted, 1977, BSBI, (*Watsonia*, **12**: 62).

(650/4 **Lemna gibba** L., Fat Duckweed (Flora). This was Davey's own record, and we hesitate before removing it from the Cornish list, but there has been no further confirmation, and it is best regarded as doubtful).

CYPERACEAE

(654/3 **Eriophorum latifolium** Hoppe, Broad-leaved Cottongrass. This species has been recorded (Flora) for both vice-counties and for Scilly, but we have not been able to trace an authentic specimen, and think these records could have been errors for forms of *E. angustifolium*, a view shared by Lousley 1971).

INDEX OF FAMILIES AND GENERA